BIOLOGY

ROBERT J. BROOKER
University of Minnesota–Minneapolis

ERIC P. WIDMAIER
Boston University

LINDA E. GRAHAM
University of Wisconsin–Madison

PETER D. STILING
University of South Florida

Boston   Burr Ridge, IL   Dubuque, IA   New York   San Francisco   St. Louis
Bangkok   Bogotá   Caracas   Kuala Lumpur   Lisbon   London   Madrid   Mexico City
Milan   Montreal   New Delhi   Santiago   Seoul   Singapore   Sydney   Taipei   Toronto

McGraw-Hill Higher Education

The McGraw-Hill Companies are extremely proud and pleased to present you with this preliminary version of **Biology**, by Rob Brooker, Eric Widmaier, Linda Graham, and Peter Stiling. This preview copy consists of the complete first two units of our forthcoming new majors-level introductory biology textbook.

Additional units of the book are being placed on the text's website — *www.brookerbiology.com* — for examination, with all chapters to be available by January 31, 2007. The complete, printed textbook will be mailed to you for your review at the beginning of March, allowing you and your colleagues time to consider this textbook and its media support materials for adoption for summer or autumn course use.

We believe that Rob Brooker and his co-authors have created a new book that provides the most up-to-date, comprehensive and accurate content, as well as a beautiful and pedagogical illustration program. The text will also be supported by the most innovative instructor and student media supplement package available today.

After examining this preview edition, we think you will agree. We hope you enjoy this first look at this exceptional new text — the Next Step in Biology.

Patrick Reidy
Executive Editor

Michael Lange
V.P. New Product Launches

Chad Grall
Marketing Director

Janice Roerig-Blong
Publisher

ABOUT THE AUTHORS

Robert J. Brooker

Robert J. Brooker (Ph.D., Yale University) received his B.A. in biology at Wittenberg University in 1978. At Harvard, he studied the lactose permease, the product of the *lacY* gene of the *lac* operon. He continues working on transporters at the University of Minnesota, where he has an active research team composed of undergraduates, graduate students, post-doctoral fellows, and laboratory technicians. At the University of Minnesota, Dr. Brooker teaches undergraduate courses in biology, genetics, and cell biology. In addition to many other publications, he has written two editions of the undergraduate genetics text *Genetics: Analysis & Principles,* McGraw-Hill, copyright 2005.

Eric P. Widmaier

Eric P. Widmaier received his Ph.D. in 1984 in endocrinology from the University of California at San Francisco. His research is focused on the control of body mass and metabolism in mammals, the mechanisms of hormone action, and the postnatal development of adrenal gland function. Dr. Widmaier is currently Professor of Biology at Boston University. Among other publications, he is a co-author of *Vander's Human Physiology: The Mechanisms of Body Function*, 10th edition, published by McGraw-Hill, copyright 2006.

Linda E. Graham

Linda E. Graham received her Ph.D. in botany from the University of Michigan, Ann Arbor. Her research explores the evolutionary origin of land-adapted plants, focusing on their cell and molecular biology as well as ecological interactions. Dr. Graham is now Professor of Botany at the University of Wisconsin-Madison. She teaches undergraduate courses in biology and plant biology. She is the co-author of, among other publications, *Algae*, copyright 2000, a major's textbook on algal biology, and *Plant Biology*, copyright 2006, both published by Prentice Hall/Pearson.

Peter D. Stiling

Peter Stiling obtained his Ph.D. from University College, Cardiff, Wales in 1979. Subsequently, he became a Post-doc at Florida State University and later spent two years as a lecturer at the University of the West Indies, Trinidad. During this time, he began photographing and writing about butterflies and other insects, which led to publication of several books on local insects. Dr. Stiling is currently a Professor of Biology at the University of South Florida at Tampa. He teaches graduate and undergraduate courses in ecology and environmental science. He has published many scientific papers and is the author of *Ecology: Theories and Applications*, 4th edition by Prentice Hall/Pearson, copyright 2002. Dr. Stiling's research interests include plant-insect relationships, parasite-host relationships, biological control, restoration ecology, and the effects of elevated carbon dioxide levels on plant herbivore interactions.

Left to right: Eric Widmaier, Linda Graham, Peter Stiling, and Rob Brooker

BRIEF CONTENTS

A New Biology Book with a Modern Perspective

In addition to being active researchers and experienced writers, our author team has taught majors biology for years. We have taught with the same books that you have. Our goal in creating something new is to offer something better—a comprehensive, modern textbook featuring an evolutionary focus with an emphasis on scientific inquiry.

Through our classroom experiences and research work, we became inspired by the prospect that a new Biology text could move biology education forward. In listening to educators and students, it became clear that we needed to concentrate our efforts on seven crucial areas. These are described briefly below. We will return to each in more detail in the pages that follow.

1. **Experimentation** During the 1970s and 1980s, biological information began to expand at an exponential rate. Biology textbooks grew and to some extent the content suffered as the scientific process was squeezed out by the avalanche of new details. We are committed to striking a better balance between general concepts and experimentation by showing the connection between scientific inquiry and the principles that are learned from such experimentation, especially through the Feature Investigation sections in every chapter.

2. **Modern content** Science is a moving target. Although the content and organization of our Biology textbook is not a dramatic departure from other books, we have added modern content that will better prepare students for future careers in biology. Toward this end, we have received content reviews from over three hundred faculty members from around the world. We are convinced they have helped us produce a book with the most up-to-date content possible.

Striking examples where we feel the content demonstrates a modern approach with an emphasis on recent experimentation include the following:

- Chapter 6 of our Cell Biology Unit explores cell biology at the level of "systems biology" in which the cell is viewed as a group of interacting parts. This allows students to understand how the parts of a cell work together.

- Our Genetics Unit takes a "molecular first" approach so that students will first understand what a gene is, and then consider how genes affect the traits of organisms.

- The Evolution Unit often takes a molecular perspective, and highlights cladistic methods to generate evolutionary relationships. This approach connects evolution at the molecular level and at the level of organisms in their native environments.

- The Diversity Unit has incorporated the newest information regarding evolutionary relationships among modern species. The connection between evolutionary innovation and reproductive success allows students to appreciate why organisms have certain types of traits.

- In our Plant Biology Unit, a much more modern connection has been made between plant structure, function and genetics. Recent information from *Arabidopsis* is often discussed.

- Each chapter in our Animal Biology Unit ends with a section on the modern Impact on Public Health, including the molecular basis of many diseases. In addition, Neuroscience is covered as a mini-Unit of its own, with three complete chapters incorporating some of the most recent information in this exciting area of biology.

- The Ecology Unit also incorporates an evolutionary theme and has an expanded discussion of species interactions. This approach provides students with a deeper understanding of evolutionary adaptations that organisms have.

3. **Evolutionary Perspective** A study of the processes and outcomes of evolution serves to unify the field of biology and the units of our text. Whether describing evolutionary mechanisms at the molecular level or surveying the diversity of life through a view of modern systematics, an understanding of evolution serves to connect and integrate the disciplines of biology.

4. **A Visual Outline** We were determined to create a new art program using both graphics and photography to serve as a "visual outline." We have worked with a large team of scientific illustrators, photographers, educators and students to build an accurate, up-to-date and visually appealing new illustration program that is easy to follow, realistic and instructive.

5. **Ensuring Accuracy** We chose to work as a team of authors to create this new Biology text because the information in our discipline is increasing so rapidly. Each member of our team has experience researching and writing in our respective areas allowing us to combine efforts to stay abreast of the field. Likewise, we have worked with a much larger team of reviewers, advisors, editors, and accuracy checkers to ensure that this text is as current and accurate as humanly possible,

6. **A Learning System** Starting with a simple outline at the beginning of each chapter, we have focused on the crucial topics in a clear and easy to follow manner. We emphasize

critical thinking and active learning by constantly returning to how science is done and through several pedagogical devices including our Biological Inquiry Questions which appear often in figure legends throughout the text. We end each chapter with a thorough review section which returns to our outline and emphasizes higher level learning through multiple question types.

7. **Media—Teaching and Learning with Technology**
   Our new book is accompanied by a vast array of electronic teaching and learning tools. We have focused on creating new student content that is built upon learning outcomes and assessing student performance. We have also created an unprecedented array of presentation and course management tools to enable instructors to enhance their lectures and manage their classrooms more effectively. Finally, we are committed to offering several electronic book and customized print options to best fit your needs.

Experimentation in Biology Reveals General Principles

Biology is the study of life. The primary way that biologists study life is through experimentation. In this textbook, we have maintained a parallel focus on the general principles of biology and experimentation.

Each chapter is divided into a few sections focusing on general principles in biology. These sections begin with an overview of why the topic is important. We then describe the features of the topic that we and our reviewers have felt are the most important and sometimes the most difficult to grasp.

In describing the principles of biology, we have woven experimentation into each chapter. To be prepared for a career in biology, students need to understand the techniques that are used in biology and bolster their critical thinking skills. Each chapter has a Feature Investigation that shows the steps in the scientific process (for example, see Figure 10.13, p. 200). These investigations include a description of the methods and end with an analysis of the data. This deeper approach allows students to appreciate how the general principles of biology were derived from experiments.

In addition, many scientists are mentioned throughout each chapter with a brief description of how their work contributed to the general principles of biology, reinforcing a sense that biology is an enterprise carried out by scientists around the world. This will prepare students for their next step into the scientific literature in future courses.

An Emphasis on Evolution Provides a Modern Perspective

Evolution is the unifying theme that connects the various areas of biology. We have chosen to explain this theme from a modern perspective by relating the information in each chapter to the genetic material, namely the genomes of organisms. Like-wise, because most genes encode proteins, a logical extension is to also relate information to proteomes—the collection of proteins that a cell or organism can make.

We use our Genomes and Proteomes subsections as one way to integrate the various disciplines of biology. For example, let's consider our Cell Biology Unit. In this unit, we emphasize how gene regulation is responsible for the differences between a nerve and muscle cell and how descent with modification occurs at the protein level to produce families of proteins with related cellular functions. Likewise, let's consider our Ecology Unit. In this unit we explain how the modification of particular genes has enabled organisms to compete effectively in their environment. The Ecology Unit also considers how the genomes of organisms have evolved in response to environmental changes over many generations.

As a team, our authors are committed to the idea of integrating the various disciplines in Biology, not separating them. We feel it important, fun, engaging, and actually easy to highlight the evolutionary theme of biology by relating information in each chapter to Genomes and Proteomes. They are intended to provide "perspective". We keep returning to the idea that everything in biology stems from the evolution of genomes, and that genomes primarily encode proteins that ultimately provide organisms with their traits. We feel strongly that this approach provides a modern perspective that will serve our readers well in their future careers. The Genomes and Proteomes subsections are just one way that we integrate the various fields of biology. Genes, proteins, and the molecular mechanisms of life are discussed throughout the entire book.

Textbook Illustrations Are a Key to Learning

In discussions with many of our students, we have come to realize that many, probably most students, are visual learners. They read the textbook for information, but when it comes time to study, their main emphasis is on the figures. Likewise, instructors often rely heavily on good illustrations for their lectures. Therefore, a top priority in the development of our Biology textbook has been the conceptualization and rendering of the illustrations.

As you will see when you scan through this book, the illustrations are very easy to follow, particularly those that have multiple steps. We have taken the attitude that students should be able to look at the figures and understand what is going on, without having to glance back and forth between the text and art. Many figures contain text boxes that explain what the illustration is showing. In those figures with multiple steps, the boxes are numbered so that students will understand that the steps occur in a particular order. In some cases, the numbering was critical when the illustration involved features that could not be presented in a linear manner. For example, a description of hearing in Figure 45.7 is much easier to follow because we have guided the student through the process by using numbered text boxes.

Likewise, technology can help us to engage, to educate and even to inspire our students. As you will see when you skim through the pages, the drawings in this textbook are technologically advanced. They are primarily intended to educate the student and we have maintained a commitment to simplicity. Even so, the illustrations in this textbook are also aimed at being interesting and inspiring. Art elements are drawn with a strong sense of realism and three-dimensionality. The illustrations come to life, which, after all, is important to students who are interested in the study of life. We expect students to occasionally look at a figure and think, "Wow, that's cool!" We invite you to skim through the pages and see for yourself.

Accuracy Is a Top Priority

Inaccuracies in a science textbook come from two primary sources. The first is human error. Authors, editors, and illustrators occasionally make mistakes. Fortunately, such mistakes are rare. Each chapter of our Biology book has been read by dozens of people, including several accuracy checkers whose sole job was to find mistakes. Using our 360-degree developmental process (p. viii), we have worked to ensure an unprecedented level of content accuracy in our textbook.

A second and more common source of error is out-of-date material. Biology is continually changing. New information arrives on a daily basis. Some of this information makes us realize that past information was incorrect. Therefore, textbooks that fail to maintain a current perspective become progressively more inaccurate and misleading. Having an experienced author team with extensive research credentials helps to build a textbook with the most current and accurate information. In addition, over three-hundred faculty members have reviewed our Biology textbook for its content.

We are confident that our book has the most modern content that the industry has to offer. This modern perspective pushes the accuracy of our book to the highest standard possible. In future editions, we will continue to strive for cutting-edge content that maintains a high level of accuracy. In future editions, we will continue to employ the help of many reviewers and accuracy checkers to maintain our commitment to modern content and accuracy.

Our Review Process Ensures a Textbook with the Right Content

If the best writer in the world wrote a textbook single-handedly without input from others, the book would not turn out well. Extensive and open-minded reviews are essential to producing a book that is superior. As we developed our book, we took the attitude that we must always return to a previous draft, analyze it critically, and then revise it accordingly.

From an author's perspective, the review process can be pretty daunting. We turn in chapters that we think are letter perfect, and then receive back reviews that make us painfully aware that writing a textbook is harder than it looks. At the start, we created a process that would make it easier for the editors and reviewers to critically evaluate our work. The first-draft chapters were sent to many outside reviewers who are faculty that either teach General Biology, are experts in the topics found in the chapter, or both. Each first-draft chapter was reviewed by up to 15 different people.

The reviews were collected and provided to the author of a given chapter and the editorial staff. Our editors read the chapters and the reviews, and then gave each author advice on how to make the next draft better. A second important type of input also occurred at the first-draft stage. For each unit, we conducted Focus Groups in which faculty members who had reviewed the chapters of an entire unit came together for a two-day meeting to discuss the chapters with the authors and editors. While written feedback is great, face-to-face discussion often brings out bigger-picture issues that may not be found in written reviews.

At the second draft stage, we decided upon an innovation that profoundly enhanced the quality of our Biology book. Although the illustrations in a Biology textbook are very expensive to make, we realized that a strong connection between the text and illustrations is critical to produce a superior textbook. Instead of making the illustrations at the final draft stage, which is typical of textbook publishing, we made them very early in the process. This helped us in two ways. First, reviewers could see the art as the book developed, and make critical changes to it. Second, it allowed the authors and editors to develop a keen sense of consistency between the text and art.

Also at the second draft stage, we assembled the text and illustrations into a format that looked like a chapter from an actual textbook. We had to keep reminding the reviewers that "These are not finalized chapters. These are early drafts that we want you to critically evaluate." This format allowed the reviewers, authors, and editors to understand how the pieces of the book would fit together. Although it was an exhaustive and rigorous process, adopting this step early in the writing process allowed us to produce a book with a sharp consistency between the text and figures.

We Are Committed to Serving Teachers and Learners

Writing a new textbook is a daunting task. To accurately and thoroughly cover a course as wide ranging as biology, we felt it was essential that our team reflect the diversity of the field. We saw an opportunity to reach students at an early stage in their education and provide their biology training with a solid and up-to-date foundation. We have worked to balance coverage of classic research with recent discoveries that extend biological concepts in surprising new directions or that forge new concepts. Some new discoveries were selected because they highlight scientific controversies, showing students that we don't have all the answers yet. There is still a lot of work for new generations of biologists. With this in mind, we've also spotlighted discoveries made by diverse people doing research in different countries to illustrate the global nature of modern biological science.

As active teachers and writers, one of the great joys of this process for us is that we have been able to meet many more educators and students during the creation of this textbook. It is humbling to see the level of dedication our peers bring to their teaching. Likewise, it is encouraging to see the energy and enthusiasm so many students bring to their studies. We hope this book and its media package will serve to aid both faculty and students in meeting the challenges of this dynamic and exciting course. For us, this remains a work in progress and we encourage you to let us know what you think of our efforts and what we can do to serve you better.

Rob Brooker   brook005@umn.edu
Eric Widmaier   widmaier@bu.edu
Linda Graham   lkgraham@wisc.edu
Peter Stiling   pstiling@chuma1.cas.usf.edu

The Next Step in Textbook Development

- 10 developmental editors
- 7 developmental focus groups
- 7 art focus groups
- 25+ accuracy checkers
- more than 1,200 reviews by over 350 reviewers across the world
- 11 multiple-day symposia with over 215 majors biology educators participating
- an art development team who worked closely with the authors
- media board of consultants
- 3 photo consultants

The following groups of individuals have been instrumental in ensuring the highest standard of content and accuracy in this textbook. We are deeply indebted to them for their tireless efforts.

Developmental Focus Groups

Cell Unit
Russell Borski,
North Carolina State University
Peter Fajer,
Florida State University
Brad Mehrtens,
University of Illinois–Urbana/Champaign
Randall Walikonis,
University of Connecticut
Sue Simon Westendorf,
Ohio University
Mark Staves,
Grand Valley State University

Genetics Unit
Karl Aufderheide,
Texas A&M University
John Doctor,
Duquesne University
Arlene Larson,
University of Colorado–Denver
Subhash Minocha,
University of New Hampshire
John Osterman,
University of Nebraska–Lincoln
Jill Reid,
Virginia Commonwealth University

Evolution Unit
Mark Decker,
University of Minnesota–Minneapolis
Robert Dill,
Bergen Community College
Jennifer Regan,
University of Southern Mississippi
Michelle Shuster,
New Mexico State University
Fred Wasserman,
Boston University

Diversity Unit
Ernest DuBrul,
University of Toledo
Roland Dute,
Auburn University
Florence Gleason,
University of Minnesota–St. Paul
Ann Rushing,
Baylor University
Randall Yoder,
Lamar University

Plants Unit
Fred Essig,
University of South Florida
Steve Herbert,
University of Wyoming
Mike Muller,
University of Illinois–Chicago
Stuart Reichler,
University of Texas–Austin
Scott Russell,
University of Oklahoma
Rani Vajravelu,
University of Central Florida

Animals Unit
Linda Collins,
University of Tennessee–Chattanooga
William Collins,
Stony Brook University
David Kurjiaka,
Ohio University
Phil Stephens,
Villanova University
David Tam,
University of North Texas
Charles Walcott,
Cornell University

Ecology Unit
James Adams,
Dalton State College
Stanley Faeth,
Arizona State University
Barbara Frase,
Bradley University
Daniel Moon,
University of North Florida
Dan Tinker,
University of Wyoming

Media Focus Group
Russell Borski,
North Carolina State University
Mark Decker,
University of Minnesota
Jon Glase,
Cornell University
John Merrill,
Michigan State University
Melissa Michael,
University of Illinois–Urbana/Champaign

Randall Phillis, *University of Massachusetts–Amherst*
Mitch Price, *Pennsylvania State University*

Accuracy Checkers

David Asch, *Youngstown State University*
Karl Aufderheide, *Texas A&M University*
Deborah Brooker
Linda Collins, *University of Tennessee–Chattanooga*
Mark Decker, *University of Minnesota*
Laura DiCaprio, *Ohio University*
Marjorie Doyle, *University of Wisconsin–Madison*
Peter Fajer, *Florida State University*

Pete Franco, *University of Minnesota*
Barbara Frase, *Bradley University*
John Graham, *Bowling Green State University*
Eunsoo Kim, *University of Wisconsin–Madison*
Arlene Larson, *University of Colorado–Denver*
David Pennock, *Miami University*
Anthony M. Rossi, *University of North Florida*
Martin Silberberg, *McGraw-Hill chemistry author*
Kevin Strang, *University of Wisconsin–Madison*
Fred Wasserman, *Boston University*
Jane E. Wissinger, *University of Minnesota*

Class Testers

We would like to thank the students and faculty at Ohio University, UCLA, and Calvin College for class testing our book.

End-of-Chapter Questions

Robert Dill, *Bergen Community College*
Arlene Larson, *University of Colorado–Denver*

Jennifer Regan, *University of Southern Mississippi*

Photo Consultants

John Osterman, *University of Nebraska–Lincoln*
Sue Simon Westendorf, *Ohio University*

Kevin Strang, *University of Wisconsin–Madison*

General Biology Symposia

Every year McGraw Hill conducts several General Biology Symposia, which are attended by instructors from across the country. These events are an opportunity for editors from McGraw-Hill to gather information about the needs and challenges of instructors teaching the major's biology course. It also offers a forum for the attendees to exchange ideas and experiences with colleagues they might not have otherwise met. The feedback we have received has been invaluable, and has contributed to the development of Biology and its supplements.

2006

Michael Bell, *Richland College*
Scott Bowling, *Auburn University*
Peter Busher, *Boston University*
Allison Cleveland, *University of South Florida–Tampa*
Sehoya Cotner, *University of Minnesota*
Kathyrn Dickson, *California State College–Fullerton*
Cathy Donald-Whitney, *Collin County Community College*
Stanley Faeth, *Arizona State University*
Karen Gerhart, *University of California–Davis*
William Glider, *University of Nebraska–Lincoln*
Stan Guffey, *The University of Tennessee*
Bernard Hauser, *University of Florida–Gainesville*
Mark Hens, *University of North Carolina– Greensboro*
James Hickey, *Miami University of Ohio–Oxford*
Sherry Krayesky, *University of Louisiana–Lafayette*
Brenda Leady, *University of Toledo*
Michael Meighan, *University of California–Berkeley*
Comer Patterson, *Texas A&M University*
Debra Pires, *University of California–Los Angeles*
Robert Simons, *University of California–Los Angeles*
Steven D. Skopik, *University of Delaware*

Ashok Upadhyaya, *University of South Florida–Tampa*
Anthony Uzwiak, *Rutgers University*
Dave Williams, *Valencia Community College–East Campus*
Jay Zimmerman, *St. John's University*

2005

Donald Buckley, *Quinnipiac University*
Arthur Buikema, *Virginia Polytechnic Institute*
Anne Bullerjahn, *Owens Community College*
Garry Davies, *University of Alaska-Anchorage*
Marilyn Hart, *Minnesota State University*
Daniel Flisser, *Camden County College*
Elizabeth Godrick, *Boston University*
Miriam Golbert, *College of the Canyons*
Sherry Harrel, *Eastern Kentucky University*
William Hoese, *California State University–Fullerton*
Margaret Horton, *University of North Carolina at Greensboro*
Carol Hurney, *James Madison University*
James Luken, *Coastal Carolina University*
Mark Lyford, *University of Wyoming*
Gail McKenzie, *Jefferson State Junior College*
Melissa Michael, *University of Illinois at Urbana-Champaign*
Subhash C. Minocha, *University of New Hampshire*
Leonore Neary, *Joliet Junior College*

K. Sata Sathasivan,
University of Texas at Austin

David Senseman,
University of Texas–San Antonio

Sukanya Subramanian,
Collin County Community College

Randall Terry,
Lamar University

Sharon Thoma,
University of Wisconsin–Madison

William Tyler,
Indian River Community College

2004

Jonathan Akin,
Northwestern State University of Louisiana

David Asch,
Youngstown State University

Diane Bassham,
Iowa State University

Donald Buckley,
Quinnipiac University

Ruth Buskirk,
University of Texas, Austin

Charles Creutz,
University of Toledo

Lydia Daniels,
University of Pittsburgh

Laura DiCaprio,
Ohio University

Michael Dini,
Texas Tech University

John Doctor,
Duquesne University

Ernest DuBrul,
University of Toledo

John Elam,
Florida State University

Samuel Hammer,
Boston University

Marilyn Hart,
Minnesota State University

Marc Hirrel,
University of Central Arkansas

Carol Johnson,
Texas A&M University

Dan Krane,
Wright State University

Karin Krieger,
University of Wisconsin–Green Bay

Josephine Kurdziel,
University of Michigan

Martha Lundell,
University of Texas, San Antonio

Roberta Maxwell,
University of North Carolina–Greensboro

John Merrill,
Michigan State University

Melissa Michael,
University of Illinois at Urbana-Champaign

Peter Niewarowski,
University of Akron

Ronald Patterson,
Michigan State University

Peggy Pollak,
Northern Arizona University

Uwe Pott,
University of Wisconsin, Green Bay

Mitch Price,
Pennsylvania State University

Steven Runge,
University of Central Arkansas

Thomas Shafer,
University of North Carolina, Wilmington

Richard Showman,
University of South Carolina

Michèle Shuster,
New Mexico State University

Dessie Underwood,
California State University–Long Beach

Mike Wade,
Indiana University

Elizabeth Willott,
University of Arizona

Carl Wolfe,
University of North Carolina, Charlotte

Reviewers

James K. Adams,
Dalton State College

Sylvester Allred,
Northern Arizona University

Jonathan W. Armbruster,
Auburn University

Joseph E. Armstrong,
Illinois State University

David K. Asch,
Youngstown State University

Amir M. Assadi-Rad,
Delta College

Karl J. Aufderheide,
Texas A&M University

Anita Davelos Baines,
University of Texas–Pan American

Lisa M. Baird,
University of San Diego

Diane Bassham,
Iowa State University

Donald Baud,
University of Memphis

Vernon W. Bauer,
Francis Marion University

Ruth E. Beattie,
University of Kentucky

Michael C. Bell,
Richland College

Steve Berg,
Winona State University

Arlene G. Billock,
University of Louisiana at Lafayette

Kristopher A. Blee,
California State University, Chico

Heidi B. Borgeas,
University of Tampa

Russell Borski,
North Carolina State University

Scott A. Bowling,
Auburn University

Robert Boyd,
Auburn University

Eldon J. Braun,
University of Arizona

Michael Breed,
University of Colorado, Boulder

Randy Brewton,
University of Tennessee, Knoxville

Peggy Brickman,
University of Georgia

Cheryl Briggs,
University of California, Berkeley

Peter S. Brown,
Mesa Community College

Mark Browning,
Purdue University

Cedric O. Buckley,
Jackson State University

Don Buckley,
Quinnipiac University

Arthur L. Buikema, Jr.,
Virginia Tech University

Anne Bullerjahn,
Owens Community College

Ray D. Burkett,
Southeast Tennessee Community College

Stephen P. Bush,
Coastal Carolina University

Peter E. Busher,
Boston University

Jeff Carmichael,
University of North Dakota

Clint E. Carter,
Vanderbilt University

Patrick A. Carter,
Washington State University

Merri Lynn Casem,
California State University, Fullerton

Domenic Castignetti,
Loyola University of Chicago

Maria V. Cattell

David T. Champlin,
University of Southern Maine

Jung H. Choi,
Georgia Institute of Technology

Curtis Clark,
Cal Poly Pomona

Allison Cleveland,
University of South Florida

Janice J. Clymer,
San Diego Mesa College

Linda T. Collins,
University of Tennessee at Chattanooga

Jay L. Comeaux,
Louisiana State University

Bob Connor II,
Owens Community College

Daniel Costa,
University of California at Santa Cruz

Sehoya Cotner,
University of Minnesota

Mack E. Crayton III,
Xavier University of Louisiana

Louis Crescitelli,
Bergen Community College
Charles Creutz,
University of Toledo
Karen A. Curto,
University of Pittsburgh
Mark A. Davis,
Macalester College
Mark D. Decker,
University of Minnesota
Jeffery P. Demuth,
Indiana University
Phil Denette,
Delgado Community College
Donald W. Deters,
Bowling Green State University
Hudson R. DeYoe,
University of Texas–Pan American
Laura DiCaprio,
Ohio University
Randy DiDomenico,
University of Colorado, Boulder
Robert S. Dill,
Bergen Community College
Kevin Dixon,
University of Illinois–Urbana/Champaign
John S. Doctor,
Duquesne University
Warren D. Dolphin,
Iowa State University
Cathy A. Donald-Whitney,
Collin County Community College
Robert P. Donaldson,
George Washington University
Kristiann Dougherty,
Valencia Community College
Ernest F. Dubrul,
University of Toledo
Jeffry L. Dudycha,
William Patterson University of New Jersey
Charles Duggins, Jr.,
University of South Carolina
Roland R. Dute,
Auburn University
William D. Eldred,
Boston University
Johnny El-Rady,
University of South Florida

Dave Eldridge,
Baylor University
Inge Eley,
Hudson Valley Community College
Frederick B. Essig,
University of South Florida
Sharon Eversman,
Montana State University
Stan Faeth,
Arizona State University
Peter Fajer,
Florida State University
Paul Farnsworth,
University of Texas at San Antonio
Paul D. Ferguson,
University of Illinois at Urbana/Champaign
Margaret F. Field,
Saint Mary's College of California
Jorge A. Flores,
West Virginia University
Irwin Forseth,
University of Maryland
David Foster,
North Idaho College
Paul Fox,
Danville Community College
Wayne D. Frasch,
Arizona State University
Adam J. Fry,
University of Connecticut
Caitlin R. Gabor,
Texas State University–San Marcos
Anne M. Galbraith,
University of Wisconsin–La Crosse
John R. Geiser,
Western Michigan University
Nicholas R. Geist,
Sonoma State University
Patricia A. Geppert,
The University of Texas at San Antonio
Frank S. Gilliam,
Marshall University
Chris R. Gissendanner,
University of Louisiana at Monroe
Florence K. Gleason,
University of Minnesota
Elizabeth Godrick,
Boston University

James M. Grady,
University of New Orleans
John S. Graham,
Bowling Green State University
Barbara E. Graham-Evans,
Jackson State University
Christine E. Gray,
Blinn College
Stan Guffey,
University of Tennessee
Rodney D. Hagley,
University of North Carolina, Wilmington
Gary L. Hannan,
Eastern Michigan University
Kyle E. Harms,
Louisiana State University
M. C. Hart,
Minnesota State University–Mankato
Carla Ann Hass,
The Pennsylvania State University
Brian T. Hazlett,
Briar Cliff University
Harold Heatwole,
North Carolina State University
Mark D. Hens,
University of North Carolina
Stephen K. Herbert,
University of Wyoming
Albert A. Herrera,
University of Southern California
David L. Herrin,
University of Texas at Austin
Helen Hess,
College of the Atlantic
R. James Hickey,
Miami University
Tracey E. Hickox,
University of Illinois, Urbana-Champaign
Mark A. Holbrook,
University of Iowa
Ella Ingram,
Rose-Hulman Institute of Technology
Jeffrey Jack,
University of Louisville
Judy Jernstedt,
University of California, Davis

Lee Johnson,
The Ohio State University
Robyn Jordan,
University of Louisiana at Monroe
Walter S. Judd,
University of Florida
David Julian,
University of Florida
Stephen R. Kelso,
University of Illinois at Chicago
Heather R. Ketchum,
Blinn College
Stephen J. King,
University of Missouri–Kansas City
John Z. Kiss,
Miami University
Ted Klenk,
Valencia Community College
David M. Kohl,
University of California, Santa Barbara
Anna Koshy,
Houston Community College System
Sherry Krayesky,
University of Louisiana at Lafayette
John Krenetsky,
Metropolitan State College at Denver
Karin E. Krieger,
University of Wisconsin–Green Bay
Paul Kugrens,
Colorado State University
Josephine Kurdziel,
University of Michigan
David T. Kurjiaka,
Ohio University
Allen Kurta,
Eastern Michigan University
Paul K. Lago,
University of Mississippi
Ellen Shepherd Lamb,
University of North Carolina at Greensboro
Pamela Lanford,
University of Maryland
Marianne M. Laporte,
Eastern Michigan University
Arlen T. Larson,
University of Colorado at Denver

John Latto,
University of California, Berkeley

Brenda Leady,
University of Toledo

Shannon Erickson Lee,
California State University–Northridge

Tali D. Lee,
University of Wisconsin–Eau Claire

Michael Lentz,
University of North Florida

Jennifer J. Lewis,
San Juan College

Pauline A. Lizotte,
Valencia Community College

Jason L. Locklin,
Temple College

Robert Locy,
Auburn University

James A. Long,
Boise State University

David Lonzarich,
University of Wisconsin–Eau Claire

James B. Ludden,
College of DuPage

Albert MacKrell,
Bradley University

P. T. Magee,
University of Minnesota

Christi Magrath,
Troy University

Richard Malkin,
University of California, Berkeley

Charles H. Mallery,
University of Miami

Kathleen A. Marrs,
IUPUI, Indianapolis

Diane L. Marshall,
University of New Mexico

Peter J. Martinat,
Xavier University of Louisiana

Joel Maruniak,
University of Missouri

Kamau Mbuthia,
Bowling Green State University

Greg McCormac,
American River College

Andrew McCubbin,
Washington State University

David L. McCulloch,
Collin County Community College

Tanya K. McKinney,
Xavier University of Louisiana

Brad Mehrtens,
University of Illinois at Urbana–Champaign

Michael Meighan,
University of California, Berkeley

Douglas Meikle,
Miami University

Allen F. Mensinger,
University of Minnesota, Duluth

John Merrill,
Michigan State University

Richard Merritt,
Houston Community College

Brian T. Miller,
Middle Tennessee State University

Hugh A. Miller III,
East Tennessee State University

Thomas E. Miller,
Florida State University

Sarah L. Milton,
Florida Atlantic University

Dennis J. Minchella,
Purdue University

Subhash C. Minocha,
University of New Hampshire

Patricia Mire,
University of Louisiana at Lafayette

Daniela S. Monk,
Washington State University

Daniel C. Moon,
University of North Florida

Janice Moore,
Colorado State University

Mathew D. Moran,
Hendrix College

Jorge A. Moreno,
University of Colorado, Boulder

Roderick M. Morgan,
Grand Valley State University

James V. Moroney,
Louisiana State University

Molly R. Morris,
Ohio University

Michael Muller,
University of Illinois at Chicago

Michelle Mynlieff,
Marquette University

Allan D. Nelson,
Tarleton State University

Raymond L. Neubauer,
University of Texas at Austin

Jacalyn S. Newman,
University of Pittsburgh

Colleen J. Nolan,
St. Mary's University

Shawn E. Nordell,
St. Louis University

Margaret Nsofor,
Southern Illinois University, Carbondale

Dennis W. Nyberg,
University of Illinois at Chicago

Nicole S. Obert,
University of Illinois, Urbana-Champaign

David G. Oppenheimer,
University of Florida

John C. Osterman,
University of Nebraska–Lincoln

Brian Palestis,
Wagner College

Julie M. Palmer,
University of Texas at Austin

C. O. Patterson,
Texas A&M University

Ronald J. Patterson,
Michigan State University

Linda M. Peck,
University of Findlay

David Pennock,
Miami University

Shelley W. Penrod,
North Harris College

Beverly J. Perry,
Houston Community College System

Chris Petersen,
College of the Atlantic

Jay Phelan,
UCLA

Eric R. Pianka,
The University of Texas at Austin

Thomas Pitzer,
Florida International University

Peggy E. Pollak,
Northern Arizona University

Richard B. Primack,
Boston University

Lynda Randa,
College of Dupage

Marceau Ratard,
Delgado Community College

Robert S. Rawding,
Gannon University

Jennifer Regan,
University of Southern Mississippi

Stuart Reichler,
University of Texas at Austin

Jill D. Reid,
Virginia Commonwealth University

Anne E. Reilly,
Florida Atlantic University

Linda R. Richardson,
Blinn College

Laurel Roberts,
University of Pittsburgh

Kenneth R. Robinson,
Purdue University

Chris Ross,
Kansas State University

Anthony M. Rossi,
University of North Florida

Kenneth H. Roux,
Florida State University

Ann E. Rushing,
Baylor University

Scott Russell,
University of Oklahoma

Christina T. Russin,
Northwestern University

Charles L. Rutherford,
Virginia Tech University

Margaret Saha,
College of William and Mary

Kanagasabapathi Sathasivan,
The University of Texas at Austin

Stephen G. Saupe,
College of St. Benedict

Jon B. Scales,
Midwestern State University

Daniel C. Scheirer,
Northeastern University

H. Jochen Schenk,
California State University, Fullerton

John Schiefelbein,
University of Michigan

Deemah N. Schirf,
University of Texas at San Antonio

Mark Schlueter,
College of Saint Mary

Scott Schuette,
Southern Illinois University, Carbondale

Dean D. Schwartz,
Auburn University

Timothy E. Shannon,
Francis Marion University

Richard M. Showman,
University of South Carolina

Michele Shuster,
New Mexico State University

Robert Simons,
UCLA

J. Henry Slone,
Francis Marion University

Phillip Snider, Jr.,
Gadsden State Community College

Nancy G. Solomon,
Miami University

Lekha Sreedhar,
University of Missouri–Kansas City

Bruce Stallsmith,
University of Alabama, Huntsville

Susan J. Stamler,
College of Dupage

Mark P. Staves,
Grand Valley State University

William Stein,
Binghamton University

Philip J. Stephens,
Villanova University

Antony Stretton,
University of Wisconsin–Madison

Gregory W. Stunz,
Texas A&M University–Corpus Christi

Julie Sutherland,
College of Dupage

David Tam,
University of North Texas

Roy A. Tassava,
Ohio State University

Sharon Thoma,
University of Wisconsin–Madison

Shawn A. Thomas,
College of St. Benedict/St. John's University

Daniel B. Tinker,
University of Wyoming

Marty Tracey,
Florida International University

Marsha Turell,
Houston Community College

J. M. Turbeville,
Virginia Commonwealth University

Rani Vajravelu,
University of Central Florida

Neal J. Voelz,
St. Cloud State University

Samuel E. Wages,
South Plains College

Jyoti R. Wagle,
Houston Community College System–Central

Charles Walcott,
Cornell University

Randall Walikonis,
University of Connecticut

Jeffrey A. Walker,
University of Southern Maine

Delon E. Washo-Krupps,
Arizona State University

Frederick Wasserman,
Boston University

Steven A. Wasserman,
University of California, San Diego

R. Douglas Watson,
University of Alabama at Birmingham

Cindy Martinez Wedig,
University of Texas–Pan American

Arthur E. Weis,
University of California–Irvine

Sue Simon Westendorf,
Ohio University

Howard Whiteman,
Murray State University

Susan Whittemore,
Keene State College

David L. Wilson,
University of Miami

Robert Winning,
Eastern Michigan University

Michelle D. Withers,
Louisiana State University

Clarence C. Wolfe,
Northern Virginia Community College

Gene K. Wong,
Quinnipiac University

Richard P. Wunderlin,
University of South Florida

Joanna Wysocka-Diller,
Auburn University

H. Randall Yoder,
Lamar University

Marilyn Yoder,
University of Missouri–Kansas City

Scott D. Zimmerman,
Southwest Missouri State University

International Reviewers

Heather Addy,
University of Calgary

Mari L. Acevedo,
University of Puerto Rico at Arecibo

Heather E. Allison,
University of Liverpool, UK

David Backhouse,
University of New England

Andrew Bendall,
University of Guelph

Marinda Bloom,
Stellenbosch University, South Africa

Tony Bradshaw,
Oxford-Brookes University, UK

Alison Campbell,
University of Waikato

Bruce Campbell,
Okanagan College

Clara E. Carrasco, Ph.D.,
University of Puerto Rico–Ponce Campus

Keith Charnley,
University of Bath, UK

Ian Cock,
Griffith University

Margaret Cooley,
University of NSW

R. S. Currah,
University of Alberta

Logan Donaldson,
York University

Theo Elzenga,
Rijks Universiteit Groningen, Netherlands

Neil C. Haave,
University of Alberta

Tom Haffie,
University of Western Ontario

Louise M. Hafner,
Queensland Uni of Technology

Annika F. M. Haywood,
Memorial Univ of Newfoundland

William Huddleston,
University of Calgary

Shin-Sung Kang,
KyungBuk Univ.

Wendy J. Keenleyside,
University of Guelph

Christopher J. Kennedy,
Simon Fraser University

Bob Lauder,
Lancaster University

Richard C. Leegood,
Sheffield University, UK

Thomas H. MacRae,
Dalhousie University

R. Ian Menz,
Flinders University

Kirsten Poling,
University of Windsor

Jim Provan,
Queens University, Belfast, UK

Richard Roy,
McGill University

Han A.B. Wösten,
Utrecht University, Netherlands

ACKNOWLEDGMENTS

The lives of most science-textbook authors do not revolve around an analysis of writing techniques. Instead, we are people who understand science and are inspired by it, and we want to communicate that information to other people. Simply put, we need a lot of help to get it right.

Editors are a key component that help the authors modify the content of their book so it is logical, easy to read, and inspiring. The editorial team for this Biology textbook has been a catalyst that kept this project rolling. The members played various roles in the editorial process. Lisa Bruflodt (Senior Developmental Editor) has been the master organizer. Frankly, this is a ridiculously hard job. Coordinating the efforts of dozens of people and keeping them on schedule is not always fun. Lisa's success at keeping us on schedule has been truly amazing. We are also grateful to Kris Tibbetts (Director of Development) who was involved in the early steps of the book, and kept the focus groups on track.

Our Biology book also has had 6 additional developmental editors who scrutinized each draft of their respective chapters with an emphasis on improving content, clarity, and readability. These developmental editors analyzed educational materials and reviewers' comments, and gave the authors advice on how to improve succeeding drafts. They also provided a list of the general principles that most instructors want in their Biology textbook. These general principles have been a cornerstone for the organization of our chapters.

Suzanne Olivier (Lead Freelance Developmental Editor) did an outstanding job of coordinating the staff of developmental editors. She also played an important role in editing chapters in the Genetics and Plant Biology units. Her early editing of the Genetics Unit, in particular, set the tone for many of the pedagogical features that became established throughout the entire textbook. Other developmental editors focused on particular units. Alice Fugate was involved with the Chemistry, Cell Biology, and Animal Biology Units. Her knack for getting the level of the writing appropriate for majors biology was invaluable, as was her attention to detail. Joni Fraser focused on the Cell Biology, Diversity, and Ecology Units. Somehow she successfully juggled the tasks of addressing all the reviewers' concerns while maintaining the necessary chapter length. Patricia Longoria played an important role in the early editing of the Diversity and Plant Biology Units. Patricia contributed many useful ideas for content and expression, and her unfailing enthusiasm smoothed the way over rocky parts of the process. Robin Fox edited three key chapters in the Genetics Unit. Her attention to detail and the explanation of mathematical principles were invaluable. And finally, Alan Titche was also involved with Animal Biology Unit, and played a major role in developing some of the most challenging chapters in that Unit. We would also like to thank Dr. Jim Deshler and Dr. Mary Erskine for their valuable contributions to the writing of several chapters in the Animal Biology Unit.

Deborah Brooker (Art/Text Coordinating Editor) analyzed all of the chapters in the textbook with one primary question in mind. Do the written text and figures tell a parallel story? With excruciating care, she made sure that the text and figures are consistent, and that the figures, by themselves, are accurate and easy to follow.

Imagineering Media Services Inc., of Ontario, Canada, did a fantastic job of illustrating our Biology book. They were involved early in the process by first making rough sketches based on the material in the first drafts, and then later progressed to drawings with finer detail. Their ability to make realistic, three-dimensional drawings is second to none. We're particularly grateful to Kierstan Hong, who provided a critical line of communication between the publisher, authors, and illustrators throughout most of this process, and also to Mark Mykytiuk, who also played a lead role in overseeing the art development. We would also like to gratefully acknowledge our photography researchers at Pronk & Associates of Ontario, Canada, and particularly to Fiona D'souza for keeping us on schedule. Likewise, we are grateful to John Leland (Photo Research Coordinator) at McGraw-Hill for his coordination of the photo selection process.

We would also like to thank our advisors and contributors:

Media Board of Advisors

Mark Decker,
University of Minnesota–Minneapolis

Naomi Friedman,
Developmental Editor

Jon Glase,
Cornell University

John Merrill,
Michigan State University

Melissa Michael,
University of Illinois–Urbana/Champaign

Randall Phyllis,
University of Massachusetts

Mitch Price,
Pennsylvania State University

Tutorial Questions

Scott Bowling,
Auburn University

Don Buckley,
Quinnipiac University

Ernest DuBrul,
University of Toledo

Jon Glase,
Cornell University

Kari Beth Krieger,
University of Wisconsin–Green Bay

Patricia Mire,
University of Louisiana–Lafayette

Michael Muller,
University of Illinois at Chicago

Allan Smits,
Quinnipiac University

Test Questions

Russell Borski,
North Carolina State University

Robert Dunn,
*North Carolina State
University*

John Godwin,
*North Carolina State
University*

Harold Heatwole,
*North Carolina State
University*

James Mickle,
*North Carolina State
University*

Gerald Van Dyke,
*North Carolina State
University ARIS*

Brad Mehrtens,
*University of Illinois–
Urbana/Champaign*

Instructor's Manual

Daniel Moon,
University of North Florida

Student Study Guide

Michelle Shuster,
New Mexico State University

Amy Marion,
New Mexico State University

Lecture Outlines

Brenda Leady,
University of Toledo

Animations

Kevin Dixon,
*University of Illinois–
Urbana/Champaign*

Another important aspect of the editorial process is the actual design, presentation, and layout of materials. It's confusing if the text and art aren't on the same page, or if a figure is too large or two small. We are indebted to the tireless efforts of Joyce Berendes (Lead Project Manager) and Wayne Harms (Design Manager) of McGraw-Hill. Their artistic talents, ability to size and arrange figures, and attention to the consistency of the figures have been remarkable. We also wish to thank John Joran (Designer) who cleverly crafted both the interior and exterior designs.

We would like to acknowledge the ongoing efforts of the superb marketing staff at McGraw-Hill. Kent Peterson (Vice President, Director of Marketing) oversees a talented staff of people who work tirelessly to promote our book. Special thanks to Chad Grall (Marketing Director), Wayne Vincent (Internet Marketing Manager), Debra Hash (Senior Marketing Manager) and Heather Wagner (Systems and Promotions Marketing Manager) for their ideas and enthusiasm for this book. The proposal of making a video website for the book *www.brookerbiology.com* was scary for the authors but actually turned out to be fun.

Finally, other staff members at McGraw-Hill Higher Education have ensured that the authors and editors were provided with adequate resources to achieve the goal of producing a superior textbook. These include Kurt Strand (President, Science, Engineering, and Math), Marty Lange (Vice President, Editor-in-Chief), Michael Lange (Vice President, New Product Launches), Janice Roerig-Blong (Publisher) and Patrick Reidy (Executive Editor). In particular, Michael and Patrick communicated with the authors on a regular basis regarding the progress of this project. They attended most of the focus groups and author meetings, and even provided occasional input regarding the content of the book. The bottom line is that the author team is grateful that you have believed in this project, and have provided us with the resources to make it happen.

Student Supplements

Designed to help students maximize their learning experience in biology—we offer the following options to students:

ARIS

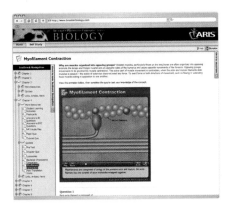

ARIS (Assessment, Review, and Instruction System) is an electronic study system that offers students a digital portal of knowledge. Students can readily access a variety of **digital learning objects** which include:

- chapter level quizzing
- pretests
- animations
- videos
- flashcards
- answers to Biological Inquiry Questions
- answers to all end-of-chapter questions
- MP3 and MP4 downloads of selected content
- learning outcomes and assessment capability woven around key content

Student Study Guide

ISBN: 0-07-299588-2

Helping students focus their time and energy on important concepts, the study guide offers students a variety of tools:

1. Practice Questions—approximately 10–12 multiple choice questions
2. Active Learning Questions—approximately 5–8 open-ended questions that ask the student to explore something and delve into content a little deeper, reinforcing content through experiential learning.
3. Outline/Summary of Fundamental Concepts—efficient listing of key concepts.
4. Key Terms
5. Strategies for Difficult Concepts

Content Delivery Flexibility

Brooker et al., *Biology* is available in many formats in addition to the traditional textbook to give instructors and students more choices when deciding on the format of their biology text. Choices include:

Volumes

The complete text has been split into three natural segments to allow instructors more flexibility and students more purchasing options.

Volume 1—Units 1 (Chemistry), 2 (Cell), and 3 (Genetics)
Volume 2—Units 6 (Plants) and 7 (Animals)
Volume 3—Units 4 (Evolution), 5 (Diversity), and 8 (Ecology)

Color Custom by Chapter

For even more flexibility, we offer the Brooker: *Biology* text in a full-color, custom version that allows instructors to pick the chapters they want included. Students pay for only what the instructor chooses.

eBook

The entire text is available electronically through the ARIS website. This electronic text offers not only the text in a digital format but includes embedded links to figures, tables, animations, and videos to make full use of the digital tools available and further enhance student understanding.

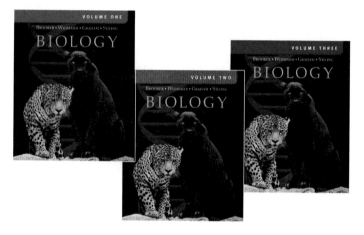

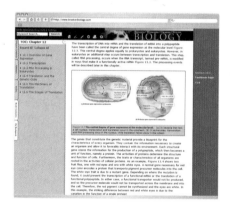

Instructor Supplements

Dedicated to providing high quality and effective supplements for instructors, the following Instructor supplements were developed for *Biology:*

ARIS with Presentation Center

Assessment, Review, and Instruction System, also known as ARIS, is an electronic homework and course management system designed for greater flexibility, power, and ease of use than any other system. Whether you are looking for a preplanned course or one you can customize to fit your course needs, ARIS is your solution.

In addition to having access to all student digital learning objects, ARIS allows instructors to:

Build Assignments

- Choose from pre-built assignments or create your own custom content by importing your own content or editing an existing assignment from the pre-built assignment.

- Assignments can include quiz questions, animations, and videos . . . anything found on the website.

- Create announcements and utilize full course or individual student communication tools

- Assign **unique multi-level tutorial questions** developed by content experts that provide intelligent feedback through a series of questions to help students truly understand a concept; not just repeat an answer.

Track Student Progress

- Assignments are automatically graded
- Gradebook functionality allows full course management including:
  - Dropping the lowest grades
  - Weighting grades / manually adjusting grades
  - Exporting your gradebook to Excel, WebCT or BlackBoard

- Manipulating data allowing you to track student progress through multiple reports

Offer More Flexibility

- **Sharing Course Materials with Colleagues** — Instructors can create and share course materials and assignments with colleagues with a few clicks of the mouse allowing for multiple section courses with many instructors (and TAs) to continually be in synch if desired.
- **Integration with BlackBoard or WebCT**—once a student is registered in the course, all student activity within McGraw-Hill's ARIS is automatically recorded and available to the instructor through a fully integrated grade book that can be downloaded to Excel, WebCT, or Blackboard.

Presentation Center

Build instructional materials wherever, whenever, and however you want!

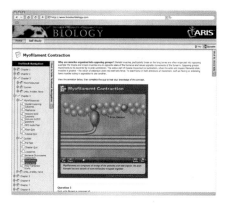

ARIS Presentation Center is an online digital library containing assets such as photos, artwork, animations, PowerPoints, and other media types that can be used to create customized lectures, visually enhanced tests and quizzes, compelling course websites, or attractive printed support materials.

Access to your book, access to all books!
The Presentation Center library includes thousands of assets from many McGraw-Hill titles. This ever-growing resource gives instructors the power to utilize assets specific to an adopted textbook as well as content from all other books in the library.

Nothing could be easier!
Accessed from the instructor side of your textbook's ARIS website, Presentation Center's dynamic search engine allows you to explore by discipline, course, textbook chapter, asset type, or keyword. Simply browse, select, and download the files you need to build engaging course materials. All assets are copyright McGraw-Hill Higher Education but can be used by instructors for classroom purposes.

Instructor's Testing and Resource CD-ROM

ISBN: 0-07-295658-5
This cross-platform CD-ROM provides these resources for instructors:

- **Instructor's Manual**—This manual contains instructional strategies and activities, student misconceptions,

etymology of key terms, "Beyond the Book" interesting facts, and sources for additional web resources.
- **Test Bank**—The test bank offers multiple-choice and true/false questions that can be used for homework assignments or the preparation of exams.
- **Computerized Test Bank**—This software can be utilized to quickly create customized exams. The user-friendly program allows instructors to sort questions by format or level of difficulty; edit existing questions or add new ones; and scramble questions and answer keys for multiple versions of the same test.

Student Response System

Wireless technology brings interactivity into the classroom or lecture hall. Instructors and students receive immediate feedback through wireless response pads that are easy to use and engage students. This system can be used by instructors to:

- Take attendance
- Administer quizzes and tests
- Create a lecture with intermittent questions
- Manage lectures and student comprehension through the use of the gradebook
- Integrate interactivity into their PowerPoint presentations

Transparencies
ISBN: 0-07-295657-7
This boxed set of overhead transparencies includes every piece of line art in the textbook plus every table. The images have been modified to ensure maximum readability in both small and large classroom settings.

BIOLOGY LABORATORY MANUAL, First Edition
Darrell S. Vodopich, *Baylor University*
Randy Moore, *University of Minnesota*
ISBN: 0-07-3323985

This laboratory manual is designed to accompany Brooker et al: *Biology.* The experiments and procedures are simple, safe, easy to perform, and especially appropriate for large classes. Few experiments require a second class-meeting to complete the procedure. Each exercise includes many photographs, traditional topics, and experiments that help students learn about life. Procedures within each exercise are numerous and discrete so that an exercise can be tailored to the needs of the students, the style of the instructor, and the facilities available.

BIOLOGICAL INVESTIGATIONS LAB MANUAL, First Edition
Warren D. Dolphin, *Iowa State University*
ISBN: 0-07-332399-3

Developed to accompany Brooker et al: *Biology;* this lab manual focuses on labs that are investigative and ask students to use more critical thinking and hands-on learning. The author emphasizes investigative, quantitative, and comparative approaches to studying the life sciences.

A VISUAL JOURNEY

Our art program was painstakingly designed in conjunction with the text development to ensure 1) the concept is accurately portrayed, 2) consistency is maintained between the text and art, and 3) it's appropriately placed on the page. The art serves as a visual outline for students, often offering textboxes that explain difficult concept. For multistep processes, these textboxes are numbered so that the student can easily follow the process from beginning to end.

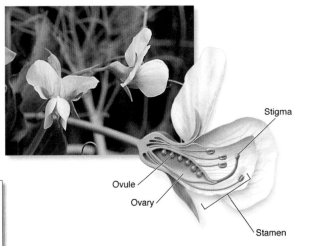

Figure 16.3   Flower structure in pea plants. The pea flower produces both male and female gametes. Sperm nuclei form in the pollen produced within the stamens; egg cells form in ovules within the ovary. A modified petal encloses the stamens and ovaries, encouraging self-fertilization.

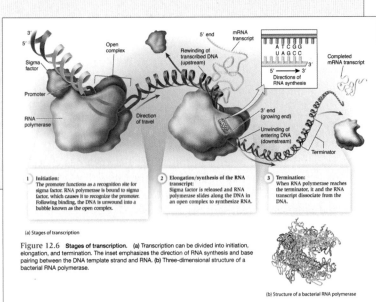

(a) Stages of transcription

1   Initiation: The promoter functions as a recognition site for sigma factor. RNA polymerase is bound to sigma factor, which causes it to recognize the promoter. Following binding, the DNA is unwound into a bubble known as the open complex.

2   Elongation/synthesis of the RNA transcript: Sigma factor is released and RNA polymerase slides along the DNA in an open complex to synthesize RNA.

3   Termination: When RNA polymerase reaches the terminator, it and the RNA transcript dissociate from the DNA.

Figure 12.6   Stages of transcription.   (a) Transcription can be divided into initiation, elongation, and termination. The inset emphasizes the direction of RNA synthesis and base pairing between the DNA template strand and RNA. **(b)** Three-dimensional structure of a bacterial RNA polymerase.

(b) Structure of a bacterial RNA polymerase

---

adaptations—processes and structures by which organisms adjust to short-term or long-term changes in their environment.

Regulation and Homeostasis As we have just seen, one way that organisms can respond to environmental variation is to change themselves. The growth of thick fur in the wintertime is an example. A common reason for certain adaptations, including this example, is to maintain homeostasis (from the Greek meaning "to stay the same"). Although life is a dynamic process, living cells and organisms regulate their cells and bodies to maintain relatively stable internal conditions, a process called **homeostasis**. The degree to which homeostasis is achieved varies among different organisms. For example, most mammals and birds maintain a relatively constant body temperature in spite of changing environmental temperatures (Figure 1.2d), while reptiles and amphibians do not. By comparison, all organisms continually regulate their cellular metabolism so that nutrient molecules are used at an appropriate rate, and new cellular components are synthesized when they are needed.

Growth and Development All living things grow and develop; **growth** produces more or larger cells, while **development** produces organisms with a defined set of characteristics. Among unicellular organisms such as bacteria, new cells are relatively small, and they increase in volume by the synthesis of additional cellular components. Multicellular organisms, such as plants and animals, begin life at a single-cell stage (for example, a fertilized egg) and then undergo multiple cell divisions to develop into a complete organism with many cells (Figure 1.2e).

Reproduction All living organisms have a finite lifespan and will eventually die. To sustain life over many generations, organisms must **reproduce** (Figure 1.2f). A key feature of reproduction is that offspring tend to have characteristics that greatly resemble those of their parent(s). The reason for this is that all living organisms contain genetic material composed of **DNA (deoxyribonucleic acid)**, which provides a blueprint for the organization, development, and function of living things. As discussed in Unit III, DNA harbors **genes**, which contribute to the characteristics or traits of organisms. During reproduction, a copy of this blueprint is transmitted from parents to offspring. The central dogma of genetics is that most genes are transcribed into a type of RNA (ribonucleic acid) molecule called messenger RNA (mRNA) that is then translated into a polypeptide with

For example, the long snout of an anteater is an adaptation that enhances its ability to obtain food, namely ants (Figure 1.2g). The long snout occurred via biological evolution in which modern anteaters evolved from organisms that did not have such long snouts. Unit IV is devoted to the topic of evolution, while Unit V surveys the evolutionary diversity among different forms of life.

Living Organisms Can Be Viewed at Different Levels of Organization

As we have just learned, life exhibits a set of characteristics, beginning with the concept of organization. The organization of living organisms can be analyzed in a hierarchical manner, starting with the tiniest level of organization, and progressing to levels that are physically much larger and more complex. Figure 1.3 depicts a scientist's view of biological organization at different levels.

1. **Atoms:** An **atom** is the smallest component of an element that has the chemical properties of the element. All matter is composed of atoms.
2. **Molecules and macromolecules:** As discussed in Unit I, atoms bond with each other to form **molecules**. When many molecules bond together to form a polymer, this is called a **macromolecule**. Carbohydrates, proteins, and nucleic acids (for example, DNA and RNA) are important macromolecules found in living organisms.
3. **Cells:** Molecules and macromolecules associate with each other to form larger structures such as membranes. A cell is formed from the association of these larger structures.
4. **Tissues:** In the case of multicellular organisms such as plants and animals, many cells of the same type associate with each other to form **tissues**. An example is muscle tissue.
5. **Organs:** An **organ** is composed of two or more types of tissue. For example, the heart of a parrot is composed of several types of tissues, including muscle, nervous, and connective tissue.
6. **Organism:** All living things can be called organisms. A single organism possesses the set of characteristics that define life. Biologists classify organisms as belonging to a particular **species**, which is a related group of organisms that share a distinctive form and set of attributes in nature.

The members of the same species are closely related genetically. In Units VI and VII, we will examine plants and animals at the level of cells, tissues, organs, and complete organisms.

7. **Population:** A group of organisms of the same species that occupy the same environment is called a **population**.
8. **Community:** A biological **community** is an assemblage of populations of different species. The types of species that are found in a community are determined by the environment and by the interactions of species with each other.
9. **Ecosystem:** Researchers may extend their work beyond living organisms and also study the environment. Ecologists analyze **ecosystems**, which are formed by

interactions of a community of organisms with their physical environment. Unit VIII considers biology from populations to ecosystems.
10. **Biosphere:** The **biosphere** includes all of the places on the Earth where living organisms exist, encompassing the air, water, and land.

Modern Forms of Life Are Connected by an Evolutionary History

Life began on Earth as primitive cells about 3.5 to 4 billion years ago. Since that time, those primitive cells underwent evolutionary changes that ultimately gave rise to the species we see today.

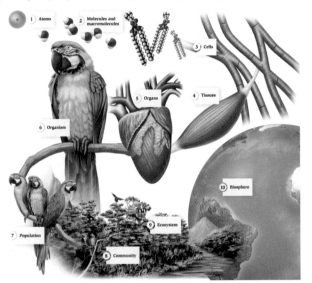

Figure 1.3   The levels of biological organization.

BIOLOGICAL INQUIRY QUESTIONS

These questions are designed to help students delve more deeply into a concept or experimental approach described in the art. These questions challenge a student to analyze the content of the figure they are looking at.

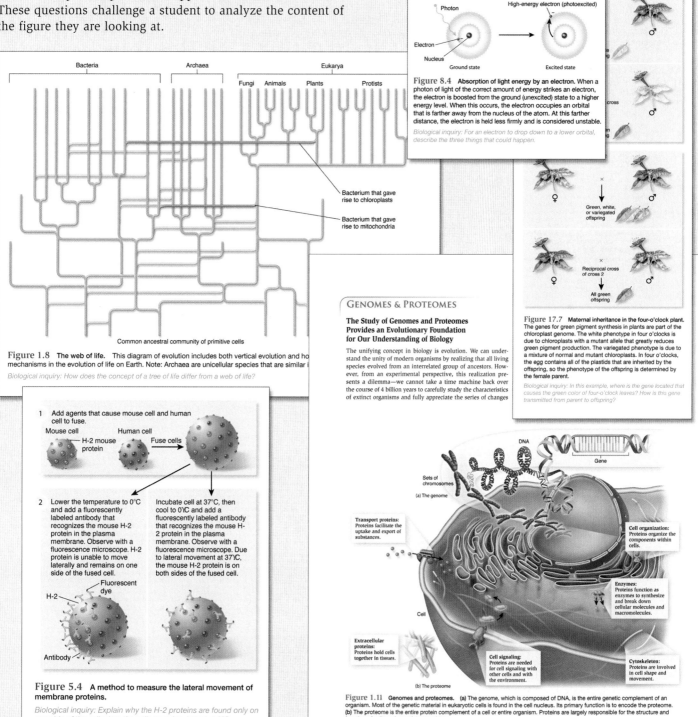

Bacteria   Archaea   Eukarya

Fungi   Animals   Plants   Protists

Bacterium that gave rise to chloroplasts

Bacterium that gave rise to mitochondria

Common ancestral community of primitive cells

Figure 1.8   The web of life. This diagram of evolution includes both vertical evolution and ho[rizontal] mechanisms in the evolution of life on Earth. Note: Archaea are unicellular species that are similar [...]

Biological inquiry: How does the concept of a tree of life differ from a web of life?

Photon

High-energy electron (photoexcited)

Electron

Nucleus

Ground state   Excited state

Figure 8.4   Absorption of light energy by an electron. When a photon of light of the correct amount of energy strikes an electron, the electron is boosted from the ground (unexcited) state to a higher energy level. When this occurs, the electron occupies an orbital that is farther away from the nucleus of the atom. At this farther distance, the electron is held less firmly and is considered unstable.

Biological inquiry: For an electron to drop down to a lower orbital, describe the three things that could happen.

Correns ' crosses

♂

cross

♀   ♂

Green, white, or variegated offspring

♀   Reciprocal cross of cross 2   ♂

All green offspring

Figure 17.7   Maternal inheritance in the four-o'clock plant. The genes for green pigment synthesis in plants are part of the chloroplast genome. The white phenotype in four o'clocks is due to chloroplasts with a mutant allele that greatly reduces green pigment production. The variegated phenotype is due to a mixture of normal and mutant chloroplasts. In four o'clocks, the egg contains all of the plastids that are inherited by the offspring, so the phenotype of the offspring is determined by the female parent.

Biological inquiry: In this example, where is the gene located that causes the green color of four-o'clock leaves? How is this gene transmitted from parent to offspring?

GENOMES & PROTEOMES

The Study of Genomes and Proteomes Provides an Evolutionary Foundation for Our Understanding of Biology

The unifying concept in biology is evolution. We can understand the unity of modern organisms by realizing that all living species evolved from an interrelated group of ancestors. However, from an experimental perspective, this realization presents a dilemma—we cannot take a time machine back over the course of 4 billion years to carefully study the characteristics of extinct organisms and fully appreciate the series of changes

---

1   Add agents that cause mouse cell and human cell to fuse.

Mouse cell   Human cell   Fuse cells

H-2 mouse protein

2   Lower the temperature to 0°C and add a fluorescently labeled antibody that recognizes the mouse H-2 protein in the plasma membrane. Observe with a fluorescence microscope. H-2 protein is unable to move laterally and remains on one side of the fused cell.

Incubate cell at 37°C, then cool to 0°C and add a fluorescently labeled antibody that recognizes the mouse H-2 protein in the plasma membrane. Observe with a fluorescence microscope. Due to lateral movement at 37°C, the mouse H-2 protein is on both sides of the fused cell.

Fluorescent dye

H-2

Antibody

Figure 5.4   A method to measure the lateral movement of membrane proteins.

Biological inquiry: Explain why the H-2 proteins are found only on one side of the cell when the cells were incubated at 0°C.

DNA

Gene

Sets of chromosomes

(a) The genome

Transport proteins: Proteins facilitate the uptake and export of substances.

Cell organization: Proteins organize the components within cells.

Enzymes: Proteins function as enzymes to synthesize and break down cellular molecules and macromolecules.

Cell

Extracellular proteins: Proteins hold cells together in tissues.

Cell signaling: Proteins are needed for cell signaling with other cells and with the environment.

Cytoskeleton: Proteins are involved in cell shape and movement.

(b) The proteome

Figure 1.11   Genomes and proteomes. (a) The genome, which is composed of DNA, is the entire genetic complement of an organism. Most of the genetic material in eukaryotic cells is found in the cell nucleus. Its primary function is to encode the proteome. (b) The proteome is the entire protein complement of a cell or entire organism. Proteins are largely responsible for the structure and function of cells and complete organisms.

Biological inquiry: Biologists sometimes say that the genome is a storage unit, while the proteome is largely the functional unit of life. Explain this statement.

EXPERIMENTAL & MODERN CONTENT

FEATURE INVESTIGATION

Nirenberg and Leder Found That RNA Triplets Can Promote the Binding of tRNA to Ribosomes

In 1964, Nirenberg and Leder discovered that RNA molecules containing any three nucleotides (that is, any triplet) can stim- ulate ribosomes to bind a tRNA molecule. In other words, an RNA triplet can act like a codon within an mRNA molecule. Ribosomes bind RNA triplets, and then a tRNA. Ribosomes bind RNA triplets, and then a tRNA with the appropriate anti- codon subsequently binds to the ribosome.

Figure 12.14 Nirenberg and Leder's use of triplet binding assays to decipher the genetic code.

Overview

HYPOTHESIS A triplet RNA can bind to a ribosome and promote the binding of the tRNA that carries the amino acid that the triplet RNA specifies.

STARTING MATERIALS Components of an *in vitro* translation system, including ribosomes and tRNAs. Preparations containing all of the different tRNA molecules were given 1 radiolabeled amino acid; the other 19 amino acids were nonlabeled. For example, in 1 sample, radiolabeled glycine was added and the other 19 amino acids were nonlabeled. In a different sample, radiolabeled proline was added and the other 19 amino acids were nonlabeled. The tRNA preparation also contained the enzymes that attach amino acids to tRNAs.

Steps

Experimental level   **Conceptual level**

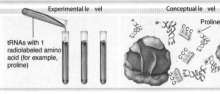

1 Mix together triplet RNAs of a specific sequence and ribosomes. In the example shown here, the triplet is 5'–CCC–3'. Add a tRNA sample to this mixture that contains 1 radiolabeled amino acid. (Note: Only 3 tubes are shown here. Because there are 20 different amino acids, this would be done in 20 different tubes.)

tRNAs with 1 radiolabeled amino acid (for example, proline)

Proline

Ribosome

2 Allow time for triplet RNA to bind to the ribosome, and for the appropriate tRNA to bind to the triplet RNA.

Radiolabeled proline

3 Pour mixture through a filter that allows the passage of unbound tRNA but does not allow the passage of ribosomes.

Ribosomes trapped on filter

Filter

Data & Analysis

5 THE DATA

Triplet	Radiolabeled amino acid trapped on the filter	Triplet
5' – AAA – 3'	Lysine	5' – GAC – 3'
5' – ACA – 3', 5' – ACC – 3'	Threonine	5' – GCC – 3'
5' – AGA – 3'	Arginine	5' – GGU – 3', 5' – GGC – 3'
5' – AUA – 3', 5' – AUU – 3'	Isoleucine	5' – GUU – 3'
5' – CCC – 3'	Proline	5' – UAU – 3'
5' – CGC – 3'	Arginine	5' – UGU – 3'
5' – GAA – 3'	Glutamic acid	5' – UUG – 3'

During bacterial translation, the mRNA lies on the surface of the 30S subunit, within a space between the 30S and 50S sub- units (Figure 12.18b). As a polypeptide is synthesized, it exits through a hole within the 50S subunit. Ribosomes contain dis- crete sites where tRNAs bind and the polypeptide is synthesized. In 1964, James Watson proposed a two-site model for tRNA bind- ing to the ribosome. These sites are known as the **peptidyl site (P site)** and **aminoacyl site (A site)**. In 1984, Knud Nierhaus and Hans-Jorg Rheinberger expanded this to a three-site model (Figure 12.18b). The third site is known as the **exit site (E site)**. Later, we will examine the roles of these sites in the synthesis of a polypeptide.

GENOMES & PROTEOMES

Comparisons of Small Subunit rRNAs Among Different Species Provide a Basis for Establishing Evolutionary Relationships

Translation is a fundamental process that is vital for the exis- tence of all living species. The components that are needed for translation arose very early in the evolution of life on our planet. In fact, they arose in an ancestor that gave rise to all known liv- ing species. For this reason, all organisms have translational components that are evolutionarily related to each other. For example, the rRNA found in the small subunit of ribosomes is similar in all forms of life, though it is slightly larger in eukary- otic species (18S) than in bacterial species (16S). In other words, the gene for the small subunit rRNA (SSU rRNA) is found in the genomes of all organisms.

One way that geneticists explore evolutionary relationships is to compare the sequences of evolutionarily related genes. At the molecular level, gene evolution involves changes in DNA sequences. After two different species have diverged from each other during evolution, the genes of each species have an oppor- tunity to accumulate changes, or mutations, that alter the se- quences of those genes. After many generations, evolutionarily related species contain genes that are similar but not identical to each other, because each species will accumulate different mutations. In general, if a very long time has elapsed since two species diverged evolutionarily, their genes tend to be quite dif- ferent. In contrast, if two species diverged relatively recently on an evolutionary time scale, their genes tend to be more similar.

Figure 12.19 compares a portion of the sequence of the small subunit rRNA gene from three mammalian and three bacterial species. The colors highlight different types of comparisons. The sequences shaded in yellow are identical in five or six species. Sequences that are identical in different species are said to be **evolutionarily conserved**. Presumably, these sequences were found in the primordial gene that gave rise to modern species and, because these sequences may have some critical function, have not been able to change over evolutionary time. Those sequences shaded in green are identical in all three mammals, but differ compared to one or more bacterial species. Actually, if you scan the mammalian species, you may notice that all three sequences are identical to each other in this region. The sequences shaded in red are identical in two or three bacterial species, but differ compared to the mammalian small subunit rRNA genes. The sequences from *E. coli* and *Serratia marcescens* are more similar to each other than the sequence from *Bacillus subtilis* is to either of them. This is consistent with the idea that *E. coli* and *S. marcescens* are more closely related evolutionarily than either of them is to *B. subtilis*.

12.6 The Stages of Translation

Like transcription, the process of translation occurs in three stages called initiation, elongation, and termination. Figure 12.20 provides an overview of the process. During initiation, mRNA, the first tRNA, and ribosomal subunits assemble into a complex. Next, in the elongation stage, the ribosome moves from the start codon in the mRNA toward the stop codon, syn- thesizing a polypeptide according to the sequence of codons in the mRNA. Finally, the process is terminated when the ribo- some reaches a stop codon and the complex disassembles, releas- ing the completed polypeptide. In this section, we will examine the steps in this process as they occur in living cells.

GATTAAGAGGGACGGCCGGGGGCATTCGTATTGCGCCGCTAGAGGTGAAATTC Human
GATTAAGAGGGACGGCCGGGGGCATTCGTATTGCGCCGCTAGAGGTGAAATTC Mouse
GATTAAGAGGGACGGCCGGGGGCATTCGTATTGCGCCGCTAGAGGTGAAATTC Rat
CAAGCTTGAGTCTCGTAGAGGGGGGTAGAATTCCAGGTGTAGCGGTGAAATGC E. coli
CAAGCTGAGTCTCGTAGAGGGGGGTAGAATTCCAGGTGTAGCGGTGAAATGC S. marcescens
GAGACTTGAGTACAGAAGAGAGAGTGGAATTCCACGTGTAGCGGTGAAATGC B. subtilis

Figure 12.19 Comparison of small subunit rRNA gene sequences from three eukaryotes and three bacterial species. Note the many similarities (yellow) and differences (green and red) among the sequences.

GENOMES AND PROTEOMES

Providing an evolutionary foundation for our understand- ing of biology, each Genomes and Proteomes subsection describes modern information regarding the genomic com- position of organisms and how this relates to proteomes (their protein composition) and evolution.

FEATURE INVESTIGATION

Focusing on hypothesis testing and discovery based science, the Feature Investigations describe a key experiment, including 1) an overview of the hypothesis or goal of the experiment, 2) the steps of the experiment, and 3) ending with an analysis of data. This encourages an appre- ciation of the scientific process.

END-OF-CHAPTER MATERIALS

The end-of-chapter materials offer students many different opportunities to focus in on key concepts and help them work at improving their knowledge:

Chapter Summary
The Chapter Summary provides the student with an overview of the biological principles and experimental approaches that have been described in the chapter. The summary is organized according to the sections of each chapter, and presents a bulleted list of key concepts.

Test Yourself
These multiple-choice questions are designed to provide students with the sense of how well they understand the material in the chapter. Answers are provided on the ARIS website.

Conceptual Questions
The aim of conceptual questions is to test a student's knowledge of biological principles, such as how a biological mechanism works or the features of a biological process or structure.

Experimental Questions
These questions challenge the student to consider the experiments found in a chapter and to critically evaluate technical procedures and analyze biological data.

Collaborative Questions
Broad in nature, students may benefit by discussing these questions with their peers.

CHAPTER SUMMARY

3.1   The Carbon Atom and the Study of Organic Molecules

- Organic chemistry is the science of studying carbon-containing molecules, which are found in living organisms. Wöhler's work with urea marked the birth of organic chemistry. (Figure 3.1)
- One property of the carbon atom that makes life possible is its ability to form four covalent bonds with other atoms. Carbon can form both polar and nonpolar bonds. The combination of different elements and different types of bonds allows a vast number of organic compounds to be formed from only a few chemical elements. (Figures 3.2, 3.3)
- Organic molecules may occur in various shapes. The structures of molecules determine their functions.

3.2   Classes of Organic Molecules and Macromolecules

- The four major classes of organic molecules are carbohydrates, lipids, proteins, and nucleic acids. Macromolecules are large organic molecules that are composed of many thousands of atoms. Some macromolecules are polymers because they are formed by linking together many smaller molecules called monomers.
- Carbohydrates are composed of carbon, hydrogen, and oxygen atoms. Most cells can break down carbohydrates, releasing energy and storing it in newly created bonds in ATP.
- Carbohydrates include monosaccharides (the simplest sugars), disaccharides, and polysaccharides. The polysaccharides starch (in plant cells) and glycogen (in animal cells) provide an efficient means of storing energy. The plant polysaccharide cellulose serves a support or structural function. (Figures 3.6, 3.7, 3.8)

TEST YOURSELF

1. Molecules that contain the element _____ are considered organic molecules.
   a. hydrogen
   b. carbon
   c. oxygen
   d. nitrogen
   e. calcium

2. _____ was the first scientist to synthesize an organic molecule. The organic molecule synthesized was _____.
   a. Kolbe, urea
   b. Wöhler, urea
   c. Wöhler, acetic acid
   d. Kolbe, acetic acid
   e. Wöhler, glucose

3. The versatility of carbon to serve as the backbone for a variety of different molecules is due to
   a. the ability of carbon atoms to form four covalent bonds.
   b. the fact that carbon usually forms ionic bonds with many different atoms.
   c. the abundance of carbon in the environment.
   d. the ability of carbon to form covalent bonds with many different types of atoms.
   e. both a and d.

CONCEPTUAL QUESTIONS

1. Define isomers.
2. List the four classes of organic molecules and give a function of each.
3. Explain the difference between saturated and unsaturated fatty acids.
4. List the seven characteristics of life and explain a little about each.
5. Give the levels of organization from the simplest to most complex.
6. Discuss the difference between discovery-based science and hypothesis testing.
7. What are the steps in the scientific method, also called hypothesis testing?
8. When conducting an experiment, explain how a control sample and an experimental sample differ from each other.

EXPERIMENTAL QUESTIONS

1. Before the experiments conducted by Anfinsen, what were the common beliefs among scientists about protein folding?
2. Explain the hypothesis tested by Anfinsen.
3. Why did Anfinsen use urea and β-mercaptoethanol in his experiments? Explain the result that was crucial to the discovery that the tertiary structure of a protein is dependent on the primary structure.
4. List the seven characteristics of life and explain a little about each.
5. Give the levels of organization from the simplest to most complex.
6. List the taxonomic groups from most inclusive to least inclusive.
7. Explain how actin filaments are involved in movement.
8. Explain the function of the Golgi apparatus.

COLLABORATIVE QUESTIONS

1. Discuss several types of carbohydrates.
2. Discuss some of the roles that proteins play in organisms. Discuss several differences between plant and animal cells.
3. Discuss the relationship between the nucleus, the rough endoplasmic reticulum, and the Golgi apparatus.
4. Discuss the two categories of transport proteins found in plasma membranes.

www.brookerbiology.com
This website includes answers to the Biological Inquiry questions found in the figure legends and all end-of-chapter questions.

Chapter Summary

Test Yourself

Conceptual Questions

Experimental Questions

Collaborative Questions

CONTENTS

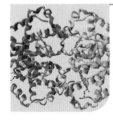
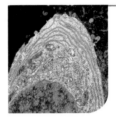

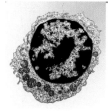

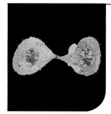
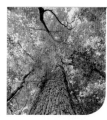

UNIT III   Genetics

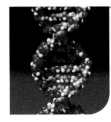

Chapter 11
Nucleic Acid Structure and DNA Replication

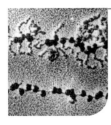

Chapter 12
Gene Expression at the Molecular Level

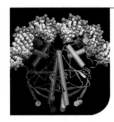

Chapter 13
Gene Regulation

Chapter 14
Mutation, DNA Repair, and Cancer

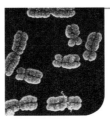

Chapter 15
Eukaryotic Chromosomes, Mitosis, and Meiosis

Chapter 16
Simple Patterns of Inheritance

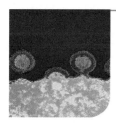

UNIT IV Evolution

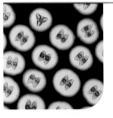

Chapter 29
The Kingdom Fungi

Chapter 30
Plants and the Conquest of Land

Chapter 31
The Diversity of Modern Gymnosperms and Angiosperms

Chapter 32
An Introduction to Animal Diversity

Chapter 33
The Invertebrates

Chapter 34
The Vertebrates

UNIT VI   Plants

Chapter 35
An Introduction to Flowering Plants

Chapter 36
Flowering Plants: Behavior

Chapter 37
Flowering Plants: Nutrition

Chapter 38
Flowering Plants: Transport

Chapter 39
Flowering Plants: Reproduction and Development

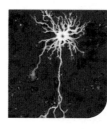
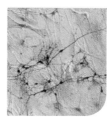

Chapter 46
The Muscular-Skeletal System and Locomotion

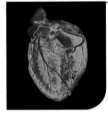

Chapter 47
Circulatory Systems

Chapter 48
Respiratory Systems

Chapter 49
Excretory Systems and Salt and Water Balance

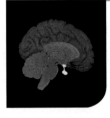

Chapter 50
Endocrine Systems

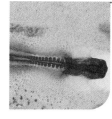
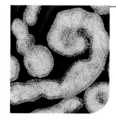

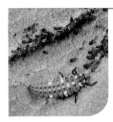

1

AN INTRODUCTION TO BIOLOGY

CHAPTER OUTLINE

Spotted and black jaguars.

Biology is the study of life. The diverse forms of life found on Earth provide biologists with an amazing array of organisms to study. In many cases, the investigation of living things leads to unforeseen discoveries that no one would have imagined. For example, researchers determined that the venom from certain poisonous snakes contains a chemical that lowers blood pressure in humans (**Figure 1.1a**). By analyzing that chemical, drugs were later developed to treat high blood pressure. Biologists also found that nine-banded armadillos usually give birth to identical quadruplets (**Figure 1.1b**). Because of this unique way of producing young, nine-banded armadillos are studied to learn more about multiple births and other reproductive issues. The ancient Romans discovered that the bark of the white willow tree can be used to fight fever (**Figure 1.1c**). Modern chemists determined that willow bark contains a substance called salicylic acid, which led to the development of the related compound acetylsalicylic acid, more commonly known as aspirin. In the last century, biologists studied soil bacteria that naturally produce "chemical weapons" to kill competing bacteria in their native environment (**Figure 1.1d**). These chemicals have been characterized and used to develop antibiotics such as streptomycin to treat bacterial infections. As you may have seen, jellyfish naturally produce a greenish glow (**Figure 1.1e**), which is due to a molecule they make called green fluorescent protein (GFP). Scientists have been able to transfer GFP to other organisms and use it as a research tool to study the functions of cells. GFP transferred to mice makes them glow in the dark! Finally, for many decades, biologists have known that the Pacific yew tree produces a toxin in its bark and needles that kills insects (**Figure 1.1f**). Since the 1990s, this toxin, known by the drug name Taxol®, has been used to treat patients with ovarian and breast cancer. These are but a few of the many discoveries that make biology an intriguing discipline. The study of life not only reveals the fascinating characteristics of living species but also leads to the development of drugs and research tools that benefit the lives of people.

To make new discoveries, biologists view life from many different perspectives. What is life made of? How is it organized? How do organisms reproduce? Sometimes, the questions posed by biologists are fundamental and even philosophical in nature. Where did we come from? Can we live forever? What is the physical basis for memory? Can we save endangered species? Biologists are scientific explorers looking for answers to some of the world's most enduring mysteries. Unraveling these mysteries presents an exciting challenge to the best and brightest minds. Our society has been substantially impacted by discoveries in biology, and future biologists will continue to make important advances. The rewards of a career in biology include the excitement of forging into uncharted territory, the thrill of making discoveries that affect the health and lives of people, and the impact of biology on the preservation of the environment and endangered species. For these and many other compelling reasons, students seeking challenging and rewarding careers may wish to choose biology as a lifelong pursuit.

In this chapter, we will begin our survey of biology by examining the basic features that are common to all living organisms. We will consider how evolution has led to the development of modern genomes—the entire genetic compositions of organisms—which can explain the unity and diversity that we observe among modern species. In the second section, we will explore the general approaches that scientists follow when making new discoveries.

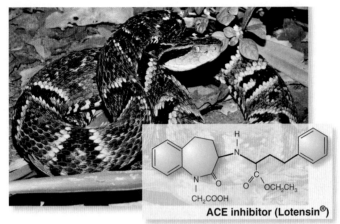

(a) A chemical in the venom of the Brazilian arrowhead viper lowers blood pressure. Derivatives of this chemical, called acetylcholinesterase (ACE) inhibitors, are now commonly used to treat high blood pressure in people.

(b) The nine-banded armadillo usually gives birth to identical quadruplets. Armadillos are studied by researchers to learn more about the mechanisms that cause multiple births.

(c) The bark of the white willow contains a chemical that is closely related to aspirin. Modern aspirin, acetylsalicylic acid, was developed after analyzing this chemical in willow trees.

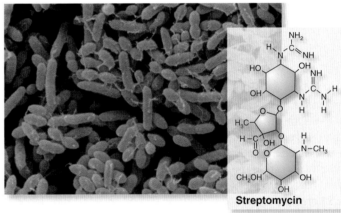

(d) This soil bacterium (*Streptomycin griseus*) naturally produces a molecule called streptomycin, which it uses to kill competing bacteria in the soil. Doctors administer streptomycin to people as an antibiotic to treat bacterial infections.

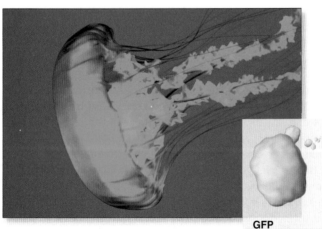

(e) Jellyfish naturally produce a green glow caused by green fluorescent protein (GFP). GFP can be transferred to other organisms, such as mice, and used as a research tool to study the functions of cells.

(f) The bark and needles of the Pacific yew tree produce a toxin that kills insects. This toxin, called Taxol, is effective in the treatment of ovarian and breast cancer.

Figure 1.1   Amazing discoveries in biology.

1.1 The Properties of Life: Past and Present

Unity and *diversity* are two words that often are used to describe the living world. Unity can be viewed from both modern and prehistorical perspectives. In this section, we first examine how all modern forms of life display a common set of characteristics that distinguish them from nonliving objects. This unity of common traits is rooted in the phenomenon of biological evolution. Life on Earth is united by an evolutionary past in which modern organisms have evolved from pre-existing organisms.

This evolutionary unity does not mean that organisms are exactly alike. Rather, the Earth has many different types of environments, ranging from tropical rain forests to salty oceans, hot and dry deserts, and cold mountaintops. Diverse forms of life have evolved to prosper in the myriad of environments that the Earth has to offer. In this section, we will also begin to examine the diversity that exists within the biological world.

A Set of Characteristics Is Common to All Forms of Modern Life

A fitting way to begin a biology textbook is to distinguish living organisms from nonliving objects. At first, the distinction might seem intuitively obvious. A person is alive, but a rock is not. However, the distinction between living and nonliving may seem less obvious when we consider microscopic entities. Is a bacterium alive? Is a virus alive? Is a chromosome alive? Biologists have wrestled with such questions and have determined that all living organisms display seven characteristics that set them apart from nonliving things.

Cells and Organization The concept of organization is so fundamental to biology that the term **organism** (which comes from the same Latin root, *organum*) can be applied to all living things. Organisms maintain an internal order that is separated from the environment (**Figure 1.2a**). The simplest unit of such organization is the **cell**, which we will examine in Unit II. The **cell theory** states that all organisms are made of cells. Unicellular organisms are composed of one cell, while multicellular organisms such as plants and animals contain many cells. In plants and animals, each cell has internal order, and the cells within the body have specific arrangements and functions.

Energy Use and Metabolism The maintenance of organization requires energy. Therefore, all living organisms acquire energy from the environment and use that energy to maintain their internal order. Cells use energy by catalyzing a variety of chemical reactions that are responsible for the breakdown of nutrients and the synthesis of the components that make up individual cells and living organisms. These chemical reactions are collectively known as **metabolism**. Plants, algae, and certain bacteria can directly harness light energy to produce their own nutrients in the process of **photosynthesis** (**Figure 1.2b**).

(a) Cells and organization: Organisms maintain an internal order. The simplest unit of organization is the cell.

(b) Energy use and metabolism: To maintain their internal order, energy is needed by organisms. Energy is utilized in chemical reactions collectively known as metabolism.

(c) Response to environmental changes: Organisms react to environmental changes to promote their survival.

(d) Regulation and homeostasis: Organisms regulate their cells and bodies to maintain relatively stable internal conditions, a process called homeostasis.

(e) Growth and development: Growth produces more or larger cells, while development produces organisms with a defined set of characteristics.

(f) Reproduction: To sustain life over many generations, organisms must reproduce. Due to genetic material, offspring tend to have traits like their parents.

(g) Biological evolution: Populations of organisms change over the course of many generations. Evolution results in traits that promote survival and reproductive success.

Figure 1.2 Seven characteristics that are common to life.

They are primary producers of food on Earth. In contrast, some organisms, such as animals and fungi, are consumers—they must eat other organisms as food to obtain energy.

Response to Environmental Changes To survive, living organisms must be able to respond to environmental changes. For example, bacterial cells have mechanisms to sense that certain nutrients in the environment are in short supply while others are readily available. Also, plants can respond to changes in the angle of the sun. If you place a plant in a window, it will grow toward the light (**Figure 1.2c**). In the winter, many species of mammals develop a thicker coat of fur to protect them from the cold temperatures. Responses to environmental changes are examples of **adaptations**—processes and structures by which organisms adjust to short-term or long-term changes in their environment.

Regulation and Homeostasis As we have just seen, one way that organisms can respond to environmental variation is to change themselves. The growth of thick fur in the wintertime is an example. A common reason for certain adaptations, including this example, is to maintain homeostasis (from the Greek meaning "to stay the same"). Although life is a dynamic process, living cells and organisms regulate their cells and bodies to maintain relatively stable internal conditions, a process called **homeostasis**. The degree to which homeostasis is achieved varies among different organisms. For example, most mammals and birds maintain a relatively constant body temperature in spite of changing environmental temperatures (**Figure 1.2d**), while reptiles and amphibians do not. By comparison, all organisms continually regulate their cellular metabolism so that nutrient molecules are used at an appropriate rate, and new cellular components are synthesized when they are needed.

Growth and Development All living things grow and develop; **growth** produces more or larger cells, while **development** produces organisms with a defined set of characteristics. Among unicellular organisms such as bacteria, new cells are relatively small, and they increase in volume by the synthesis of additional cellular components. Multicellular organisms, such as plants and animals, begin life at a single-cell stage (for example, a fertilized egg) and then undergo multiple cell divisions to develop into a complete organism with many cells (**Figure 1.2e**).

Reproduction All living organisms have a finite life span and will eventually die. To sustain life over many generations, organisms must **reproduce** (**Figure 1.2f**). A key feature of reproduction is that offspring tend to have characteristics that greatly resemble those of their parent(s). The reason for this is that all living organisms contain genetic material composed of **DNA (deoxyribonucleic acid)**, which provides a blueprint for the organization, development, and function of living things. As discussed in Unit III, DNA harbors **genes**, which contribute to the characteristics or traits of organisms. During reproduction, a copy of this blueprint is transmitted from parents to offspring. The central dogma of genetics is that most genes are transcribed into a type of RNA (ribonucleic acid) molecule called messenger RNA (mRNA) that is then translated into a polypeptide with a specific amino acid sequence. This process is called molecular gene expression. Polypeptides are the structural units of functional proteins. The functioning of proteins is largely responsible for the traits of living organisms.

Biological Evolution The first six characteristics of life, which we have just considered, apply to individual organisms over the short run. Over the long run, another universal characteristic of life is **biological evolution**, which refers to the phenomenon that populations of organisms change over the course of many generations. As a result of evolution, some organisms become more successful at survival and reproduction. Populations become better adapted to the environment in which they live. For example, the long snout of an anteater is an adaptation that enhances its ability to obtain food, namely ants (**Figure 1.2g**). The long snout occurred via biological evolution in which modern anteaters evolved from organisms that did not have such long snouts. Unit IV is devoted to the topic of evolution, while Unit V surveys the evolutionary diversity among different forms of life.

Living Organisms Can Be Viewed at Different Levels of Organization

As we have just learned, life exhibits a set of characteristics, beginning with the concept of organization. The organization of living organisms can be analyzed in a hierarchical manner, starting with the tiniest level of organization, and progressing to levels that are physically much larger and more complex. **Figure 1.3** depicts a scientist's view of biological organization at different levels.

1. **Atoms:** An **atom** is the smallest component of an element that has the chemical properties of the element. All matter is composed of atoms.
2. **Molecules and macromolecules:** As discussed in Unit I, atoms bond with each other to form **molecules**. When many molecules bond together to form a polymer, this is called a **macromolecule**. Carbohydrates, proteins, and nucleic acids (for example, DNA and RNA) are important macromolecules found in living organisms.
3. **Cells:** Molecules and macromolecules associate with each other to form larger structures such as membranes. A cell is formed from the association of these larger structures.
4. **Tissues:** In the case of multicellular organisms such as plants and animals, many cells of the same type associate with each other to form **tissues**. An example is muscle tissue.
5. **Organs:** An **organ** is composed of two or more types of tissue. For example, the heart of a parrot is composed of several types of tissues, including muscle, nervous, and connective tissue.
6. **Organism:** All living things can be called organisms. A single organism possesses the set of characteristics that define life. Biologists classify organisms as belonging to a particular **species**, which is a related group of organisms that share a distinctive form and set of attributes in nature.

The members of the same species are closely related genetically. In Units VI and VII, we will examine plants and animals at the level of cells, tissues, organs, and complete organisms.

7. **Population:** A group of organisms of the same species that occupy the same environment is called a **population**.

8. **Community:** A biological **community** is an assemblage of populations of different species. The types of species that are found in a community are determined by the environment and by the interactions of species with each other.

9. **Ecosystem:** Researchers may extend their work beyond living organisms and also study the environment. Ecologists analyze **ecosystems**, which are formed by interactions of a community of organisms with their physical environment. Unit VIII considers biology from populations to ecosystems.

10. **Biosphere:** The **biosphere** includes all of the places on the Earth where living organisms exist, encompassing the air, water, and land.

Modern Forms of Life Are Connected by an Evolutionary History

Life began on Earth as primitive cells about 3.5 to 4 billion years ago. Since that time, those primitive cells underwent evolutionary changes that ultimately gave rise to the species we see today.

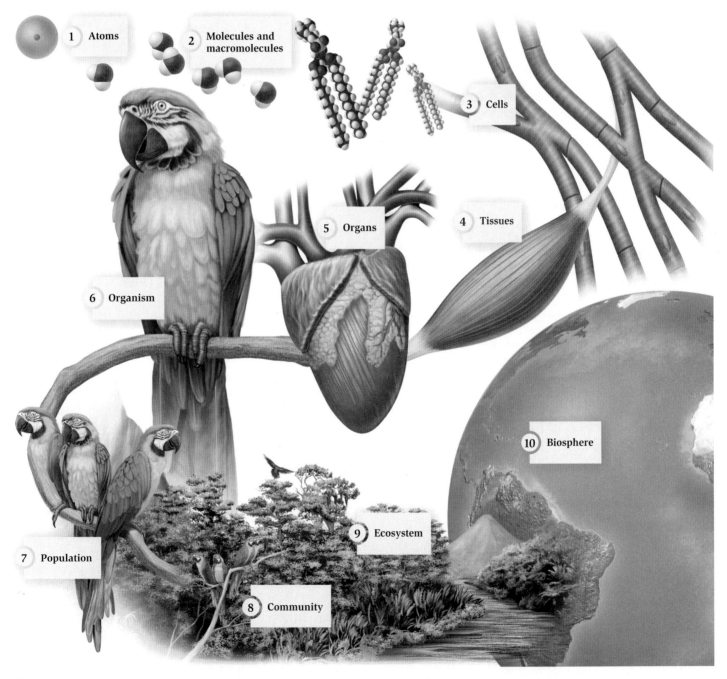

Figure 1.3   The levels of biological organization.

Figure 1.4   An example of modification of a structure for a new function.   The bird shown in the photograph has used a modified milk carton in which to build its nest. By analogy, evolution also involves the modification of pre-existing structures for a new function.

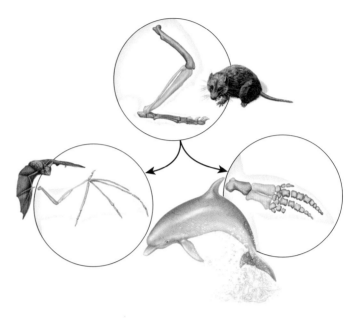

Figure 1.5   An example showing a modification that has occurred as a result of biological evolution.   The wing of a bat and the flipper of a dolphin were modified from a limb that was used for walking in a pre-existing ancestor.

Biological inquiry: Among mammals, give two examples of how the tail has been modified for different purposes.

Understanding the evolutionary history of species often provides key insights regarding the structure and function of an organism's body. As a metaphor to help you appreciate this idea, **Figure 1.4** shows a photograph of a bird that is using a milk carton in which to build a nest. If we did not know that the milk carton had served an earlier purpose, namely to contain milk, we might wonder why the bird had made a nesting site that resembled a milk carton. Obviously, we do not worry about this because we immediately grasp that the milk carton had a previous history, and that it has been modified by a person to serve a new purpose—a nesting site for a bird. Understanding history allows us to make sense out of this nest.

Likewise, evolutionary change involves modifications of characteristics in pre-existing populations. Over long periods of time, populations may change such that structures with a particular function may become modified to serve a new function. For example, the wing of a bat is used for flying, while the flipper of a dolphin is used for swimming (**Figure 1.5**). Both structures were modified from a limb that was used for walking in a pre-existing ancestor.

Evolutionary change occurs by two mechanisms, vertical descent with mutation and horizontal gene transfer. Let's take a brief look at each of these mechanisms.

Vertical Descent with Mutation   The traditional way to view evolution involves a progression of changes in a series of ancestors. Such a series is called a **lineage**. **Figure 1.6** shows a portion of the lineage that gave rise to modern horses. This type of evolution is called **vertical evolution** because biologists have traditionally depicted such evolutionary change in a

vertical diagram like the one shown in Figure 1.6. In this mechanism of evolution, new species evolve from pre-existing species by the accumulation of **mutations**, which are changes in the genetic material of organisms. But why would some mutations accumulate in a population and eventually change the characteristics of an entire species? One reason is that a mutation may alter the traits of organisms in a way that increases their chances of survival or reproduction. When a mutation causes such a beneficial change, the mutation is more likely to increase in a population over the course of many generations, a process called **natural selection**, which is discussed in Units IV and V. Evolution also involves the accumulation of neutral changes that do not benefit a species, and even rare changes that may be harmful.

Horizontal Gene Transfer   In addition to vertical evolution, which produces a lineage, species also evolve by another process that involves genetic exchanges between different species. Sexually reproducing species usually mate with members of their own species. Similarly, asexual species such as bacteria can occasionally transfer genetic material between cells, but again, that tends to occur most readily between members of the same bacterial species. However, on relatively rare occasions, genetic exchanges occur between different species. For example, you may have heard in the news media that resistance to antibiotics among bacteria is a growing medical problem. Genes that confer antibiotic resistance are sometimes transferred between different bacterial species (**Figure 1.7**).

When genes are transferred from one species to another, this event is called **horizontal gene transfer**. In a lineage in

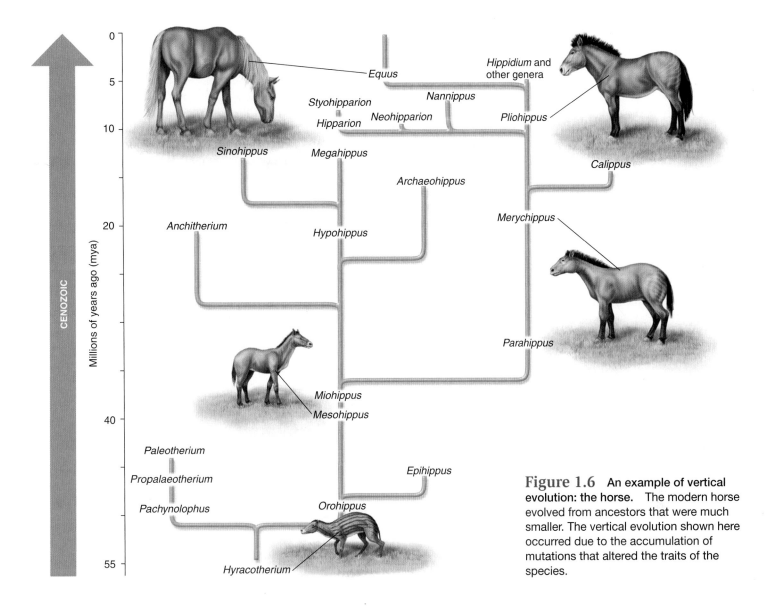

Figure 1.6 An example of vertical evolution: the horse.   The modern horse evolved from ancestors that were much smaller. The vertical evolution shown here occurred due to the accumulation of mutations that altered the traits of the species.

which the timescale is depicted on a vertical axis, horizontal gene transfer is shown as a horizontal line between two different species (**Figure 1.8**). Genes that are transferred horizontally may be acted upon by natural selection to eventually promote changes in an entire species. This has been an important mechanism of evolutionary change, particularly among bacterial species. In addition, during the early stages of evolution, which occurred a few billion years ago, horizontal gene transfer was an important part of the process that gave rise to all modern species.

Traditionally, biologists have described evolution using diagrams that depict the vertical evolution of species on a long timescale. This is the type of evolutionary tree that was shown in Figure 1.6. For many decades, the simplistic view held that all living organisms evolved from a common ancestor, resulting in a "tree of life," which could describe the vertical evolution that gave rise to all modern species. Now that we understand the great importance of horizontal gene transfer in the evolution of life on Earth, biologists have needed to re-evaluate the concept of evolution as it occurs over time. Rather than a tree of

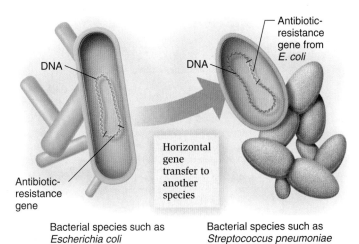

Figure 1.7 An example of horizontal gene transfer: antibiotic resistance.   One bacterial species may transfer a gene to a different bacterial species, such as a gene that confers resistance to an antibiotic.

life, a more appropriate way to view the unity of living organisms is to describe it as a "web of life," which accounts for both vertical evolution and horizontal gene transfer. Figure 1.8 illustrates such a diagram.

The Classification of Living Organisms Allows Biologists to Appreciate the Unity and Diversity of Life

As biologists discover new species, they try to place them in groups based on their evolutionary history. This is an arduous task because researchers estimate that the Earth has between 10 and 100 million different species! The rationale for categorization is usually based on vertical descent. Species with a recent common ancestor are grouped together, while species whose common ancestor is in the very distant past are placed into different groups. The grouping of species is termed **taxonomy**.

Let's first consider taxonomy on a broad scale. You may have noticed that Figure 1.8 showed three main groups of organisms.

All forms of life can be placed into three large categories or domains called **Bacteria**, **Archaea**, and **Eukarya** (**Figure 1.9**). Bacteria and Archaea are microorganisms that are also termed **prokaryotic** because their cell structure is relatively simple. At the molecular level, bacterial and archaeal cells show significant differences in their lipid composition, metabolic pathways, and mechanisms of gene expression. By comparison, organisms in domain Eukarya are **eukaryotic** and have larger cells with internal compartments that serve various functions. A defining distinction between prokaryotic and eukaryotic cells is that eukaryotic cells have a **cell nucleus** in which the genetic material is surrounded by a membrane. The organisms in domain Eukarya have been further subdivided into four major categories or kingdoms called Animalia (animals), Plantae (plants), Protista (protists), and Fungi. However, as discussed in Chapter 26 and Unit V, the traditional view of four eukaryotic kingdoms is now under revision as biologists have gathered new information regarding the evolutionary relationships of these organisms.

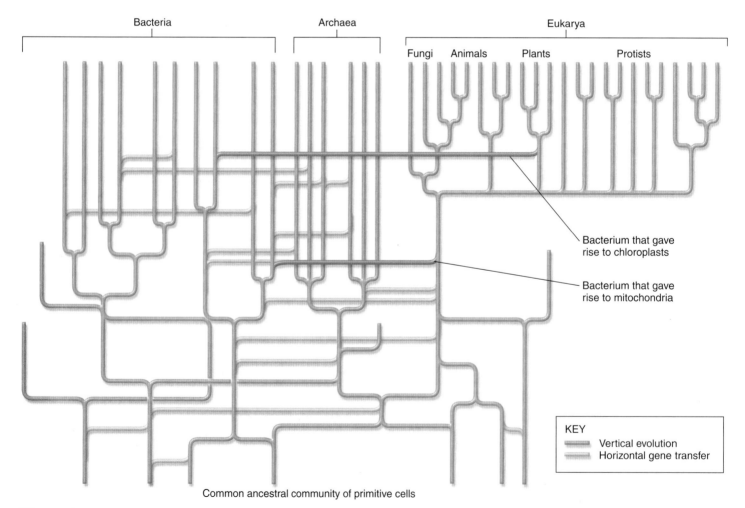

Figure 1.8   The web of life.   This diagram of evolution includes both vertical evolution and horizontal gene transfer as important mechanisms in the evolution of life on Earth. Note: Archaea are unicellular species that are similar in structure to bacteria.

Biological inquiry: How does the concept of a tree of life differ from a web of life?

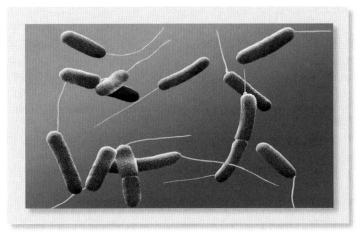

(a) Domain Bacteria: Unicellular prokaryotes that inhabit many diverse environments on Earth.

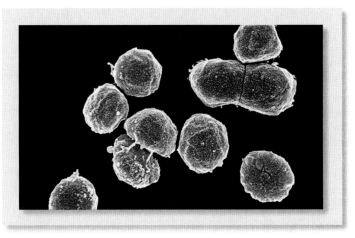

(b) Domain Archaea: Unicellular prokaryotes that are less common than bacteria. Some live in extreme environments such as hot springs.

Kingdom Animalia: Multicellular organisms that usually have a nervous system and are capable of locomotion. They must eat other organisms to live.

Kingdom Plantae: Multicellular organisms that can carry out photosynthesis.

Kingdom Protista: Unicellular and small multicellular organisms that are now subdivided into several different kingdoms based on their evolutionary relationships.

Kingdom Fungi: Unicellular and multicellular organisms that have a cell wall but cannot carry out photosynthesis. Fungi usually survive on decaying organic material.

(c) Domain Eukarya

Figure 1.9   **The three domains of life.**   Two of these domains, **(a)** Bacteria and **(b)** Archaea, are prokaryotes, while the third domain, **(c)** Eukarya, comprises species that are eukaryotes.

Taxonomy involves multiple levels in which particular species are placed into progressively smaller and smaller groups of organisms that are more closely related to each other evolutionarily (**Figure 1.10**). Such an approach emphasizes the unity and diversity of different species. As an example, let's consider the jaguars, shown on the cover of your textbook. The broadest grouping for the jaguar is the domain, namely Eukarya, followed by progressively smaller divisions, from kingdom (Animalia) to species. In the animal kingdom, jaguars are part of a phylum, Chordata, which is subdivided into classes. Jaguars are in a class called Mammalia, which includes all mammals. The common ancestor that gave rise to mammals arose over 200 million years ago. Mammalia is subdivided into several smaller orders. The jaguar is in the order Carnivora. The order is in turn divided into families; the jaguar and all other cats belong to the family Felidae. The genus *Panthera* is the smallest group of different species that contains the jaguar. As you can see in Figure 1.10, the genus contains only four modern species, the jaguar and other types of large cats. Therefore, the genus has species that are very similar to each other in form, and have evolved from a common (extinct) ancestor that lived relatively recently on an evolutionary timescale, approximately 5 million years ago.

Biologists use a two-part description, called a **binomial**, to provide each species with a unique scientific name. The scientific name of the jaguar is *Panthera onca*. The first part is the genus and the second part is the specific epithet or species descriptor. By convention, the genus name is capitalized, while the specific epithet is not. Both names are italicized. All scientific names are Latinized.

Taxonomic group	Jaguar is found in:	Approximate time when the common ancestor for this group arose	Approximate number of modern species in this group	
Domain	Eukarya	2,000 mya	> 5,000,000	
Kingdom	Animalia	600 mya	> 1,000,000	
Phylum	Chordata	525 mya	50,000	
Class	Mammalia	200 mya	5,000	
Order	Carnivora	60 mya	270	
Family	Felidae	40 mya	38	
Genus	*Panthera*	5 mya	4	
Species	*onca*	1.5 mya	1	

Figure 1.10 Taxonomic and evolutionary groupings leading to the jaguar.

GENOMES & PROTEOMES

The Study of Genomes and Proteomes Provides an Evolutionary Foundation for Our Understanding of Biology

The unifying concept in biology is evolution. We can understand the unity of modern organisms by realizing that all living species evolved from an interrelated group of ancestors. However, from an experimental perspective, this realization presents a dilemma—we cannot take a time machine back over the course of 4 billion years to carefully study the characteristics of extinct organisms and fully appreciate the series of changes that have led to modern species. Fortunately though, evolution has given experimental biologists a wonderful puzzle to study, namely the genomes of modern species. The term **genome** refers to *the complete genetic makeup of an organism* (**Figure 1.11a**). The genome is critical to life because it performs these functions:

- *Acts as a stable informational unit:* The genome of every organism stores information that provides a blueprint to create their characteristics.

- *Provides continuity from generation to generation:* The genome is copied and transmitted from generation to generation.

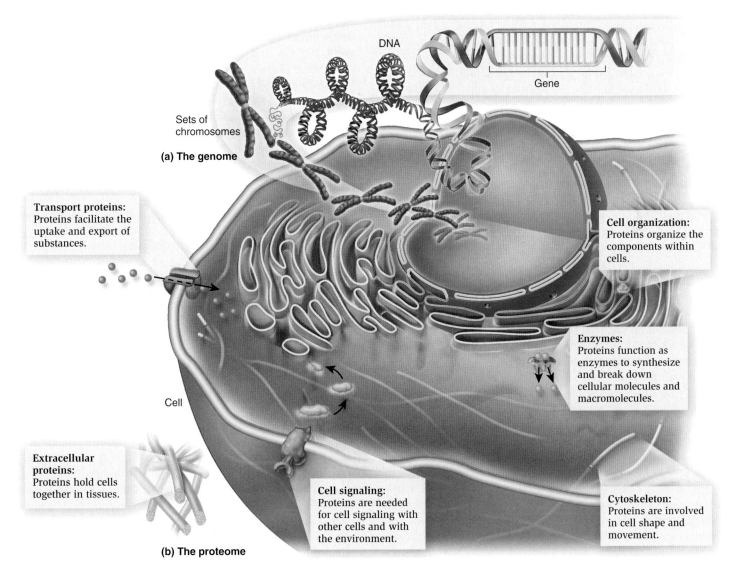

(a) The genome

(b) The proteome

Transport proteins: Proteins facilitate the uptake and export of substances.

Extracellular proteins: Proteins hold cells together in tissues.

Cell signaling: Proteins are needed for cell signaling with other cells and with the environment.

Cell organization: Proteins organize the components within cells.

Enzymes: Proteins function as enzymes to synthesize and break down cellular molecules and macromolecules.

Cytoskeleton: Proteins are involved in cell shape and movement.

Figure 1.11   **Genomes and proteomes.**   (a) The genome, which is composed of DNA, is the entire genetic complement of an organism. Most of the genetic material in eukaryotic cells is found in the cell nucleus. Its primary function is to encode the proteome. (b) The proteome is the entire protein complement of a cell or entire organism. Proteins are largely responsible for the structure and function of cells and complete organisms.

Biological inquiry: Biologists sometimes say that the genome is a storage unit, while the proteome is largely the functional unit of life. Explain this statement.

- *Acts as an instrument of evolutionary change:* Every now and then, the genome undergoes a mutation that may alter the characteristics of an organism. In addition, a genome may acquire new genes by horizontal gene transfer. The accumulation of such changes over the course of many generations produces the evolutionary changes that alter species and produce new species.

The evolutionary history and relatedness of all living organisms can be illuminated by genome analysis. The genome of every organism carries the results and the evidence of millions of years of evolution. The genomes of prokaryotes usually contain a few thousand genes, while those of eukaryotes may contain tens of thousands. An exciting advance in biology over the past couple of decades has been the ability to analyze the DNA sequence of genomes, a technology called **genomics**. For instance, we can compare the genomes of a frog, a giraffe, and a petunia and discover intriguing similarities and differences. These comparisons help us to understand how new traits evolved. For example, all three types of organisms have the same kinds of genes that are needed for the breakdown of nutrients such as sugars. In contrast, only the petunia carries genes that allow it to carry out photosynthesis.

An extension of genome analysis is the study of **proteomes**, which refers to *the complete complement of proteins that a cell or organism can make.* The function of most genes is to encode polypeptides that become units in proteins. As shown in **Figure 1.11b**, these include transport proteins; extracellular proteins; proteins that function in cell organization, in cell signaling, and as enzymes; and proteins that form a cytoskeleton. Proteins are the key participants in maintaining cell structure and carrying out most cell functions. Therefore, the genome of each species carries the information to make its proteome, the hundreds or thousands of proteins that each cell of that species makes. Proteins are largely responsible for the structures and functions of cells and organisms. The technical approach called **proteomics** involves the analysis of the proteome of a single species and the comparison of the proteomes of different species. Proteomics helps us to understand how the various levels of biology are related to one another, from the molecular level—at the level of protein molecules—to the higher levels, such as how the functioning of proteins produces the characteristics of cells and organisms, and the ability of populations of organisms to survive in their natural environments.

As a concrete way to understand the unifying theme of evolution in biology, a recurring theme in the chapters that follow is a brief topic called "Genomes & Proteomes" that will allow you to appreciate how evolution produced the characteristics of modern species. These topics explore how the genomes of different species are similar to each other, and how they are different. You will learn how genome changes affect the proteome and thereby control the traits of modern species. Ultimately, these concepts provide you with a way to relate information at the molecular level to the traits of organisms and their survival within ecosystems.

Along these lines, the cover of your textbook provides food for thought. The cats on the cover are jaguars. A black jaguar is sometimes called a panther, but it is still the same species, *Panthera onca*, as a spotted jaguar. How are the genomes of the spotted and black jaguars different? How are their proteomes different? Can this information tell us anything about the ecosystem in which these animals live? Does this have anything to do with evolutionary change? If we analyzed the genomes of spotted and black jaguars, we would discover that they are overwhelmingly similar to each other (**Figure 1.12a**). Of the 20,000 or so genes, the majority would be identical to each other or nearly so. However, based on their differences in appearance, we would expect the DNA sequence within one particular gene to be different, namely a gene that plays a role in producing pigment in the fur. At the level of the proteome, this slight genome difference causes the spotted jaguar to make proteins (enzymes) that synthesize a background coat pigment that is tan, while a black jaguar makes a background coat pigment that is black. Under bright light, you can see that a black jaguar actually has spots, but the dark background pigment greatly masks their appearance (**Figure 1.12b**).

Do spotted versus black coats have any impact on the life of these animals? The answer is yes. The spotted animals are thought to be better hunters in lighter grassland environments. The black animals are more likely to survive in darker forests, where they are less likely to be seen by their prey. In nature, mixed populations of spotted and black jaguars are often observed on the edges of forests, where both light and dark environments exist. Therefore, biologists have speculated that this is an example of evolutionary change. Genetic mutations have occurred that promote the survival and reproductive success of these animals, which vary in light and dark environments.

1.2 Biology as a Scientific Discipline

What is science? Surprisingly, the definition of science is not easy to state. Most people have an idea of what science is, but actually articulating that idea proves difficult. In biology, we might define **science** as *the observation, identification, experimental investigation, and theoretical explanation of natural phenomena.*

Science is conducted in different ways and at different levels. Some biologists study the molecules that compose life, while others try to understand how organisms survive in their natural environments. In some cases, experiments are designed to test the validity of ideas that are suggested by researchers. In this section, we will examine how biologists follow a standard approach, called the **scientific method**, to test their ideas. We will learn that scientific insight is not based on intuition. Instead, scientific knowledge makes predictions that can be experimentally tested.

Even so, not all discoveries are the result of researchers following the scientific method. Some discoveries are simply made

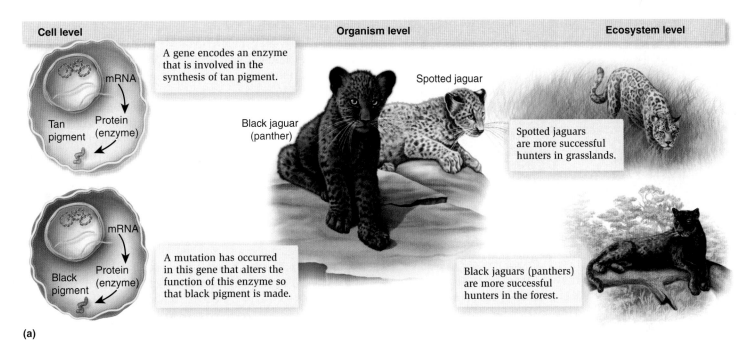

| Cell level | Organism level | Ecosystem level |

A gene encodes an enzyme that is involved in the synthesis of tan pigment.

Tan pigment — Protein (enzyme)

mRNA

Black jaguar (panther)

Spotted jaguar

Spotted jaguars are more successful hunters in grasslands.

mRNA

Black pigment — Protein (enzyme)

A mutation has occurred in this gene that alters the function of this enzyme so that black pigment is made.

Black jaguars (panthers) are more successful hunters in the forest.

(a)

(b)

Figure 1.12 How the study of genomes and proteomes can provide us with connections to different biological levels. (a) Spotted jaguars differ from panthers because they make an enzyme that produces a tan pigment, while a mutation in the same gene in panthers results in black pigment. With regard to hunting success, the spotted jaguars are better in grasslands, while the panthers are better in the forest. (b) A close-up view of a panther, showing its spots.

by gathering new information. As described earlier in Figure 1.1, the characterization of many plants and animals has led to the development of many important medicines and research tools. In this section, we will also consider how researchers often set out on "fact-finding missions" that are aimed at uncovering new information that may eventually lead to new discoveries in biology.

Biologists Investigate Life at Different Levels of Organization

Earlier in Figure 1.3, we examined the various levels of biological organization. The study of these different levels depends not only on the scientific interests of biologists but also on the tools that are available to them. Prior to the development of high-quality microscopes, biologists primarily focused their attention on characteristics they could observe with their unaided eyes. They studied the activities of organisms in their natural environments, a branch of biology called **ecology** (**Figure 1.13a**). In addition, researchers have examined the structures and functions of plants and animals, which are disciplines called **anatomy** and **physiology** (**Figure 1.13b**). As microscope technology improved, many researchers shifted their attention to the study of

cells. **Cell biology**, which is the study of cells, became an important branch of biology in the early 1900s and remains so today (**Figure 1.13c**). In the 1970s, genetic tools became available to study single genes and the proteins they encode. This genetic technology enabled researchers to study individual molecules, such as proteins, in living cells. Genetic technology spawned the field of **molecular biology**. Together with the efforts of chemists and biochemists, molecular biologists focus their efforts on the structure and function of the molecules of life (**Figure 1.13d**). Such researchers want to understand how biology works at the molecular and even atomic levels. Overall, the 20th century saw a progressive increase in the number of biologists who used a reductionist approach to understand biology. **Reductionism** involves reducing complex systems to simpler components as a way to understand how the system works. In biology, reductionists study the parts of a cell or organism as individual units.

In the 1980s, the pendulum began to swing in the other direction. Scientists have invented new tools that allow us to study groups of genes (genomic techniques) and groups of proteins (proteomic techniques). Biologists now use the term **systems biology** to describe research that is aimed at understanding how the properties of life arise by complex interactions.

Ecologists study species in their native environments.

(a) Ecology—population/ community/ecosystem levels

Anatomists and physiologists study how the structure of organisms are related to their functions.

(b) Anatomy and physiology— tissue/organ/organism levels

Cell biologists often use the microscope to learn how cells function.

(c) Cell biology—cellular levels

Molecular biologists and biochemists study the molecules and macromolecules that make up cells.

(d) Molecular biology— molecular/atomic levels

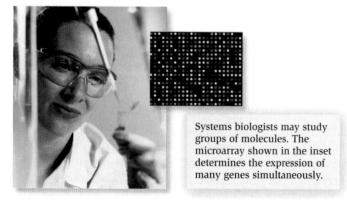

Systems biologists may study groups of molecules. The microarray shown in the inset determines the expression of many genes simultaneously.

(e) Systems biology—all levels, shown here at the molecular level

Figure 1.13   Biological investigation at different levels.

This term is often applied to the study of cells. In this context, systems biology may involve the investigation of groups of proteins with a common goal (**Figure 1.13e**). For example, a systems biologist may conduct experiments that try to characterize an entire cellular process, which is driven by dozens of different proteins. Systems biology is not new. Animal and plant physiologists have been studying the functions of complex organ systems for centuries. Likewise, ecologists have been characterizing ecosystems for a very long time. The novelty and excitement of systems biology in recent years has been the result of new experimental tools that allow us to study complex interactions at the molecular level. As described throughout this textbook, the investigation of genomes and proteomes has provided important insights regarding many interesting topics in systems biology. For example, as discussed in Chapter 6, systems biology has enabled researchers to understand how the various parts of a cell work together as an integrated system.

A Hypothesis Is a Proposed Idea, While a Theory Is a Broad Explanation Backed by Extensive Evidence

Let's now consider the process of science. In biology, a **hypothesis** is a proposed explanation for a natural phenomenon. It is a proposition based on previous observations or experimental studies. For example, with knowledge of seasonal changes, you might hypothesize that maple trees drop their leaves in the autumn because of the shortened amount of daylight. An alternative hypothesis might be that the trees drop their leaves because of colder temperatures. In biology, a hypothesis requires more work by researchers to either accept or reject it.

A useful hypothesis must make predictions that can be shown to be correct or incorrect. The validity of the predictions is usually determined by additional observations or experimentation. If the predictions do not agree with new data, the hypothesis is rejected. Alternatively, a hypothesis may be correct so that further work will not disprove it. Even so, a hypothesis is never really proven but rather always remains provisional. Researchers accept the possibility that perhaps they have not yet conceived of the correct hypothesis. However, after many experiments, biologists may say that they accept a hypothesis, but they should never say that the hypothesis is proven.

By comparison, the term **theory**, as it is used in biology, is a broad explanation of some aspect of the natural world that is substantiated by a large body of evidence. Biological theories incorporate observations, hypothesis testing, and the laws of other disciplines such as chemistry and physics. The power of theories is that they allow us to make many predictions regarding the properties of living organisms. As an example, let's consider the theory that DNA is the genetic material, and that it is organized into units called genes. An overwhelming body of evidence has substantiated this theory. Thousands of living species have been analyzed, and all of them have been found to use DNA as their genetic material, and to express genes that produce the proteins that lead to their characteristics. This theory makes many valid predictions. For example, certain types of mutations in genes are expected to affect the traits of organisms. This prediction has been confirmed experimentally. Similarly, genetic material is copied and transmitted from parents to offspring. By comparing the DNA of parents and offspring, this prediction has also been confirmed. Furthermore, the theory explains the observation that offspring resemble their parents. Overall, two key attributes of a scientific theory are consistency with a vast amount of known data, and the ability to make many correct predictions. Two other important biological theories that we have touched on in this chapter are the cell theory and the theory of evolution by natural selection.

The meaning of the term *theory* is sometimes muddled because it is used in different situations. In everyday language, a "theory" is often viewed as little more than a guess or a hypothesis. For example, a person might say, "My theory is that Professor Simpson did not come to class today because he went to the beach." However, in biology, a theory is much more than a guess. A theory is an established set of ideas that explains a vast amount of data and offers valid predictions that can be tested. Like a hypothesis, a theory can never be proven to be true. Scientists acknowledge that they do not know everything. Even so, biologists would say that theories are extremely likely to be true, based on all known information. In this regard, theories are viewed as **knowledge**, which is the awareness and understanding of information.

Discovery-Based Science and Hypothesis Testing Are Scientific Approaches That Help Us Understand Biology

The path that leads to an important discovery is rarely a straight line. Rather, scientists ask questions, make observations, ask modified questions, and may eventually conduct experiments to test their hypotheses. The first attempts at experimentation may fail, and new experimental approaches may be needed. To suggest that scientists follow a rigid scientific method is an oversimplification of the process of science. Scientific advances often occur as scientists dig deeper and deeper into a topic that interests them. Curiosity is the key phenomenon that sparks scientific inquiry. As discussed next, researchers typically follow two general types of approaches—discovery-based science and hypothesis testing.

Discovery-Based Science The collection and analysis of data without the need for a preconceived hypothesis is called **discovery-based science** or simply **discovery science**. The information gained from discovery-based science may have practical applications that benefit people. Drug companies, for example, may test hundreds or even thousands of drugs to determine if any of them are useful in the treatment of disease (**Figure 1.14a**). Once a drug has been discovered that is effective in disease treatment, researchers may dig deeper and try to understand how the drug exerts its effects. In this way, discovery-based science may help us learn about basic concepts in medicine

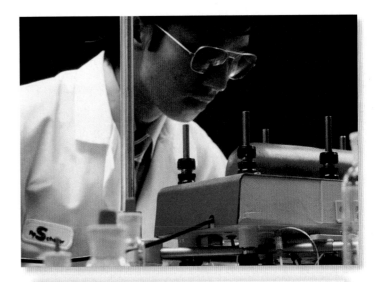

Drug companies may screen hundreds or thousands of different compounds trying to discover ones that may prove effective in the treatment of a particular disease.

(a) Drug discovery

Genetic researchers search through the genomes of humans and other species trying to discover new genes. Such discoveries may help us understand molecular biology and provide insight into the causes of inherited diseases in people.

(b) Discovery of genes

Figure 1.14 Discovery-based science.

and biology. Another example involves the study of genomes (**Figure 1.14b**). Over the past few decades, researchers have identified and begun to investigate newly discovered genes within the human genome without already knowing the function of the gene they are studying. The goal is to gather additional clues that may eventually allow them to propose a hypothesis that explains the gene's function. Discovery-based science often leads to hypothesis testing.

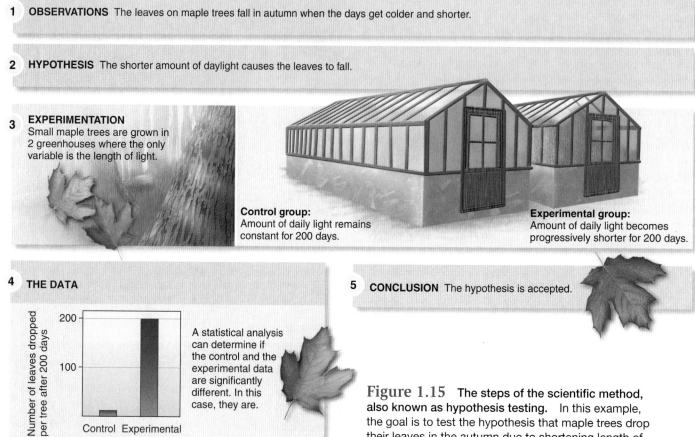

1 **OBSERVATIONS** The leaves on maple trees fall in autumn when the days get colder and shorter.

2 **HYPOTHESIS** The shorter amount of daylight causes the leaves to fall.

3 **EXPERIMENTATION**
Small maple trees are grown in 2 greenhouses where the only variable is the length of light.

Control group:
Amount of daily light remains constant for 200 days.

Experimental group:
Amount of daily light becomes progressively shorter for 200 days.

4 **THE DATA**

A statistical analysis can determine if the control and the experimental data are significantly different. In this case, they are.

(graph: y-axis "Number of leaves dropped per tree after 200 days" marked 100, 200; x-axis "Control group" and "Experimental group")

5 **CONCLUSION** The hypothesis is accepted.

Figure 1.15 The steps of the scientific method, also known as hypothesis testing. In this example, the goal is to test the hypothesis that maple trees drop their leaves in the autumn due to shortening length of daylight.

Hypothesis Testing In biological science, the scientific method, also known as **hypothesis testing**, is often followed to test the validity of a hypothesis. This strategy may be described as a five-stage process:

1. Observations are made regarding natural phenomena.
2. These observations lead to a hypothesis that tries to explain the phenomena. As mentioned, a useful hypothesis is one that is testable because it makes specific predictions.
3. Experimentation is conducted to determine if the predictions are correct.
4. The data from the experiment are analyzed.
5. The hypothesis is accepted or rejected.

The scientific method is intended to be an objective way to gather knowledge.

As an example, let's return to our scenario of maple trees dropping their leaves in autumn. By observing the length of daylight throughout the year, and comparing that data with the time of the year when leaves fall, one hypothesis might be that shorter daylight causes the leaves to fall (**Figure 1.15**). This hypothesis makes a prediction—exposure of maple trees to shorter daylight will cause their leaves to fall. To test this prediction, researchers would design and conduct an experiment.

Although hypothesis testing may follow many paths, certain experimental features are common to this approach. First, data are often collected in two parallel manners. One set of experi-

ments is done on the **control sample**, while another set is conducted on the **experimental sample**. In an ideal experiment, the control and experimental samples differ by only one factor. For example, an experiment could be conducted in which two groups of trees would be observed and the only difference between their environments would be the length of light each day. To conduct such an experiment, researchers would grow small trees in a greenhouse where they could keep factors such as temperature and water the same between the control and experimental samples, while providing them with different amounts of daylight. In the control group, the number of hours of light provided by light bulbs would be kept constant each day, while in the experimental group, the amount of light each day would become progressively shorter to mimic seasonal light changes. The researchers would then record the amount of leaves that were dropped by the two groups of trees over a certain period of time.

Another key feature of hypothesis testing is data analysis. The result of experimentation is a set of data from which a biologist tries to draw conclusions. Biology is a quantitative science. As such, data often come in the form of numbers that may or may not have important meaning. When experimentation involves a control and experimental sample, a common form of analysis is to determine if the data collected from the two samples are significantly different from each other. In this regard, the word *significant* means statistically significant. Biologists apply statistical analyses to their data to determine if the control and experimental samples are likely to be different from each other because of the single variable that is different between the two samples. When they are statistically significant, this means that the differences between the control and experimental data are not likely to have occurred as a matter of random chance. In our tree example shown in Figure 1.15, the trees in the control sample dropped far fewer leaves than did those in the experimental sample. A statistical analysis could determine if the data collected from the two greenhouses are significantly different from each other. If the two sets of data are found not to be significantly different, we would reject our hypothesis. Alternatively, if the differences between the two sets of data are significant, as shown in Figure 1.15, we would accept our hypothesis, though it is not proven.

As described next, discovery-based science and hypothesis testing are often used together to learn more about a particular scientific topic. As an example, let's look at how both approaches have led to successes in the study of the disease called cystic fibrosis.

The Study of Cystic Fibrosis Provides Examples of Both Discovery-Based Science and Hypothesis Testing

Let's consider how biologists made discoveries related to cystic fibrosis (CF), which affects about 1 in every 3,500 Americans. Persons with CF produce abnormally thick and sticky mucus that obstructs the lungs and causes life-threatening lung infections. The thick mucus also blocks the pancreas, which prevents the digestive enzymes that this organ produces from reaching the intestine. For this reason, CF patients tend to have excessive appetites but poor weight gain. Persons with this disease may also experience liver damage because the thick mucus can obstruct the liver. The average life span for people with CF is currently in their mid- to late 30s. Fortunately, as more advances have been made in treatment, this number has steadily increased.

Because of its medical significance, many scientists are interested in this disorder and have conducted studies aimed at gaining greater information regarding its underlying cause. The hope is that a better understanding of the disorder may lead to improved treatment options, and perhaps even a cure. As described next, discovery-based science and hypothesis testing have been critical to gaining a better understanding of this disorder.

The CF Gene and Discovery-Based Science In 1945, Dorothy Anderson determined that cystic fibrosis is a genetic disorder. Persons with CF have inherited two faulty *CF* genes, one from each parent. Over 40 years later, researchers used discovery-based science to identify the *CF* gene. Their search for the *CF* gene did not require any preconceived hypothesis regarding the function of the gene. Rather, they used genetic strategies that are similar to those described in Chapter 20. In 1989, research groups headed by Lap-Chi Tsui, Francis Collins, and John Riordan identified the *CF* gene.

The discovery of the gene made it possible to devise diagnostic testing methods to determine if a person carries a faulty *CF* gene. In addition, the identification of the *CF* gene may provide a potential treatment option for people with this disorder.

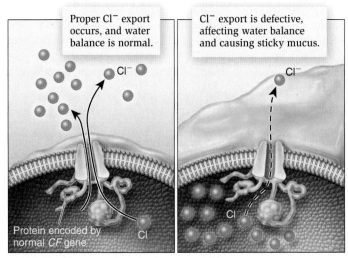

Lung cell with nomal *CF* gene   Lung cell with faulty *CF* gene

Figure 1.16   A hypothesis that suggests an explanation of the function of the gene that is defective in patients with cystic fibrosis.   The normal *CF* gene, which does not carry a mutation, encodes a transporter protein that transports chloride ions (Cl⁻) across the plasma membrane to the outside of the cell. In persons with CF, this transporter is defective due to a mutation in the *CF* gene.

Biological inquiry: Explain how discovery-based science helped researchers to hypothesize that the CF gene encodes a transporter protein.

As discussed in Chapter 20, gene therapy is a technology in which persons with a faulty gene are given treatments that involve the introduction of the normal gene into their bodies. Clinical trials are underway to determine if the *CF* gene from normal individuals can be used to overcome the symptoms of the faulty gene in CF patients.

The characterization of the *CF* gene provided important clues regarding its function. Researchers observed striking similarities between the *CF* gene and other genes that were already known to encode proteins called transporters that function in the transport of substances across membranes. Based on this observation, as well as other kinds of data, the researchers hypothesized that the function of the normal *CF* gene is to encode a transporter. In this way, the identification of the *CF* gene led researchers to conduct experiments that were aimed at testing a hypothesis of its function.

The CF Gene and Hypothesis Testing Based on the characterization of the *CF* gene and on other studies showing that patients with the disorder have an abnormal regulation of salt balance across their plasma membranes, researchers hypothesized that the normal *CF* gene encodes a protein that transports chloride ions (Cl⁻), a component of common table salt (NaCl), across the membrane of cells (**Figure 1.16**). This hypothesis led to experimentation in which researchers tested normal cells and cells from CF patients for their ability to transport Cl⁻. The CF cells were found to be defective in chloride transport. In 1990, scientists successfully transferred the normal gene to CF cells in the laboratory.

The introduction of the normal *CF* gene into the cells from CF patients corrected the defect in chloride transport. Overall, the results showed that the *CF* gene encodes a protein that transports Cl⁻ across the plasma membrane. A mutation in this gene causes it to encode a defective transporter protein, leading to a salt imbalance that affects water levels outside the cell, which explains the thick and sticky mucus in CF patients. In this example, hypothesis testing has provided a way to accept or reject an idea regarding how a disease is caused by a genetic change.

FEATURE INVESTIGATION

Observation and Experimentation Form the Core of Biology

Because biology is the study of life, a biology textbook that focuses only on a description of living organisms would miss the main point. Biology is largely about the process of discovery. Therefore, a recurring theme of this textbook is discovery-based science and hypothesis testing. While each chapter contains many examples of data collection and experiments, a consistent element is a "Feature Investigation"—an actual study by current or past researchers. Some of these involve discovery-based science in which biologists collect and analyze data in an attempt to make discoveries that are not hypothesis driven. Alternatively, most Feature Investigations involve hypothesis testing in which a hypothesis is stated, and the experiment and resulting data are presented.

The Feature Investigations allow you to appreciate the connection between science and scientific theories. We hope you will find this a more interesting and rewarding way to learn about biology. As you read a Feature Investigation, you may find yourself thinking about different approaches and alternative hypotheses. Different people can view the same data and arrive at very different conclusions. As you progress through the experiments in this textbook, you will enjoy biology far more if you try to develop your own skills at formulating hypotheses, designing experiments, and interpreting data.

Finally, it is worthwhile to point out that science is a social discipline. After performing observations and experiments, scientists report their conclusions to the scientific community (**Figure 1.17**). They comment on each other's ideas and work, eventually shaping together the information that builds into scientific theories over many years. As you develop your skills at scrutinizing experiments, it is satisfying to discuss your ideas with other people, including fellow students and faculty members. Importantly, you do not need to "know all the answers" before you enter into a scientific discussion. Instead, a more rewarding way to view science is as an ongoing and never-ending series of questions.

Figure 1.17   **The social aspects of science.**   At scientific meetings, researchers gather together to discuss new data and discoveries. Research that is conducted by professors, students, lab technicians, and industrial participants is sometimes hotly debated.

CHAPTER SUMMARY

- Biology is the study of life. Discoveries in biology help us understand how life exists, and they also have many practical applications such as the development of drugs to treat human diseases. (Figure 1.1)

1.1   The Properties of Life: Past and Present

- Seven characteristics are common to all forms of life. All living things (1) are composed of cells; (2) use energy; (3) respond to environmental changes; (4) regulate their internal conditions (homeostasis); (5) grow and develop; (6) reproduce; and (7) evolve over the course of many generations. (Figure 1.2)

- Living organisms can be viewed at different levels of complexity: atoms, molecules and macromolecules, cells, tissues, organs, organisms, populations, communities, ecosystems, and the biosphere. (Figure 1.3)

- Changes in species often occur as a result of modification of pre-existing structures. (Figures 1.4, 1.5)

- Vertical evolution involves mutations in a lineage that alter the characteristics of species over many generations. During this process, natural selection results in the survival of individuals with greater reproductive success. Over the long run, this process alters species and may produce new species. (Figure 1.6)

- Horizontal gene transfer is the transfer of genes between different species. Along with vertical evolution, it is also an important force in biological evolution. (Figures 1.7, 1.8)

- Taxonomy involves the grouping of species according to their evolutionary relatedness to other species. Going from broad to narrow, each species is placed into a domain, kingdom, phylum, class, order, family, and genus. (Figures 1.9, 1.10)

- The genome is the genetic composition of a species. It provides a blueprint for the traits of an organism, is transmitted from parents to offspring, and acts as an instrument for evolutionary change. The proteome is the collection of proteins that a cell or organism can make. Each chapter in this textbook has a brief discussion of "Genomes & Proteomes" for you to understand this fundamental concept in biology. (Figure 1.11)

- An understanding of genomes and proteomes helps us to understand the characteristics of individuals and how they survive in their native environments. (Figure 1.12, and book cover)

1.2 Biology as a Scientific Discipline

- Biological science involves the observation, identification, experimental investigation, and theoretical explanation of natural phenomena.

- Biologists study life at different levels, ranging from ecosystems to molecular components in cells. (Figure 1.13)

- A hypothesis is a proposal to explain a natural phenomenon. A biological theory is a broad explanation that makes many valid predictions. A theory is based on vast amounts of data.

- Discovery-based science is an approach in which researchers conduct experiments without a preconceived hypothesis. It is a fact-finding mission. (Figure 1.14)

- The scientific method, also called hypothesis testing, is a series of steps to test the validity of a hypothesis. The experimentation often involves a comparison between control and experimental samples. (Figure 1.15)

- The study of cystic fibrosis is an interesting example in which both discovery-based science and hypothesis testing have provided key insights regarding the nature of the disease. (Figure 1.16)

- Each chapter in this textbook has a "Feature Investigation" to help you appreciate how science has led to key discoveries in biology.

- Advances in science often occur when scientists gather together and discuss their data. (Figure 1.17)

TEST YOURSELF

1. The process where living organisms maintain a relatively stable internal condition is
   a. adaptation.
   b. evolution.
   c. metabolism.
   d. homeostasis.
   e. development.

2. Populations of organisms change over the course of many generations. Many of these changes result in increased survival and reproduction. This phenomenon is
   a. evolution.
   b. homeostasis.
   c. development.
   d. genetics.
   e. metabolism.

3. All of the places on Earth where living organisms are found is
   a. the ecosystem.
   b. a community.
   c. the biosphere.
   d. a viable land mass.
   e. a population.

4. Horizontal evolution is the result of
   a. accumulation of mutations over many generations.
   b. transfer of genetic material between individuals of different species.
   c. transfer of genetic material from parent to offspring.
   d. all of the above.
   e. a and c only.

5. The scientific name for humans is *Homo sapiens*. The name *Homo* is the _____ to which humans are classified.
   a. kingdom
   b. phylum
   c. order
   d. genus
   e. species

6. The complete genetic makeup of an organism is called
   a. the genus.
   b. the genome.
   c. the proteome.
   d. the genotype.
   e. the phenotype.

7. A proposed explanation for a natural phenomenon is
   a. a theory.
   b. a law.
   c. a prediction.
   d. a hypothesis.
   e. an assay.

8. In science, a theory should
   a. be equated with knowledge.
   b. be supported by a substantial body of evidence.
   c. provide the ability to make many correct predictions.
   d. all of the above.
   e. b and c only.

9. Conducting research without a preconceived hypothesis is called
   a. discovery-based science.
   b. the scientific method.
   c. hypothesis testing.
   d. a control experiment.
   e. none of the above.

10. What is the purpose of using a control in scientific experiments?
    a. A control allows the researcher to practice the experiment first before actually conducting it.
    b. A researcher can compare the results in the experimental group and control group to determine if a single variable is causing a particular outcome in the experimental group.

c. A control provides the framework for the entire experiment so the researcher can recall the procedures that should be conducted.

d. A control allows the researcher to conduct other experimental changes without disturbing the original experiment.

e. All of the above.

CONCEPTUAL QUESTIONS

1. List the seven characteristics of life and explain a little about each.

2. Give the levels of organization from the simplest to most complex.

3. List the taxonomic groups from most inclusive to least inclusive.

EXPERIMENTAL QUESTIONS

1. Discuss the difference between discovery-based science and hypothesis testing.

2. What are the steps in the scientific method, also called hypothesis testing?

3. When conducting an experiment, explain how a control sample and an experimental sample differ from each other.

COLLABORATIVE QUESTIONS

1. Discuss the terms genomes and proteomes.

2. Discuss the levels of organization of life.

www.brookerbiology.com

This website includes answers to the Biological Inquiry questions found in the figure legends and all end-of-chapter questions.

2

THE CHEMICAL BASIS OF LIFE I: ATOMS, MOLECULES, AND WATER

CHAPTER OUTLINE

Crystals of sodium chloride (NaCl).

iology—the study of life—is founded on the principles of chemistry and physics. All living organisms are a collection of atoms and molecules bound together and interacting with each other through the forces of nature. Throughout this textbook, we will see how chemistry can be applied to living organisms as we discuss the components of cells, the functions of proteins, the flow of nutrients in plants and animals, and the evolution of new genes. This chapter lays the groundwork for understanding these interactions. We begin with an overview of **inorganic chemistry**—that is, the nature of atoms and molecules with the exception of those that contain rings or chains of carbon. Such carbon-containing molecules form the basis of **organic chemistry** and are covered in Chapter 3.

2.1 Atoms

All life is composed of atoms, which in turn are composed of smaller, subatomic particles. A major role of the physicist is to uncover the properties of subatomic particles. Chemists, by contrast, are interested in the properties of atoms and molecules. Chemistry and physics merge when one attempts to understand the mechanisms by which atoms and molecules interact. When atoms and molecules are studied in the context of a living organism, the science of biochemistry emerges. No living creature is immortal, but atoms never "die." Instead, they exist *ad infinitum* as solitary atoms, or as components of a single molecule, or they shuttle between countless molecules over vast eons of time. In this section, we explore the physical properties of atoms so we can understand how atoms combine to form molecules of biological importance.

Atoms Are the Smallest Functional Units in Living Organisms

Atoms are the smallest functional units of matter that form all chemical substances and that cannot be further broken down into other substances by ordinary chemical or physical means. Many types of atoms are known. The simplest atom, hydrogen, is approximately 1 angstrom (10^{-10} meters) in diameter, roughly one-millionth the diameter of a human hair. Each specific type of atom—nitrogen, hydrogen, oxygen, and so on—occurs as a **chemical element**.

Three subatomic particles—**protons, neutrons**, and **electrons**—are found within atoms. The protons and neutrons are confined to a very small volume at the center of an atom, the **atomic nucleus**, whereas the electrons are found in regions at various distances from the nucleus. The numbers of protons and electrons in a given type of atom are identical, but the number of neutrons may vary. Each of the subatomic particles has a different electric charge. Protons have one unit of positive charge, electrons have one unit of negative charge, and neutrons are electrically neutral (**Table 2.1**).

Table 2.1	Characteristics of Major Subatomic Particles		
Particle	Location	Charge	Mass relative to electron
Electron	Around the nucleus	−1	1
Proton	Nucleus	+1	1,836
Neutron	Nucleus	0	1,839

Because the protons are located in the atomic nucleus, the nucleus has a net positive charge equal to the number of protons it contains. The entire atom has no net electric charge, however, because the number of negatively charged electrons around the nucleus is equal to the number of positively charged protons in the nucleus. As shown in Table 2.1, the masses of protons and neutrons are similar to each other and much greater than the mass of electrons.

FEATURE INVESTIGATION

Rutherford Determined the Modern Model of the Atom

Nobel laureate Ernest Rutherford was born in 1871 in New Zealand, but he did his greatest work at McGill University in Montreal, Canada, and later at the University of Manchester in England. At that time, scientists knew that atoms contained charged particles but had no idea how those particles were arranged. Neutrons had not yet been discovered, and many scientists believed that the positive charge and the mass of an atom were evenly dispersed throughout the atom.

In a now-classic experiment, Rutherford aimed a fine beam of positively charged alpha particles (helium nuclei) at an extremely thin sheet of gold foil only 400 atoms thick (**Figure 2.1**). Surrounding the gold foil was a zinc sulfide screen that registered any alpha particles passing through or bouncing off the foil, much like film in a camera detects light. Rutherford hypothesized that if the positive charges of the gold atoms were uniformly distributed, most of the alpha particles would be slightly deflected as they passed through the foil, because one of the most important features of electric charge is that like charges repel each other. Due to their much smaller mass, he did not expect electrons to have any impact on the ability of an alpha particle to move through the metal foil.

Although some of the alpha particles were indeed deflected as they passed through the foil, more than 98% of them passed right through as if the foil was not there, and a few bounced nearly straight back! To explain the 98% that passed right through, Rutherford concluded that most of the volume of an atom is empty space. To explain the few alpha particles that bounced back, he postulated that most of the atom's positive charge was localized in a highly compact area. The existence of this small, dense region of highly concentrated positive charge—which today we call the atomic nucleus—explains how some alpha particles could be so strongly deflected by the gold foil. Alpha particles would bounce back if they directly collided with

Figure 2.1   Rutherford's gold foil experiment demonstrating that most of the volume of an atom is empty space.

HYPOTHESIS Atoms in gold foil are composed of diffuse, evenly distributed positive charges that should usually cause α-particles to be slightly deflected as they pass through.

STARTING MATERIALS Thin sheet of gold foil, α-particle emitter, zinc sulfide detection screen.

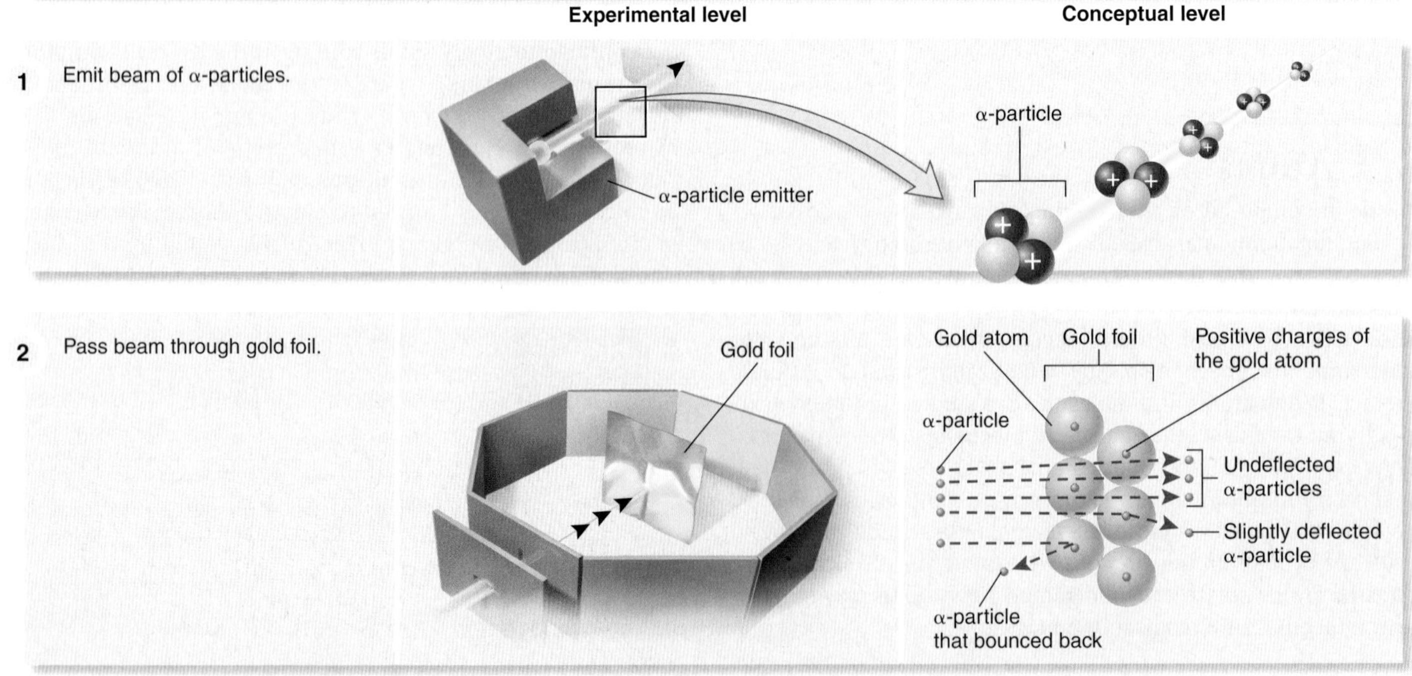

Experimental level   Conceptual level

1   Emit beam of α-particles.

α-particle

α-particle emitter

2   Pass beam through gold foil.

Gold foil

Gold atom   Gold foil   Positive charges of the gold atom

α-particle

Undeflected α-particles

Slightly deflected α-particle

α-particle that bounced back

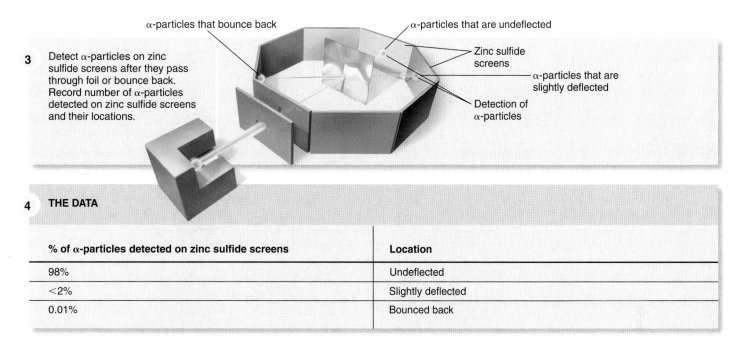

3 Detect α-particles on zinc sulfide screens after they pass through foil or bounce back. Record number of α-particles detected on zinc sulfide screens and their locations.

α-particles that bounce back

α-particles that are undeflected

Zinc sulfide screens

α-particles that are slightly deflected

Detection of α-particles

4 **THE DATA**

% of α-particles detected on zinc sulfide screens	Location
98%	Undeflected
<2%	Slightly deflected
0.01%	Bounced back

an atomic nucleus. Therefore, based on these results, Rutherford rejected his original hypothesis that atoms are composed of diffuse, evenly distributed positive charges.

From a single experiment Rutherford proposed our modern model of an atom, with its small, positively charged nucleus surrounded at relatively great distances by negatively charged electrons. Today we know that more than 99.99% of an atom's volume is outside the nucleus. Indeed, the nucleus accounts for only about 1/10,000 of an atom's diameter—most of an atom is empty space!

Electrons Occupy Orbitals Around an Atom's Nucleus

After Rutherford's experiments, scientists initially visualized an atom as a mini–solar system, with the nucleus being the sun and the electrons traveling in clearly defined orbits around it. Electrons move at terrific speeds. Some estimates suggest that the electron in a typical hydrogen atom could circle the Earth in less than 20 seconds! **Figure 2.2** shows a diagram of the two simplest atoms, hydrogen and helium, which have the smallest numbers of protons. This model of the atom is now considered an oversimplification, because electrons do not actually orbit the nucleus in a defined path. However, this depiction of an atom remains a convenient way to diagram atoms in two dimensions.

At any given moment, it is impossible to precisely predict where a given electron will be located. Electrons travel within regions surrounding the nucleus in which the probability is high of finding that electron. These areas are called **orbitals**. Thus, another way of depicting atoms is a central nucleus surrounded by cloudlike orbitals. The cloud represents the region in which a given electron is most likely to be found. Some orbitals are spherical, called *s* orbitals, while others assume a shape that is often described as similar to a propeller or dumbbell and are called *p* orbitals (**Figure 2.3**). An orbital can contain a maximum of two electrons. Consequently, any atom with more than two electrons must contain additional orbitals.

Orbitals occupy so-called energy shells or energy levels. Atoms with progressively more electrons have orbitals within energy shells that are at greater and greater distances from the nucleus. These shells are numbered so that shell number 1 is closest to the nucleus. Different energy shells may contain one or more orbitals, each orbital with up to two electrons. The innermost shell of all atoms has room for only two electrons, which spin in opposite directions within a spherical orbital (1*s*). The second shell is composed of one spherical orbital (2*s*) and three dumbbell-shaped orbitals (2*p*). Thus, the second shell can hold up to four pairs of electrons (Figure 2.3).

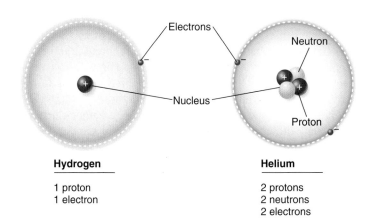

Electrons

Neutron

Nucleus

Proton

Hydrogen

1 proton
1 electron

Helium

2 protons
2 neutrons
2 electrons

Figure 2.2 **The nuclei of two simple atoms and their electrons.**   Early depictions of the atom envisioned a nucleus surrounded by electrons in discrete, measurable orbits, much like planets around the sun. This is a model of the two simplest atoms, hydrogen and helium. Note: In all figures of atoms, the sizes and distances are not to scale.

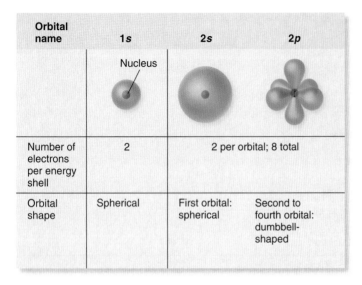

Orbital name	1s	2s	2p
	Nucleus		
Number of electrons per energy shell	2	2 per orbital; 8 total	
Orbital shape	Spherical	First orbital: spherical	Second to fourth orbital: dumbbell-shaped

Figure 2.3   **Diagrams of individual electron orbitals.** Electrons are found outside the nucleus in orbitals that may resemble spherical or dumbbell-shaped clouds. The orbital cloud represents a region of high probability of locating a particular electron.

Electrons vary in the amount of energy they have. The shell closest to the nucleus fills up with the lowest energy electrons first, and then each subsequent shell fills with higher and higher energy electrons, one shell at a time. Within a given shell, the energy of electrons can also vary among different orbitals. In the second shell, for example, the spherical orbital has lower energy, while the three dumbbell-shaped orbitals have slightly higher and roughly equal energies. In that case, therefore, two electrons fill the spherical orbital first. Any additional electrons fill the dumbbell-shaped orbitals one electron at a time.

Although electrons are actually found in orbitals of varying shapes, as shown in Figure 2.3, chemists often use more simplified diagrams when depicting the energy shells of electrons. **Figure 2.4a** illustrates an example involving nitrogen. An atom of this element has seven protons and seven electrons. Two electrons fill the first shell, and five electrons are found in the outer shell. Two of these fill the 2s orbital and are shown as a pair of electrons in the second shell. The other three electrons in the second shell are found singly in each of the three p orbitals. The diagram in Figure 2.4a makes it easy to see whether electrons are paired within the same orbital, and whether the outer shell is full. **Figure 2.4b** shows a more realistic depiction of a nitrogen atom, showing how the electrons actually occupy orbitals with different shapes.

Most atoms have outer shells that are not completely filled with electrons. Nitrogen, as we just saw, has a first shell filled with two electrons and a second shell with five electrons (Figure 2.4a). Because the second shell can actually hold eight electrons, the outer shell of a nitrogen atom is not full. As discussed later in this chapter, atoms that have unfilled energy shells tend to share, release, or obtain electrons to fill their outer shell. Those electrons in the outer shell that are available to combine

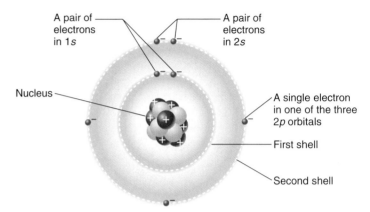

(a) Simplified depiction of a nitrogen atom (7 electrons; 2 electrons in first shell, 5 in second shell)

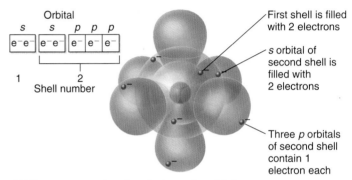

(b) Nitrogen atom showing electrons in orbitals

Figure 2.4   **Diagrams showing the multiple shells and orbitals of a nitrogen atom.** The nitrogen atom shown **(a)** simplified and **(b)** with all of its orbitals and shells. An atom's shells fill up one by one. In shells containing more than one orbital, the orbital with lowest energy fills first. Subsequent orbitals gain one electron at a time, shown schematically in boxes, where e represents an electron.

Biological inquiry: What is the difference between an energy shell and an orbital?

with other atoms are called the **valence electrons**. Such electrons allow atoms to form chemical bonds with each other.

Each Element Has a Unique Number of Protons

Each chemical element has a specific and unique number of protons that distinguishes one element from another. The number of protons in an atom is its **atomic number**. For example, hydrogen, the simplest atom, has an atomic number of 1, corresponding to its single proton. Magnesium has an atomic number of 12, corresponding to its 12 protons. The term atom refers to a particle that is electrically neutral. Therefore, the atomic number is also equal to the number of electrons in the atom, resulting in a net charge of zero.

Atomic number and electron shells are a useful means of organizing the chemical elements. **Figure 2.5** shows the first three rows of the periodic table of the elements. A one- or two-letter symbol is used as an abbreviation for each element. (Three-letter

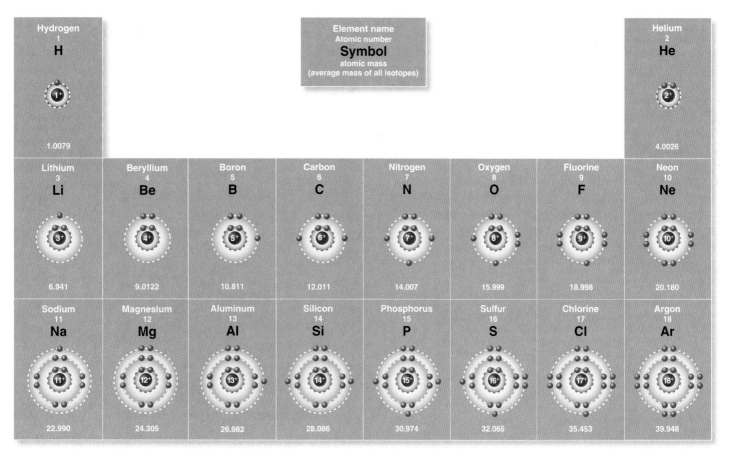

Figure 2.5 **A portion of the periodic table of the elements.**   The atoms are shown in models that depict the energy shells in different colors. The occupancy of orbitals is that of the elements in their pure state.

symbols are temporary until a two-letter symbol is chosen officially.) The elements are listed in the order of their atomic numbers. The rows indicate the number of energy shells. Hydrogen (H) has one shell, lithium (Li) has two shells, and sodium (Na) has three shells. The columns, from left to right, indicate the numbers of electrons in the outer shell. The outer shell of lithium (Li) has one electron, beryllium (Be) has two, boron (B) has three, and so forth. This organization of the periodic table tends to arrange elements based on similar chemical properties. For example, helium (He), neon (Ne), and argon (Ar) are inert gases and don't participate in chemical reactions. The inert gases have completely full outer shells. By comparison, beryllium (Be) and magnesium (Mg) are metals that have two electrons in their outer shell. The similarities of elements within a column occur because they have the same number of electrons in their outer shells, and therefore they have similar chemical bonding properties. These properties will be discussed later in this chapter.

Atoms Have a Small but Measurable Mass

Atoms are extremely minute and therefore have very little mass. A single hydrogen atom, for example, has a mass of only 1.67×10^{-24} g (grams). Protons and neutrons are nearly equal in mass, and both are more than 1,800 times the mass of an electron. Despite the great difference in mass of protons and electrons,

however, they nonetheless possess equal but opposite amounts of electric charge (see Table 2.1).

The **atomic mass** scale indicates an atom's mass relative to the mass of other atoms. By convention, the most common type of carbon atom, which has six protons and six neutrons, is assigned an atomic mass of exactly 12. On this scale, a hydrogen atom has an atomic mass of 1, indicating that it has 1/12 the mass of a carbon atom. A magnesium atom, with an atomic mass of 24, has twice the mass of a carbon atom. The term mass is sometimes confused with weight, but these two terms refer to different features of matter. Weight is derived from the gravitational pull on a given mass. If a man who weighs 154 pounds on Earth were standing on the moon, for example, he would only weigh about 25 pounds, but he would weigh 21 trillion pounds if he could stand on a neutron star. However, his mass is the same in all locations. Because we are discussing mass on Earth only, we can assume that the gravitational tug on all matter is roughly equivalent and thus the terms become essentially interchangeable for our purpose.

Atomic mass is measured in units called daltons, after the English chemist John Dalton, who postulated that matter is composed of minute, indivisible units he called atoms. One **dalton (Da)** equals 1/12 the mass of a carbon atom, or about the mass of a proton or a hydrogen atom. Thus, the most common type of carbon atom has an atomic mass of 12 daltons.

Because atoms such as hydrogen have a small mass, while atoms such as carbon have a larger mass, 1 g of hydrogen would have more atoms than 1 g of carbon. A **mole** of any substance contains the same number of particles as there are atoms in exactly 12 g of carbon. Twelve grams of carbon equals 1 mole, while 1 g of hydrogen equals 1 mole. As first described by Italian physicist Amedeo Avogadro, 1 mole of any element contains the same number of atoms—6.022×10^{23}. For example, 12 g of carbon contain 6.022×10^{23} atoms, and 1 g of hydrogen, whose atoms have 1/12 the mass of a carbon atom, also has 6.022×10^{23} atoms. This number, which is known today as **Avogadro's number**, is large enough to be somewhat mind-boggling, and thus gives us an idea of just how small atoms really are. To visualize the enormity of this number, imagine that people could move through a turnstile at a rate of 1 million people per second. It would require almost 20 billion years for 6.022×10^{23} people to move through that turnstile!

Isotopes Vary in Their Number of Neutrons

Although the number of neutrons in an atom is often equal to the number of protons, many elements can exist in multiple forms, called **isotopes**, that differ in the number of neutrons they contain. For example, the most abundant form of the carbon atom, ^{12}C, contains six protons and six neutrons, and thus has an atomic number of 6 and an atomic mass of 12 daltons, as described previously. The superscript placed to the left of ^{12}C is the sum of the protons and neutrons. The rare carbon isotope ^{14}C, however, contains six protons and eight neutrons, giving it an atomic number of 6 but an atomic mass of 14 Da. Nearly 99% of the carbon in living organisms is ^{12}C. Thus, the average atomic mass of carbon is very close to, but actually slightly greater than, 12 Da because of the existence of a small amount of heavier isotopes. This explains why the atomic masses given in the periodic table do not add up exactly to the predicted masses based on the atomic number and the number of neutrons of a given atom (Figure 2.5).

Many isotopes found in nature are inherently unstable and do not exist for long periods of time. Such isotopes are called **radioisotopes**, and they lose energy by emitting subatomic particles and/or radiation. At the very low amounts found in nature, radioisotopes usually pose no serious threat to life, but exposure of living organisms to high amounts of radioactivity can result in the disruption of cellular function and even death.

Modern medicine makes use of the high energy level of radioactive compounds in many ways. For example, solutions containing radioactive isotopes of iodine can be given to a person with an overactive thyroid gland. The thyroid is a gland in the neck that controls many important body functions. It is the only structure in the human body that uses iodine in large quantities, and so the isotope becomes concentrated in the gland. This localizes the radiation of the isotope to the thyroid, killing the hyperactive regions of the gland without harming other parts of the body. Another application makes use of the fact that radiation is easily detectable using various imaging techniques.

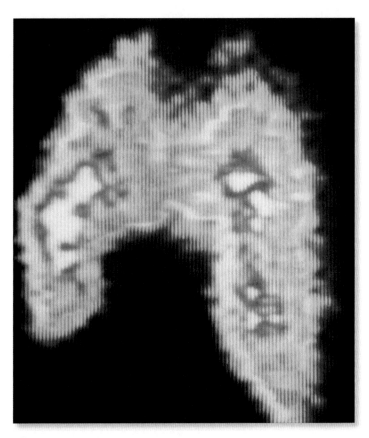

Figure 2.6 Diagnostic image of the human body using radioisotopes. A procedure called positron-emission tomography (PET) scanning highlights a region of the neck that contains the thyroid gland. A radioactive isotope of iodine was administered to the patient to reveal the size and activity of the gland. Radioactivity in this image shows up as a color.

These techniques, such as the PET scan shown in **Figure 2.6**, can detect the activities of body cells following injection of a compound that contains a radioactive isotope such as ^{131}I.

Researchers also use isotopes to study biological processes, such as tracking the movement of cellular compounds as they are shuttled between different cellular structures. For example, to determine which structures within a cell utilize cholesterol as part of their structure, researchers can incubate cells with cholesterol containing a radioactive isotope of hydrogen called tritium, ^{3}H, in place of one of its ordinary hydrogens. Cells are then examined at various times to determine where the tritium is located. For instance, much of the radioactivity will appear in the cell's plasma membrane, indicating that cholesterol is a component of the outer covering of cells.

Four Elements Constitute the Vast Majority of Living Organisms

Just four elements—oxygen, carbon, hydrogen, and nitrogen—account for the vast majority of atoms in living organisms (**Table 2.2**). These elements typically make up about 95% of the mass

Table 2.2	Chemical Elements Essential for Life in Most Organisms*	
Element	**Symbol**	**% Human body mass**
Most abundant in living organisms (approximately 95% of total mass)		
Oxygen	O	65
Carbon	C	18
Hydrogen	H	9
Nitrogen	N	3
Mineral elements (less than 1% of total mass)		
Calcium	Ca	
Chlorine	Cl	
Magnesium	Mg	
Phosphorus	P	
Potassium	K	
Sodium	Na	
Sulfur	S	
Trace elements (less than 0.01% of total mass)		
Chromium	Cr	
Cobalt	Co	
Copper	Cu	
Fluorine	F	
Iodine	I	
Iron	Fe	
Manganese	Mn	
Molybdenum	Mo	
Selenium	Se	
Silicon	Si	
Tin	Sn	
Vanadium	V	
Zinc	Zn	

* While these are the most common elements in living organisms, many other trace and mineral elements have reported functions. For example, aluminum is believed to be a cofactor for certain chemical reactions in animals, but it is generally toxic to plants.

of living organisms. Much of the hydrogen and oxygen occur in the form of water, which accounts for approximately 60% of the mass of most animals and up to 95% or more in some plants. Nitrogen is a vital element in all proteins, and carbon is a major building block of all living matter. Other vital elements in living organisms include the mineral elements, such as calcium and phosphorus, which are important constituents of the skeletons and shells of animals. Minerals like sodium and potassium are key regulators of water movement and electrical currents that occur across the surfaces of many cells.

In addition, all living organisms require trace elements. These atoms are present in extremely small quantities but still are essential for normal growth and function (Table 2.2). For example, iron plays an important role in how vertebrates store oxygen in their blood, and copper serves a similar role in some invertebrates.

2.2 Chemical Bonds and Molecules

The linkage of atoms with other atoms serves as the basis for life, and also gives life its great diversity. Two or more atoms bonded together make up a **molecule**. Atoms can combine with each other in several ways. For example, two oxygen atoms can combine to form one oxygen molecule, represented as O_2. This representation is called a **molecular formula**, and it consists of the chemical symbols for all of the atoms present (here, O for oxygen) and a subscript that tells you how many of those atoms are present in the molecule (in this case, two). The term **compound** refers to a molecule composed of two or more different elements. Examples include water (H_2O), with two hydrogen atoms and one oxygen atom, and the sugar glucose ($C_6H_{12}O_6$), which has 6 carbon atoms, 12 hydrogen atoms, and 6 oxygen atoms.

One of the most important features of compounds is their emerging physical properties. This means that the properties of a compound differ greatly from the elements that combined to form it. Let's consider sodium as an example. Pure sodium (Na), also called elemental sodium, is a soft, silvery white metal that you can cut with a knife. When sodium forms a compound with chlorine, table salt (NaCl) is made. NaCl is a white, relatively hard crystal that dissolves in water. Thus the properties of sodium in a compound can be dramatically different from its properties as an element.

The atoms in molecules are held together by chemical bonds. Important types of chemical bonds include covalent and ionic bonds. In this section, we will examine how these types of bonds form, and how they determine the structures of molecules.

Covalent Bonds Join Atoms Through the Sharing of Electrons

Covalent bonds, in which atoms share a pair of electrons, can occur between atoms whose outer shells are not full. A fundamental principle of chemistry is that *atoms tend to be most stable when their outer shells are full of electrons*. **Figure 2.7** shows this principle as it applies to the formation of hydrogen fluoride. The outer shell of a hydrogen atom is full when it contains two electrons, though a hydrogen atom has only one electron. The outer shell of a fluorine atom has seven electrons, though its outer shell would be full if it contained eight electrons. When hydrogen fluoride (HF) is made, the two atoms share a pair of electrons. This allows both of their outer shells to be full. Covalent bonds are strong chemical bonds, because the shared electrons behave as if they belong to each atom.

When the structure of a molecule is diagrammed, each covalent bond is represented by a line indicating a pair of shared electrons. For example, hydrogen fluoride is diagrammed as

H—F

A molecule of water can be diagrammed as

H—O—H

The structural formula of water indicates that the oxygen atom is covalently bound to two hydrogen atoms. Alternatively, as mentioned previously, water can be written by its shorthand molecular formula, H_2O.

Each atom forms a characteristic number of covalent bonds, which depends on the number of electrons that is needed to fill the outer shell. The atoms of some elements important for life, notably carbon, form more than one covalent bond and become linked simultaneously to two or more other atoms. **Figure 2.8** shows the number of covalent bonds that are formed by several atoms that are commonly found in the molecules of living cells.

Learning the **octet rule** may help you remember that atoms are stable when their outer shell is full. For many, but not all, types of atoms, their outer shell is full when they contain eight electrons, an octet. This rule applies to many types of atoms that are found in living organisms including carbon, nitrogen, oxygen, phosphorus, and sulfur. These atoms form a character-

istic number of covalent bonds to make an octet in their outer shell (Figure 2.8). However, the octet rule does not always apply. For example, hydrogen has an outer shell that can contain only two electrons, not eight.

In some molecules, a **double bond** occurs when atoms share two pairs of electrons rather than one pair. As shown in **Figure 2.9**, this is the case for an oxygen molecule (O_2), which can be diagrammed as

$$O=O$$

Another common example occurs when two carbon atoms form bonds in compounds. They may share one pair of electrons (single bond) or two pairs (double bond), depending on how many other covalent bonds each carbon forms with other atoms. In rare cases, carbon can even form triple bonds, where three pairs of electrons are shared between two atoms.

Electrons Are Not Always Evenly Shared Between Atoms

Some atoms attract shared electrons more readily than do other atoms. The **electronegativity** of an atom is a measure of its ability to attract electrons in a bond from another atom. When two atoms with different electronegativities form a covalent bond, the shared electrons are more likely to be closer to the atom of higher electronegativity rather than the atom of lower electronegativity. Such bonds are called **polar covalent bonds**, because the distribution of electrons around the atoms creates a polarity, or difference in electric charge, across the molecule. Water is the classic example of a molecule containing polar covalent bonds. The shared electrons at any moment tend to be closer to the oxygen atom rather than either of the hydrogens. This unequal sharing of electrons gives the molecule a region of partial negative charge and two regions of partial positive charge (**Figure 2.10**).

Atoms with high electronegativity, such as oxygen and nitrogen, have a relatively strong attraction for electrons. These atoms

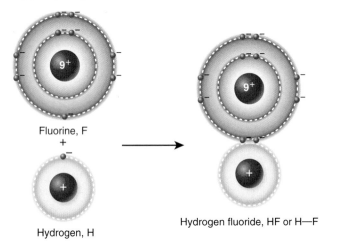

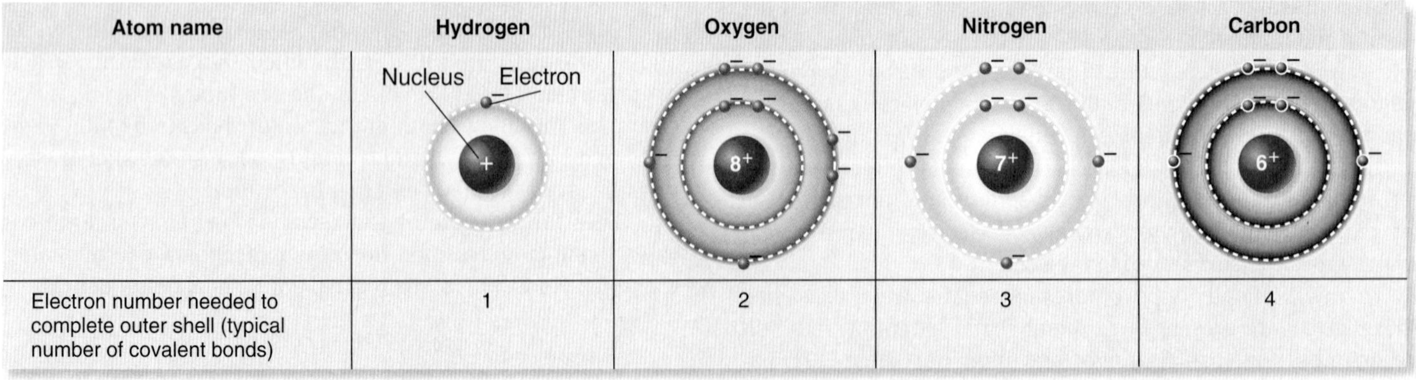

Figure 2.7 **The formation of covalent bonds.** In covalent bonds, electrons from the outer shell of two atoms are shared with each other, in order to complete the outer shells of both atoms. This simplified illustration shows hydrogen forming a covalent bond with fluorine.

Atom name	Hydrogen	Oxygen	Nitrogen	Carbon
Electron number needed to complete outer shell (typical number of covalent bonds)	1	2	3	4

Figure 2.8 **The most abundant elements found in living organisms.** These elements form different numbers of covalent bonds due to the electron configurations in their outer shells.

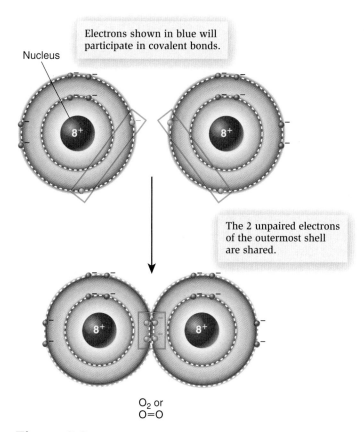

Electrons shown in blue will participate in covalent bonds.

Nucleus

The 2 unpaired electrons of the outermost shell are shared.

O₂ or
O=O

Figure 2.9 A double bond between two oxygen atoms.

Biological inquiry: Explain how an oxygen molecule obeys the octet rule.

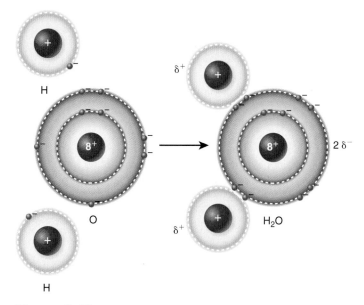

In water, the shared electrons spend more time near the oxygen atom. This gives oxygen a partial negative charge ($2\delta^-$) and each hydrogen a partial positive charge (δ^+).

δ^+

H

O

δ^+

$2\delta^-$

δ^+

H_2O

H

Figure 2.10 Polar covalent bonds in water molecules. In a water molecule, two hydrogen atoms share electrons with an oxygen atom. Because oxygen has a higher electronegativity, the shared electrons spend more time closer to oxygen. This gives oxygen a partial negative charge, designated $2\delta^-$, and each hydrogen a partial positive charge, designated δ^+.

form polar covalent bonds with hydrogen atoms, which have low electronegativity. Examples of polar bonds include O—H and N—H. In contrast, bonds between carbon atoms (C—C) and between carbon and hydrogen atoms (C—H) are electrically neutral or nonpolar. Molecules containing significant numbers of polar bonds are known as **polar molecules**, whereas molecules composed predominantly of nonpolar bonds are called **nonpolar molecules**. A single molecule may have different regions with nonpolar bonds and polar bonds. For example, the detergent molecules found in soap have polar and nonpolar ends. The nonpolar ends dissolve in the oil of your skin, and the polar ends help the detergent rinse off in water. As you will see later, the physical characteristics of polar and nonpolar molecules, especially their solubility in water, are quite different.

Hydrogen Bonds Allow Interactions Within and Between Molecules

An important result of certain polar covalent bonds is the ability of one molecule to loosely associate with another molecule through a weak interaction called a **hydrogen bond**. A hydrogen bond forms when a hydrogen atom from one polar molecule becomes electrically attracted to an electronegative atom,

such as an oxygen or nitrogen atom, in another polar molecule. Hydrogen bonds, like those between water molecules, are represented in diagrams by dashed or dotted lines to distinguish them from covalent bonds (**Figure 2.11a**). A single hydrogen bond is very weak. The strength of a hydrogen bond is only a few percent of the polar covalent bonds linking the hydrogen and oxygen within a water molecule.

Hydrogen bonds can also occur within a single large molecule. Many large molecules may have dozens, hundreds, or more hydrogen bonds within their structure. Collectively, many hydrogen bonds may add up to a strong force that helps maintain the three-dimensional structure of a molecule. This is particularly true in DNA—the molecule that makes up the genetic material of living organisms. DNA exists as two long, twisting strands of many thousands of atoms and molecules. The two strands are held together all along their length by hydrogen bonds (**Figure 2.11b**). Due to the large number of hydrogen bonds, considerable energy is needed to separate the two strands of DNA.

In contrast to the cumulative strength of many hydrogen bonds, the weakness of individual bonds is also important. When an interaction between two molecules involves relatively few hydrogen bonds, such interactions tend to be short-lived.

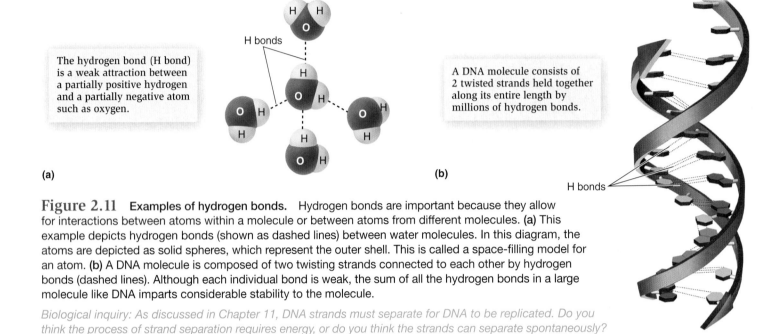

The hydrogen bond (H bond) is a weak attraction between a partially positive hydrogen and a partially negative atom such as oxygen.

H bonds

A DNA molecule consists of 2 twisted strands held together along its entire length by millions of hydrogen bonds.

H bonds

(a) (b)

Figure 2.11 **Examples of hydrogen bonds.** Hydrogen bonds are important because they allow for interactions between atoms within a molecule or between atoms from different molecules. **(a)** This example depicts hydrogen bonds (shown as dashed lines) between water molecules. In this diagram, the atoms are depicted as solid spheres, which represent the outer shell. This is called a space-filling model for an atom. **(b)** A DNA molecule is composed of two twisting strands connected to each other by hydrogen bonds (dashed lines). Although each individual bond is weak, the sum of all the hydrogen bonds in a large molecule like DNA imparts considerable stability to the molecule.

Biological inquiry: As discussed in Chapter 11, DNA strands must separate for DNA to be replicated. Do you think the process of strand separation requires energy, or do you think the strands can separate spontaneously?

The reversible nature of hydrogen bonds allows molecules to interact and then to become separated again. For example, as discussed in Chapter 7, small molecules may bind to proteins called enzymes via hydrogen bonds. The small molecules are later released after the enzymes have changed their structure.

Ionic Bonds Involve an Attraction Between Positive and Negative Ions

Atoms are electrically neutral because they contain equal numbers of negative electrons and positive protons. If an atom or molecule gains or loses one or more electrons, it acquires a net electric charge and becomes an **ion**. For example, when a sodium atom (Na), which has 11 electrons, loses one electron, it becomes a sodium ion (Na^+) with a net positive charge. A sodium ion still has 11 protons, but only 10 electrons. Ions such as Na^+ are depicted with a superscript that indicates the net charge of the ion. Some atoms can gain or lose more than one electron. For instance, a calcium atom loses two electrons to become a calcium ion, depicted as Ca^{2+}. On the other hand, a chlorine atom (Cl), which has 17 electrons, can gain an electron and become a chloride ion (Cl^-) with a net negative charge— it has 18 electrons but only 17 protons. Hydrogen atoms and most mineral and trace element atoms readily form ions. **Table 2.3** lists the ionic forms of several elements. The ions listed in this table are relatively stable because the outer electron shells of the ions are full. For example, a sodium atom has one electron in its third (outer) shell. If it loses this electron to become Na^+, it no longer has a third shell, and the second shell, which is full, becomes its outer shell. Alternatively, a Cl atom has seven electrons in its third (outer) shell. If it gains an electron to become a chloride ion (Cl^-), its outer shell becomes full with eight electrons.

Ions that have a net positive charge are called **cations**, while those that have a net negative charge are **anions**. Ionization, the process of ion formation, can occur in single atoms or in atoms that are covalently linked in molecules.

An **ionic bond** occurs when a cation binds to an anion. **Figure 2.12a** shows an ionic bond between Na^+ and Cl^- to form NaCl. The general name, salt, is given to compounds that are formed from an attraction between a positively charged ion (a cation) and negatively charged ion (an anion). Examples of salts include NaCl, KCl, and $CaCl_2$. Salts may form crystals in which the cations and anions form a regular array. **Figure 2.12b** shows a NaCl crystal in which the sodium and chloride ions are held together by ionic bonds.

Table 2.3	Ionic Forms of Some Common Elements			
Atom	Chemical symbol	Ion	Ion symbol	Electrons gained or lost
Calcium	Ca	Calcium ion	Ca^{2+}	2 lost
Chlorine	Cl	Chloride ion	Cl^-	1 gained
Hydrogen	H	Hydrogen ion	H^+	1 lost
Magnesium	Mg	Magnesium ion	Mg^{2+}	2 lost
Potassium	K	Potassium ion	K^+	1 lost
Sodium	Na	Sodium ion	Na^+	1 lost

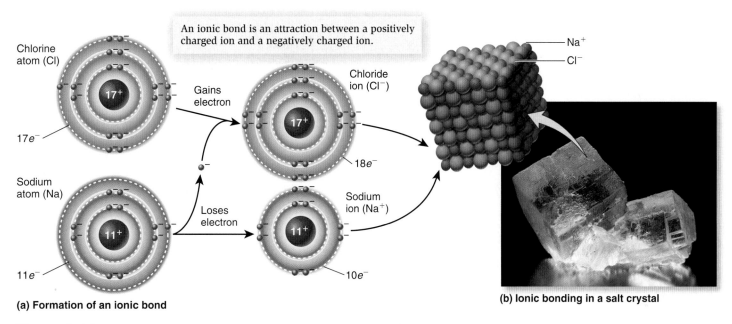

An ionic bond is an attraction between a positively charged ion and a negatively charged ion.

(a) Formation of an ionic bond

(b) Ionic bonding in a salt crystal

Figure 2.12   Ionic bonding in table salt (NaCl).   (a) When an electron is transferred from a sodium atom to a chlorine atom, the resulting ions are attracted to each other via an ionic bond. **(b)** In a salt crystal, a lattice is formed in which the positively charged sodium ions (Na^+) are attracted to negatively charged chloride ions (Cl^-).

Molecules May Change Their Shapes

When atoms combine, they can form molecules with various three-dimensional shapes, depending on the arrangements and numbers of bonds between their atoms. As an example, let's consider the arrangements of covalent bonds in a few simple molecules (**Figure 2.13**). These molecules form new orbitals that cause the atoms to have defined angles relative to each other. This gives groups of atoms very specific shapes as shown in the three examples of Figure 2.13.

Molecules containing covalent bonds are not rigid, inflexible structures. Think of a covalent bond, for example, as an axle around which the joined atoms can rotate. Within certain limits, the shape of a molecule can change without breaking its covalent bonds. As illustrated in **Figure 2.14a**, a molecule of six carbon atoms bonded together can assume a number of shapes as a result of rotations around various covalent bonds. The three-dimensional, flexible shape of molecules contributes to their biological properties. As shown in **Figure 2.14b**, the binding of one molecule to another may affect the shape of one of the molecules. An animal can taste food, for instance, because food molecules interact with receptors on its tongue. When a food molecule encounters a receptor, the two molecules recognize each other by their unique shapes, much like a key fitting into a lock. As atoms in the receptor are attracted by hydrogen bonds to atoms in the food, the shape of the receptor changes. As we will see when we look at how the brain receives information from other parts of the body, the altered shape of the receptor initiates a signal that communicates to the animal's brain that the food tastes good (see Chapter 44).

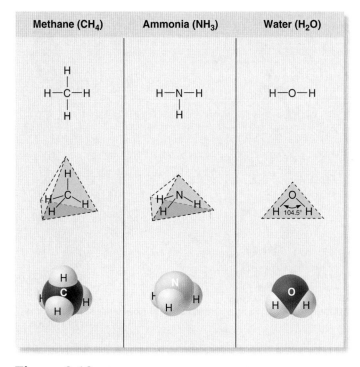

**Figure 2.13   Shapes of molecules.   Molecules may assume different shapes depending on the types of bonds between their atoms. The angles between groups of atoms are well defined. For example, in liquid water at room temperature, the angle formed by the two bonds of each hydrogen to oxygen is approximately 104.5°. This bond angle can vary slightly depending on the temperature and degree of hydrogen bonding between adjacent water molecules.

Free Radicals Are a Special Class of Highly Reactive Molecules

Recall that an atom or ion is most stable when each of its orbitals is occupied by its full complement of electrons. A molecule containing an atom with a single, unpaired electron in its outer shell is known as a **free radical**. Free radicals can react with other molecules to "steal" an electron from one of their atoms,

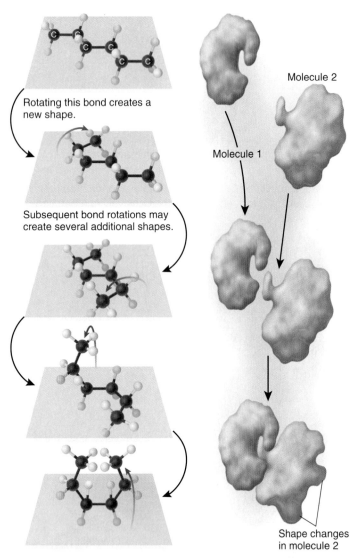

Rotating this bond creates a new shape.

Subsequent bond rotations may create several additional shapes.

Molecule 2

Molecule 1

Shape changes in molecule 2

(a) Bond rotation in a small molecule   **(b) Noncovalent interactions that may alter the shape of molecules**

Figure 2.14   Shape changes in molecules.   A single molecule may assume different three-dimensional shapes without breaking any of the covalent bonds between its atoms, as shown in **(a)** for a six-carbon molecule. Hydrogen atoms above the blue plane are shown in white; those below the blue plane are blue. **(b)** Two molecules are shown schematically as having complementary shapes that permit them to interact. Upon interacting, the flexible nature of the molecules causes molecule 2 to twist sufficiently to assume a new shape. This change in shape is often an important mechanism by which one molecule influences the activity of another.

thereby filling the orbital in the free radical. In the process, this may create a new free radical in the donor molecule, setting off a chain reaction.

Free radicals can be formed in several ways, including exposure of cells to radiation and toxins. Free radicals can do considerable harm to living cells—for example, by causing a cell's membrane to rupture or damaging the genetic material. Surprisingly, the lethal effect of free radicals is sometimes put to good use. Some cells in animals' bodies create free radicals and use them to kill invading cells such as bacteria. Likewise, people use hydrogen peroxide to kill bacteria, as in a dirty skin wound. Hydrogen peroxide can break down to create free radicals, which can then attack bacteria in the wound.

Despite the exceptional case of fighting off bacteria, though, most free radicals that arise in an organism need to be inactivated so that they do not kill healthy cells. Protection from free radicals is afforded by molecules that can donate electrons to the free radicals without becoming highly reactive themselves. Examples of such protective compounds are certain vitamins found in fruits and vegetables, and the numerous plant compounds known as flavonoids. This is one reason why a diet rich in fruits and vegetables is beneficial to our health.

Free radicals are diagrammed with a dot next to the atomic symbol. Examples of biologically important free radicals are superoxide anion, $O_2 \bullet^-$; hydroxyl radical, $OH\bullet$; and nitric oxide, $NO\bullet$. Note that free radicals can be either charged or neutral.

Chemical Reactions Change Elements or Compounds into Different Compounds

A **chemical reaction** occurs when one or more substances are changed into other substances. This can happen when two or more elements or compounds combine with each other to form a compound, when one compound breaks down into two or more molecules, or when electrons are added to or taken away from an atom. Chemical reactions share many similar properties. First, they all require a source of energy for molecules to encounter each other. Such energy is provided partly by heat. In the complete absence of any heat (a temperature called absolute zero), atoms and molecules would be totally stationary and unable to interact. Heat energy causes atoms and molecules to vibrate and move, a phenomenon known as Brownian motion. Second, chemical reactions that occur in living organisms often require more than just Brownian motion to proceed at a reasonable rate. Such reactions need to be catalyzed. As discussed in Chapter 7, a catalyst is a substance that speeds up a chemical reaction. All cells contain many kinds of catalysts called enzymes. Third, chemical reactions tend to proceed in a particular direction, but will eventually reach a state of equilibrium. As an example, let's consider a chemical reaction between methane, a component found in natural gas, and oxygen. These molecules react with each other to produce carbon dioxide and water.

$$CH_4 \ + \ 2\,O_2 \ \rightleftharpoons \ CO_2 \ + \ 2\,H_2O$$

(methane) (oxygen)   (carbon dioxide) (water)

As it is written here, methane and oxygen are the **reactants**, while carbon dioxide and water are the **products**. Whether a chemical reaction is likely to proceed in a forward or reverse direction depends on changes in free energy, as described in Chapter 7. If we began with only methane and oxygen, the forward reaction is very favorable. The reaction would produce a large amount of carbon dioxide and water, as well as heat. This is why natural gas is used as a fuel to heat homes. However, all chemical reactions will eventually reach **equilibrium** in which the rate of the forward reaction is balanced by the rate of the reverse reaction. In the case of the reaction described above, this equilibrium would occur when nearly all of the reactants had been converted to products.

A final feature common to chemical reactions in living organisms is that they occur in water environments. Just as a crystal of sodium chloride will not dissolve in air but will dissolve in water, so too do the chemical reactions in organisms require water. Next, we will examine the properties of this amazing liquid.

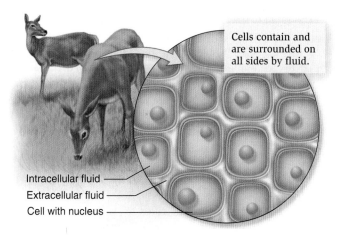

Figure 2.15 Fluids inside and outside of cells. Aqueous solutions exist in the intracellular fluid and in extracellular fluid. Chemical reactions are always ongoing in both fluids.

2.3 Properties of Water

It would be difficult to imagine life without water. People can survive for a month or more without food but usually die in less than a week without water. The bodies of organisms are composed largely of water. Up to 95% of the weight of certain plants comes from water. In people, typically 60–70% of body weight is from water. The brain is roughly 70% water, blood is about 80% water, and the lungs are nearly 90% water. Even our bones are about 20% water! In addition, water is an important liquid in the environments of living organisms. For example, many species are aquatic organisms that survive in a watery environment.

Thus far in this chapter we have considered the features of atoms and molecules, and the nature of chemical reactions between atoms and molecules. In this section, we will turn our attention to issues related to the liquid properties of living organisms, and the environment in which they live. Most of the chemical reactions that occur in nature involve molecules that are dissolved in water, including those reactions that happen inside cells and in the spaces that surround cells of living organisms (**Figure 2.15**). However, not all molecules dissolve in water. In this section, we will examine the properties of chemicals that influence whether they dissolve in water, and consider how biologists measure the amounts of dissolved substances. In addition, we examine some of the other special properties of water that make it a vital component of living organisms and their environments.

Polar Molecules and Ions Readily Dissolve in Water

Substances dissolved in a liquid are known as **solutes**, and the liquid in which they are dissolved is the **solvent**. Solutes dissolve in a solvent to form a **solution**. In all living organisms, the solvent for chemical reactions is water, which is the most abundant solvent in nature. Solutions made with water are called **aqueous solutions**. To understand why a substance dissolves in

Figure 2.16 NaCl crystals dissolving in water. The ability of water to dissolve sodium chloride crystals depends on the electrical attraction between the polar water molecules and the charged sodium and chloride ions. Water molecules surround each ion as it becomes dissolved.

water, we need to consider the chemical bonds in the solute molecule and those in water. As discussed earlier, the covalent bonds linking the two hydrogen atoms to the oxygen atom in a water molecule are polar. Therefore, the oxygen in water has a slight negative charge, and each hydrogen has a slight positive charge. To dissolve in water, a substance must be polar and electrically attracted to water molecules. For example, table salt (NaCl) is a solid crystalline substance because of the strong ionic bonds between positive sodium ions (Na^+) and negative chloride ions (Cl^-). When a crystal of sodium chloride is placed in water, the polar water molecules are attracted to the charged Na^+ and Cl^- (**Figure 2.16**). The ions become surrounded by clusters of water molecules, allowing the Na^+ and Cl^- to separate from each other and enter the water—that is, to dissolve.

Generally, molecules that contain polar covalent bonds will dissolve in water. Such molecules are said to be **hydrophilic**, which literally means "water-loving." In contrast, molecules composed predominantly of carbon and hydrogen are relatively insoluble in water, because carbon-carbon and carbon-hydrogen bonds are nonpolar. These molecules do not have partial positive and negative charges, and therefore are not attracted to water molecules. Such molecules are **hydrophobic**, or "water-fearing." Oils are a familiar example of hydrophobic molecules. Try mixing vegetable oil with water and observe the result. The two liquids separate into an oil phase and water phase. Very little oil dissolves in the water.

Although hydrophobic molecules dissolve poorly in water, they normally dissolve readily in nonpolar solvents. For example, cholesterol is a compound found in the blood and cells of animals. It is a hydrophobic molecule that is barely soluble in water but that easily dissolves in nonpolar solvents used in chemical laboratories, such as ether. Biological membranes like those that encase cells contain about 50% nonpolar compounds. Because of this, cholesterol also inserts into biological membranes, where it helps to maintain the membrane structure.

Molecules that have both polar or ionized regions at one or more sites and nonpolar regions at other sites are called **amphipathic**—consisting of two parts. When mixed with water, long amphipathic molecules may form spheres called **micelles**, with their polar (hydrophilic) regions at the surface of the micelle, where they are attracted to the surrounding water molecules. The nonpolar (hydrophobic) ends are oriented toward the interior of the micelle (**Figure 2.17**). Such an arrangement minimizes the interaction between water molecules and the nonpolar ends of the amphipathic molecules. Nonpolar molecules can dissolve in the central nonpolar regions of these clusters and thus exist in an aqueous environment in far higher amounts than would otherwise be possible based on their low solubility in water. We already considered one familiar example of amphipathic molecules, soap, which can form micelles that help to dissolve oils and nonpolar molecules found in dirt.

Instead of micelles, other amphipathic molecules form structures called bilayers. As you will learn in Chapter 5, lipid bilayers play a key role in membrane structure.

The Amount of a Dissolved Solute Is Its Concentration

Solute **concentration** is defined as the amount of a solute dissolved in a unit volume of solution. For example, if 1 gram (g) of NaCl were dissolved in enough water to make 1 liter of solution, we would say that its solute concentration is 1 g/L.

A comparison of the concentrations of two different substances on the basis of the number of grams per liter of solution does not directly indicate how many molecules of each substance are present. For example, let's compare 10 g each of glucose ($C_6H_{12}O_6$) and sodium chloride (NaCl). Because the individual molecules of glucose have more mass than those of NaCl,

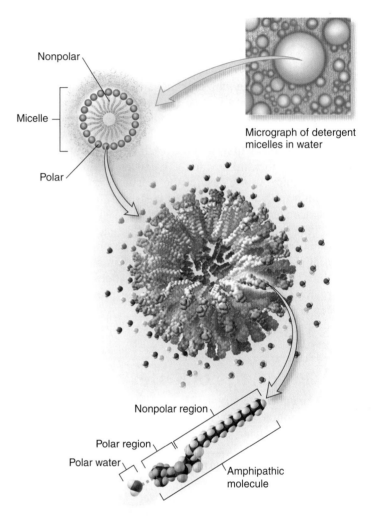

Nonpolar

Micelle

Polar

Micrograph of detergent micelles in water

Nonpolar region

Polar region

Polar water

Amphipathic molecule

Figure 2.17   **The formation of micelles by amphipathic molecules.**   In water, amphipathic molecules tend to arrange themselves so their nonpolar regions are directed away from water molecules, and the polar regions are directed toward the water and can form hydrogen bonds with it.

10 g of glucose will contain fewer molecules than 10 g of NaCl. Therefore, another way to describe solute concentration is according to the moles of dissolved solute per volume of solution. To make this calculation, we must know three things: the amount of dissolved solute, the molecular mass of the dissolved solute, and the volume of the solution.

The **molecular mass** of a molecule is equal to the sum of the atomic masses of all the atoms in the molecule. For example, glucose ($C_6H_{12}O_6$) has a molecular mass of 180 ([6 × 12] + [12 × 1] + [6 × 16] = 180). As mentioned earlier, 1 mole (abbreviated mol) of a substance is the amount of the substance in grams equal to its atomic or molecular mass. The **molarity** of a solution is defined as the number of moles of a solute dissolved in 1 L of solution. A solution containing 180 g of glucose (1 mol) dissolved in enough water to make 1 L is a 1 **molar** solution of glucose (1 mol/L). By convention, a 1 mol/L solution is usually written as 1 M, where the capital M stands for molar and is defined as mol/L. If 90 g of glucose (half its molecular mass) were dissolved in enough water to make 1 L, the solution would have a concentration of 0.5 mol/L, or 0.5 M.

The concentrations of solutes dissolved in the fluids of living organisms are usually much less than 1 mol/L. Many have concentrations in the range of millimoles per liter (1 mM = 0.001 M = 10^{-3} M), while others are present in even smaller concentrations—micromoles per liter (1 μM = 0.000001 M = 10^{-6} M) or nanomoles per liter (1 nM = 0.000000001 M = 10^{-9} M).

H$_2$O Exists as Ice, Water, and Water Vapor

Let's now consider some general features of water and how dissolved solutes affect its properties. H$_2$O is an abundant compound on Earth that exists in all three states of matter—solid (ice), liquid (water), and gas (water vapor). At the temperatures found over most regions of the planet, H$_2$O is found primarily as a liquid in which the weak hydrogen bonds between water molecules are continuously being formed, broken, and formed again. If the temperature rises, the rate at which hydrogen bonds break increases, and molecules of water escape into the gaseous state, becoming water vapor. If the temperature falls, hydrogen bonds are broken less frequently so that larger and larger clusters of water molecules are formed, until at 0°C water freezes into a crystalline matrix—ice. The H$_2$O molecules in ice tend to lie in a more "open" arrangement, which makes ice less dense than water. This is why ice floats on water (**Figure 2.18**). Compared to water, ice is also less likely to participate in most types of chemical reactions.

Changes in state, such as changes between the solid, liquid, and gaseous states of H$_2$O, involve an input or release of energy. For example, when energy is supplied to make water boil, it changes from the liquid to the gaseous state. This is called vaporization. The heat required to vaporize 1 mole of any substance at its boiling point under standard pressure is called the substance's **heat of vaporization**. For water, this value is very high. It takes more than five times as much heat to vaporize water than it does to raise the temperature of water from 0°C to 100°C. In contrast, energy is released when water freezes to form ice. Water has a high **heat of fusion**, which is the amount of heat energy that must be withdrawn or released from a substance to cause it to change from the liquid to the solid state. These two features, the high heats of vaporization and fusion, mean that water is extremely stable as a liquid. Not surprisingly, therefore, living organisms have evolved to function best within a range of temperatures consistent with the liquid phase of H$_2$O.

The temperature at which a solution freezes or vaporizes is influenced by the amounts of dissolved solutes. These are examples of **colligative properties**, which depend strictly on the concentration of dissolved solute particles, not on the specific type of particle. Pure water freezes at 0°C and vaporizes at 100°C. Addition of solutes to water lowers its freezing point below 0°C

Ice

Liquid water

Figure 2.18 **Structure of water and ice.** In its liquid form, the hydrogen bonds between water molecules continually form, break, and re-form, resulting in a changing arrangement of molecules from instant to instant. At temperatures at or below its freezing point, water forms a crystalline matrix called ice. In this solid form, hydrogen bonds are more stable. Ice has a hexagonally shaped crystal structure. The greater space between H$_2$O molecules in this crystal structure causes ice to have a lower density compared to water. For this reason, ice floats on water.

and raises its boiling point above 100°C. Adding a small amount of the compound ethylene glycol—antifreeze—to the water in your car's radiator, for instance, prevents the water from freezing in cold weather. Similarly, the presence of large amounts of solutes partly explains why the oceans do not freeze when the temperature falls below 0°C. Likewise, the colligative properties of water also account for the remarkable ability of certain ectothermic animals, which are unable to maintain warm body temperatures in cold environments, to nonetheless escape becoming frozen solid. Such "cold-blooded" animals produce antifreeze molecules that dissolve in their body fluids, thereby lower- ing the freezing point of the fluids and preventing their blood and cells from freezing in the extreme cold. The emerald rockcod (*Trematomus bernacchii*), found in the waters of Antarctica, for example, manages to live in ocean waters that are at or below 0°C (**Figure 2.19a**). Similarly, many insects such as the larvae of the parasitic wasp (*Brachon cephi*) also make use of natural antifreeze to stay alive in extreme conditions (**Figure 2.19b**).

(a) Emerald rockcod in the waters of Antarctica

(b) Wasp larvae, which can withstand freezing temperatures

Figure 2.19 Antifreeze in living organisms. Many animals, such as **(a)** the emerald rockcod (*Trematomus bernacchii*) and **(b)** the larvae of the parasitic wasp (*Brachon cephi*), can withstand extremely cold temperatures thanks to natural antifreeze molecules in their body fluids.

Water Performs Many Other Important Tasks in Living Organisms

As discussed earlier, water is the primary solvent in the fluids of all living organisms, from unicellular bacteria to the largest Sequoia tree. Water permits atoms and molecules to interact in ways that would be impossible in their nondissolved states. In Unit II we will consider a myriad of ions and molecules that are solutes in living cells. Even so, it is important to recognize that in addition to acting as a solvent, water serves many other remarkable functions that are critical for the survival of living organisms. For example, water molecules themselves take part in many chemical reactions of this general type:

$$R1\!-\!R2 + H\!-\!O\!-\!H \quad \rightarrow \quad R1\!-\!OH + H\!-\!R2$$

R is a general symbol to represent a group of atoms. In this equation, *R1* and *R2* are distinct groups of atoms. On the left side, *R1—R2* is a compound in which the groups of atoms are connected by a covalent bond. To be converted to products, a covalent bond is broken in each reactant, R1—R2 and H—O—H, and OH and H (from water) form covalent bonds with R1 and R2, respectively. Reactions of this type are known as hydrolytic reactions (*hydro*, water; *lysis*, break apart), because water is used to break apart another molecule. This process is also called **hydrolysis** (**Figure 2.20a**). As discussed in later chapters, many large molecules are broken down into smaller units by hydrolysis. Alternatively, other chemical reactions in living organisms involve the removal of a water molecule so that a covalent bond can be formed between two separate molecules. For example, let's consider a chemical reaction that is the reverse of our previous hydrolytic reaction:

$$R1\!-\!OH + H\!-\!R2 \quad \rightarrow \quad R1\!-\!R2 + H\!-\!O\!-\!H$$

Such a reaction involves the removal of a water molecule, and the formation of a covalent bond between two separate molecules. This is termed a **dehydration** or **condensation reaction**. As discussed in later chapters, this is a common reaction that is used to build larger molecules in living organisms.

Another feature of water is that it is incompressible—its volume does not significantly decrease when subjected to high pressure. This has biological importance for many organisms that use water to provide force or support (**Figure 2.20b**). For example, water forms the so-called hydrostatic skeleton of worms and some other invertebrates, and it provides turgidity (stiffness) and support for plants.

Water is also the means by which unneeded and potentially toxic waste compounds are eliminated from an animal's body (**Figure 2.20c**). In mammals, for example, the kidneys filter out soluble waste products derived from the breakdown of proteins and other compounds. The filtered products remain in solution in the watery fluid, which eventually becomes urine and is excreted.

Recall from our discussion of water's properties that it takes considerable energy in the form of heat to convert water from a liquid to a gas. This feature has great biological significance. Although everyone is familiar with the fact that boiling water is converted to water vapor, water can vaporize into the gaseous state even at ordinary temperatures. This process is known as **evaporation**. The simplest way to understand this is to imagine that in any volume of water at any temperature, some water molecules will have higher energy than others. Not every molecule is vibrating identically with the same energy. Those with highest energy escape into the gaseous state. The important point, however, is that even at ordinary temperatures it still requires the same energy to change water from liquid to gas. Thus, the evaporation of sweat from an animal's skin requires considerable energy in the form of body heat, which is then lost to the environment. Evaporation is an important mechanism by which many animals cool themselves on hot days (**Figure 2.20d**).

Another important feature for living organisms is that water has a very high heat capacity, which means that it takes a lot of heat to raise its temperature. This accounts in part for the relatively stable temperatures of large bodies of water compared to inland temperatures. Large bodies of water tend to have a moderating effect on the temperature of nearby land masses.

The hydrogen-bonding properties of water affect its ability to form droplets and to adhere to surfaces. When the molecules within a substance tend to noncovalently attract each other, this phenomenon is called cohesion. Water exhibits strong cohesion due to hydrogen bonding. Cohesion aids in the movement of water through the vessels of plants (**Figure 2.20e**). A property that is similar to cohesion is adhesion, which refers to the ability of water to adhere to another surface. Water tends to cling to surfaces to which it can hydrogen-bond. For this reason, water can coat the surfaces of the digestive tract of animals and act as a lubricant for the passage of food (**Figure 2.20f**). Surface tension is a measure of how difficult it is to break the interface between a liquid and air. In the case of water, the attractive force between hydrogen-bonded water molecules at the interface between water and air is what causes water to form droplets. The surface water molecules attract each other into a configuration (a sphere) that reduces the number of water molecules in contact with air. Likewise, surface tension allows certain insects, such as water striders, to walk on the surface of a pond without sinking (**Figure 2.20g**).

Hydrogen Ion Concentrations Are Changed by Acids and Bases

Pure water has the ability to ionize to a very small extent into hydrogen ions (H^+) and **hydroxide ions** (OH^-). In pure water, the concentrations of H^+ and OH^- are both 10^{-7} mol/L, or 10^{-7} M. An inherent property of water is that the product of the concentrations of H^+ and OH^- is always 10^{-14} M at 25°C. Therefore, in pure water, $[H^+][OH^-] = [10^{-7} \text{ M}][10^{-7} \text{ M}] = 10^{-14}$ M. (The brackets around the symbols for the hydrogen and hydroxide ions indicate concentration.)

When certain substances are dissolved in water, they may release or absorb H^+ or OH^-, thereby altering the relative concentrations of these ions. Molecules that release hydrogen ions in solution are called **acids**. Two examples are:

$$HCl \rightarrow H^+ + Cl^-$$
(hydrochloric acid)   (chloride)

$$H_2CO_3 \rightleftharpoons H^+ + HCO_3^-$$
(carbonic acid)   (bicarbonate)

Hydrochloric acid is called a **strong acid** because it completely dissociates into H^+ and Cl^- when added to water. By comparison, carbonic acid is a **weak acid** because some of it will remain in the H_2CO_3 state when dissolved in water.

Compared to an acid, a **base** has the opposite effect when dissolved in water—it lowers the H^+ concentration. This can occur in different ways. Some bases, such as sodium hydroxide (NaOH), release OH^- when dissolved in water.

$$NaOH \rightarrow Na^+ + OH^-$$

Recall that the product of $[H^+]$ and $[OH^-]$ is always 10^{-14} M. When a base such as NaOH raises the OH^- concentration, some of the hydrogen ions bind to these hydroxide ions to form water. Therefore, increasing the OH^- concentration lowers the H^+ concentration. Alternatively, other bases, such as ammonia, react with water.

$$NH_3 + H_2O \rightleftharpoons NH_4^+ + OH^-$$
(ammonia)

(a) **Water participates in chemical reactions.**

(b) **Water provides support.**

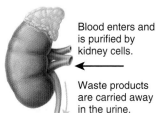

Blood enters and is purified by kidney cells.

Waste products are carried away in the urine.

(c) **Water is used to eliminate soluble wastes.**

(d) **Evaporation helps animals dissipate body heat.**

(e) **The cohesive force of water molecules aids in the movement of fluid through vessels in plants.**

(f) **Water serves as a lubricant during feeding.**

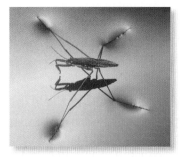

(g) **The surface tension of water explains why this water strider doesn't sink.**

Figure 2.20   Some amazing roles of water in biology. In addition to acting as a solvent, water serves many crucial functions in nature.

Both NaOH and ammonia have the same effect—they lower the concentration of H$^+$. NaOH achieves this by directly increasing the OH$^-$ concentration, while NH$_3$ reacts with water to produce OH$^-$.

The addition of acids and bases to water can greatly change the H$^+$ and OH$^-$ concentrations over a very broad range. Therefore, chemists and biologists use a log scale to describe the concentrations of these ions. The H$^+$ concentration is expressed as the solution's **pH**, which is defined as the negative logarithm to the base 10 of the H$^+$ concentration.

$$pH = -\log_{10} [H^+]$$

To understand what this equation means, let's consider a few examples. A solution with a H$^+$ concentration of 10^{-7} M has a pH of 7. A concentration of 10^{-7} M is the same as 0.1 μM. A solution in which [H$^+$] = 10^{-6} M has a pH of 6. 10^{-6} M is the same as 1.0 μM. A solution at pH 6 is said to be more **acidic**, because the H$^+$ concentration is 10-fold higher than a solution at pH 7. Note that as the acidity increases, the pH decreases. A solution where the pH is 7 is said to be neutral because [H$^+$] and [OH$^-$] are equal. An acidic solution has a pH that is below 7, while an **alkaline** solution has a pH above 7. **Figure 2.21** considers the pH values of some familiar fluids.

Why is pH of importance to biologists? The answer lies in the observation that H$^+$ and OH$^-$ can readily bind to many kinds of ions and molecules. For this reason, the pH of a solution can affect

- the shapes and functions of molecules;
- the rates of many chemical reactions;
- the ability of two molecules to bind to each other;
- the ability of ions or molecules to dissolve in water.

Due to the various effects of pH, many biological processes function best within very narrow ranges of pH, and even small shifts can have a negative effect. In living cells, the pH ranges from 6.5 to 7.8 and is carefully regulated to avoid major shifts in pH. The blood of the human body has a normal range of about pH 7.35 to 7.45 and is thus slightly alkaline. Certain diseases can reduce or increase blood pH by a few tenths of a unit. When this happens, the enzymes in the body needed for normal metabolism are rendered less functional, leading to illness and even death. As described next, living organisms have molecules called buffers to prevent such changes in pH.

Buffers Minimize Fluctuations in the pH of Fluids

What factors might alter the pH of an organism's fluids? External factors such as acid rain and other forms of pollution can reduce the pH of water entering the roots of plants. In animals, exercise generates lactic acid, and certain diseases can raise or lower the pH of blood.

Organisms have several ways to cope with changes in pH. Complex animals such as mammals, for example, can use struc-

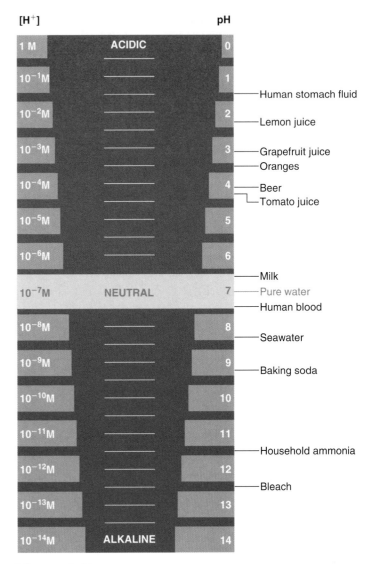

Figure 2.21   **The pH scale and the relative acidities of common substances.**

Biological inquiry: What is the OH$^-$ concentration at pH 8?

tures like the kidney to secrete acidic or alkaline compounds into the bloodstream when the blood pH becomes imbalanced. Similarly, the kidneys can transfer hydrogen ions from the body into the urine and adjust the body's pH in that way. Another mechanism by which pH balance is regulated in diverse organisms involves the actions of acid-base buffers. An acid-base **buffer** is composed of a weak acid and its related base. One such buffer is the bicarbonate pathway.

$$CO_2 + H_2O \rightleftharpoons H_2CO_3 \rightleftharpoons H^+ + HCO_3^-$$
$$\text{(carbonic acid)} \qquad \text{(bicarbonate)}$$

This buffer system can work in both directions. If the pH of an animal's blood were to increase (that is, the H$^+$ concentration decreased), the bicarbonate pathway would proceed from left to right. CO_2 would combine with water to make carbonic acid, and then the carbonic acid would dissociate into H^+ and bicarbonate. This would raise the H^+ concentration and thereby lower the pH. Alternatively, when the pH of an animal's blood decreases, this pathway runs in reverse. Bicarbonate combines with H^+ to make carbonic acid, which then dissociates to carbon dioxide and water. This process removes H^+ from the blood, restoring it to its normal pH, and the CO_2 is exhaled from the lungs. Many buffers, including this example, exist in nature. Buffers found in living organisms are adapted to function most efficiently at the normal range of pH values seen in that organism.

CHAPTER SUMMARY

2.1 Atoms

- Atoms are the smallest functional units of matter that form all chemical elements and that cannot be further broken down into other substances by ordinary chemical or physical means. Atoms are composed of protons (positive charge), electrons (negative charge), and neutrons (electrically neutral). Electrons are found in orbitals around the nucleus. (Table 2.1, Figures 2.1, 2.2, 2.3, 2.4)

- Each element contains a unique number of protons, its atomic number. The periodic table organizes all known elements by atomic number and energy shells. (Figure 2.5)

- Each atom has a small but measurable mass, measured in daltons. The atomic mass scale indicates an atom's mass relative to the mass of other atoms.

- Many atoms exist as isotopes, which differ in the number of neutrons they contain. Some isotopes are unstable radioisotopes and emit radiation. (Figure 2.6)

- Four elements—oxygen, carbon, hydrogen, and nitrogen—account for the vast majority of atoms in living organisms. In addition, living organisms require mineral and trace elements that are essential for growth and function. (Table 2.2)

2.2 Chemical Bonds and Molecules

- A molecule consists of two or more atoms bonded together. The properties of a molecule are different from the properties of the atoms that combined to form it. A compound is composed of two or more different elements.

- Atoms tend to form bonds that fill their outer shell with electrons.

- Covalent bonds, in which atoms share electrons, are strong chemical bonds. Atoms form two covalent bonds—a double bond—when they share two pairs of electrons. (Figures 2.7, 2.8, 2.9)

- The electronegativity of an atom is a measure of its ability to attract bonded electrons. When two atoms with different electronegativities combine, the atoms form a polar covalent bond because the distribution of electrons around the atoms creates polarity, or difference in electric charge, across the molecule. Polar molecules, such as water, are largely composed of polar bonds, while most nonpolar molecules are composed predominantly of nonpolar bonds. (Figure 2.10)

- An important result of polar covalent bonds is the ability of one molecule to loosely associate with another molecule through weak interactions called hydrogen bonds. (Figure 2.11)

- If an atom or molecule gains or loses one or more electrons, it acquires a net electric charge and becomes an ion. The strong attraction between two oppositely charged ions forms an ionic bond. (Table 2.3, Figure 2.12)

- The three-dimensional, flexible shape of molecules allows them to interact and contributes to their biological properties. (Figures 2.13, 2.14)

- A free radical is an unstable molecule that interacts with other molecules by "stealing" electrons from their atoms.

2.3 Properties of Water

- Chemical reactions change compounds or elements into different compounds. All chemical reactions require energy. In living organisms, chemical reactions take place in a liquid environment, and many are readily reversible. (Figure 2.15)

- Solutes dissolve in a solvent to form a solution. Solute concentration refers to the amount of a solute dissolved in a unit volume of solution. The molarity of a solution is defined as the number of moles of a solute dissolved in 1 L of solution. (Figure 2.16)

- Polar molecules are hydrophilic, while nonpolar molecules composed predominantly of carbon and hydrogen are hydrophobic. Amphipathic molecules, such as detergents, have polar and nonpolar regions. (Figure 2.17)

- Water is the solvent for chemical reactions in all living organisms, which allows atoms and molecules to interact in ways that would be impossible in their nondissolved states.

- H_2O exists as ice, water, and water vapor. (Figure 2.18)

- The colligative properties of water allow it to function as an antifreeze in certain organisms. (Figure 2.19)

- Water's high heat of vaporization and high heat of fusion make it very stable in liquid form.

- Water molecules participate in many chemical reactions in living organisms. Hydrolysis breaks down large molecules into smaller units, and dehydration reactions combine two smaller molecules into one larger one. In living organisms, water provides support, is used to eliminate wastes, dissipates body heat, aids in the movement of liquid through vessels, and serves as a lubricant. Surface tension allows insects to walk on water. (Figure 2.20)

- The pH of a solution refers to its hydrogen ion concentration. The pH of pure water is 7 (a neutral solution). Alkaline solutions have a pH higher than 7, and acidic solutions have a pH lower than 7. (Figure 2.21)
- Buffers are compounds that act to minimize pH fluctuations in the fluids of living organisms. Buffer systems can raise or lower pH as needed.

TEST YOURSELF

1. _____ make up the nucleus of an atom.
   a. Protons and electrons   d. Neutrons and electrons
   b. Protons and neutrons   e. DNA only
   c. DNA and RNA

2. Living organisms are composed mainly of
   a. calcium, hydrogen, nitrogen, and oxygen.
   b. carbon, hydrogen, nitrogen, and oxygen.
   c. hydrogen, nitrogen, oxygen, and helium.
   d. carbon, helium, nitrogen, and oxygen.
   e. carbon, calcium, hydrogen, and oxygen.

3. The ability of an atom to attract bonded electrons is
   a. polarity.   d. valence.
   b. electronegativity.   e. both a and b.
   c. solubility.

4. Hydrogen bonds differ from covalent bonds in that
   a. covalent bonds can form between any type of atom and hydrogen bonds only form between H and O.
   b. covalent bonds involve sharing of electrons and hydrogen bonds involve the complete transfer of electrons.
   c. covalent bonds result from equal sharing of electrons but hydrogen bonds involve unequal sharing of electrons.
   d. covalent bonds involve sharing of electrons between atoms but hydrogen bonds are the result of weak attractions between a hydrogen atom of a polar molecule and an electronegative atom of another polar molecule.
   e. covalent bonds are weak bonds that break easily but hydrogen bonds are strong links between atoms that are not easily broken.

5. A free radical
   a. is a positively charged ion.
   b. is an atom with one unpaired electron in its outer shell.
   c. is a stable atom that is not bonded to another atom.
   d. can cause considerable cellular damage.
   e. both b and d.

6. Chemical reactions in living organisms
   a. require energy to begin.
   b. usually require a catalyst to initiate the process.
   c. are usually reversible.
   d. occur in liquid environments, such as water.
   e. all of the above.

7. Solutes that easily dissolve in water are said to be
   a. hydrophobic.   d. all of the above.
   b. hydrophilic.   e. b and c only.
   c. polar molecules.

8. The sum of the atomic masses of all the atoms of a molecule is its
   a. atomic weight.   d. concentration.
   b. molarity.   e. polarity.
   c. molecular mass.

9. Reactions that involve water in the breaking apart of other molecules are known as _____ reactions.
   a. hydrophilic   d. anabolic
   b. hydrophobic   e. hydrolytic
   c. dehydration

10. A difference between a strong acid and a weak acid is
   a. strong acids have a higher molecular mass than weak acids.
   b. strong acids completely ionize in solution, but weak acids do not completely ionize in solution.
   c. strong acids give off two hydrogen ions per molecule, but weak acids only give off one hydrogen ion per molecule.
   d. strong acids are water-soluble, but weak acids are not.
   e. strong acids give off hydrogen ions and weak acids give off hydroxyl groups.

CONCEPTUAL QUESTIONS

1. What are the types of bonds commonly found in biological molecules?
2. Distinguish between the terms hydrophobic and hydrophilic.
3. List the special properties of water that are ideally suited to life.

EXPERIMENTAL QUESTIONS

1. Before the experiment conducted by Ernest Rutherford, how did many scientists envision the structure of an atom?
2. What was the hypothesis tested by Rutherford?
3. What were the results of the experiment? How did Rutherford interpret the results?

COLLABORATIVE QUESTIONS

1. Discuss the three basic subatomic particles.
2. Discuss several properties of water that make it possible for life to exist.

www.brookerbiology.com
This website includes answers to the Biological Inquiry questions found in the figure legends and all end-of-chapter questions.

3

THE CHEMICAL BASIS OF LIFE II: ORGANIC MOLECULES

CHAPTER OUTLINE

A model showing the structure of a protein—a type of organic macromolecule. The example here depicts the four subunits of hemoglobin, on oxygen-carrying protein.

In Chapter 2, we learned that all life is composed of sub-atomic particles that form atoms, which in turn combine to form molecules. Molecules may be simple in atomic composition, as in water (H_2O) or hydrogen gas (H_2), or may bind with other molecules to form larger molecules. Of the countless possible molecules that can be produced from the known elements in nature, certain types contain carbon and are found in all forms of life. These carbon-containing molecules are collectively referred to as **organic molecules**, so named because they were first discovered in living organisms. Among these are lipids and large, complex compounds called **macromolecules**, which include carbohydrates, proteins, and nucleic acids. In this chapter, we will survey the structures of these molecules and examine their chief functions. We begin by examining the element whose chemical properties are fundamental to the formation of biologically important molecules: carbon. This element provides the atomic scaffold upon which life is built.

3.1 The Carbon Atom and the Study of Organic Molecules

The science of studying carbon-containing molecules is known as organic chemistry. This is a relatively young area of chemical exploration, considering that inorganic chemistry has been studied for hundreds of years, albeit in a rather primitive fashion in the beginning. In this section, we will examine the bonding properties of carbon that create groups of atoms with distinct functions and shapes.

Interestingly, the study of organic molecules was long considered a fruitless endeavor because of a concept called vitalism that persisted into the 19th century. Vitalism held that organic molecules were created by, and therefore imparted with, a vital life force contained within a plant or an animal's body. Supporters of vitalism argued there was no point in trying to synthesize an organic compound, because such molecules could arise only through the intervention of mysterious qualities associated with life. As described next, this would all change due to the pioneering experiments of Friedrich Wöhler in 1828.

Wöhler's Synthesis of an Organic Compound Transformed Misconceptions About Life's Molecules

Friedrich Wöhler (**Figure 3.1a**) was a German physician and chemist who was interested in the properties of inorganic and

(a)   (b)

Figure 3.1 Wöhler and his crystals of urea. (a) Friedrich Wöhler. (b) Crystals of urea.

Biological inquiry: How did prior knowledge of urea allow Wöhler to realize he had made urea outside of the body?

organic compounds. He spent some time studying urea, which is found in urine. Urea is a natural organic product formed from the breakdown of proteins in an animal's body. In mammals, urea accumulates in the urine, which is formed by the kidneys, and then is excreted from the body. During the course of his studies, Wöhler purified urea from the urine of mammals. He noted the color, size, shape, and other characteristics of the crystals that formed when urea was isolated. This experience would serve him well in later years when he quite accidentally helped to put the concept of vitalism to rest.

In 1828, while exploring the reactive properties of ammonia and cyanic acid, Wöhler attempted to synthesize an inorganic molecule, ammonium cyanate (NH_4OCN). Instead, Wöhler discovered, to his surprise, that ammonia and cyanic acid reacted to produce a third compound, which, when heated formed familiar-looking crystals (**Figure 3.1b**). After careful analysis, he concluded that these crystals were in fact urea. He announced to the scientific community that he had synthesized urea, an organic compound, "without the use of kidneys, either man or dog." In other words, no mysterious life force was required to create this organic molecule. Subsequently, other scientists, such as Adolph Kolbe in 1845, would demonstrate that organic compounds such as acetic acid could be synthesized directly from their respective elements. These studies were a major breakthrough in the way in which scientists viewed life, and so began the field of science now called organic chemistry. From that time to the present, the fields of chemistry and biology have been understood to be intricately related.

Central to Wöhler's and Kolbe's reactions was the carbon atom. Urea and acetic acid, like all organic compounds, contain carbon atoms bound to other atoms. Let's now consider the chemical features that make carbon such an important element in living organisms.

Carbon Forms Four Covalent Bonds with Other Atoms

One of the properties of the carbon atom that makes life possible is its ability to form four covalent bonds with other atoms, including other carbon atoms. This occurs because carbon has four electrons in its outer shell, and it needs four additional electrons for its outer shell to be full (**Figure 3.2**). In living organisms, carbon atoms most commonly form covalent bonds with other carbons and with hydrogen, oxygen, nitrogen, and sulfur atoms. Bonds between two carbon atoms, between carbon and oxygen, or between carbon and nitrogen can be single or double. The combination of carbon with itself and with different elements and different types of bonds allows a vast number of organic compounds to be formed from only a few chemical elements. This is made all the more impressive because carbon bonds may occur in configurations that are linear, ringlike, or highly branched. Such molecular shapes can produce molecules with a variety of functions.

Because carbon and hydrogen have similar electronegativities, carbon-carbon and carbon-hydrogen bonds are nonpolar. As a consequence, molecules with predominantly hydrogen-

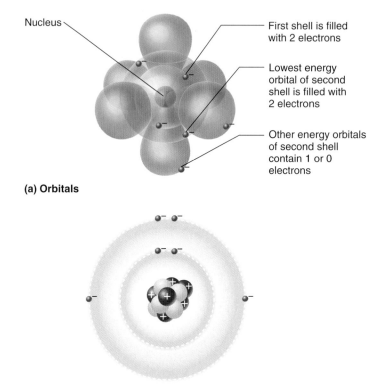

(a) Orbitals

(b) Energy shells

Figure 3.2 Models for the electron orbitals and energy shells of carbon. Carbon atoms have only four electrons in their outer (second) shell, which allows carbon to form four covalent bonds. When carbon forms four covalent bonds, the result is four hybrid orbitals of equal energy called sp^3 orbitals.

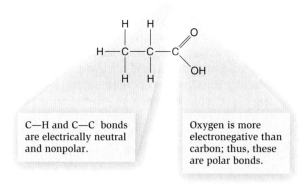

C—H and C—C bonds are electrically neutral and nonpolar.

Oxygen is more electronegative than carbon; thus, these are polar bonds.

Figure 3.3 Nonpolar and polar bonds in an organic molecule. Carbon can form both nonpolar and polar bonds, and single and double bonds.

carbon bonds, called **hydrocarbons**, tend to be poorly soluble in water. In contrast, when carbon forms polar covalent bonds with oxygen or nitrogen, for example, the molecule is much more soluble in water due to the electrical attraction of polar water molecules. The ability of carbon to form both polar and nonpolar bonds contributes to its ability to serve as the backbone for an astonishing variety of molecules (**Figure 3.3**).

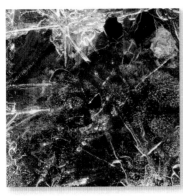

Figure 3.4 The stability of carbon bonds makes life possible even in extreme environments. **(a)** In the Russian Arctic, moss grows beneath the ice. **(b)** Deep-sea vents may reach temperatures greater than 650°F. Organisms can live near these vents, in very warm water.

(a)

(b)

One last feature of carbon that is important to biology is that carbon bonds are stable at the different temperatures associated with life. This property arises in part because the carbon atom is very small compared to most other atoms, and therefore the distance between carbon atoms forming a carbon-carbon bond is quite short. Shorter bonds tend to be stronger and more stable than longer bonds between two large atoms. Thus, carbon bonds are compatible with what we observe about life today, namely that living organisms can inhabit environments ranging from the Earth's icy poles to deep-sea vents (**Figure 3.4**).

Carbon Atoms Can Bond to Several Biologically Important Functional Groups

Aside from the simplest hydrocarbons, most organic molecules and macromolecules contain **functional groups**—groups of atoms with special chemical features that are functionally important. Each type of functional group exhibits the same properties in all molecules in which it occurs. For example, the amino group (NH_2) acts like a base. At the pH found in living organisms, amino groups readily bind H^+ to become NH_3^+, thereby removing H^+ from an aqueous solution and raising the pH. As discussed later in this chapter, amino groups are widely found in proteins and also in other types of organic molecules. **Table 3.1** describes examples of functional groups that are found in many different types of organic molecules. We will discuss each of these groups at numerous points throughout this textbook.

Table 3.1	Some Biologically Important Functional Groups That Bond to Carbon	
Functional group	**Formula**	**Examples of where found***
Amino	$R-N{\overset{H}{\underset{H}{}}}$	Amino acids (proteins)
Carbonyl**		
Ketone	$R-\overset{\overset{O}{\|}}{C}-R'$	Steroids, eicosanoids, waxes, and proteins
Aldehyde	$R-\overset{\overset{O}{\|}}{C}-H$	
Carboxyl	$R-C{\overset{O}{\underset{OH}{}}}$	Amino acids, fatty acids
Hydroxyl	$R-OH$	Steroids, alcohol, carbohydrates, some amino acids
Methyl	$R-\overset{\overset{H}{\|}}{\underset{\underset{H}{\|}}{C}}-H$	May be attached to DNA, proteins, and carbohydrates
Phosphate	$R-O-\overset{\overset{O}{\|}}{\underset{\underset{O^-}{\|}}{P}}-O^-$	Nucleic acids, ATP, attached to amino acids
Sulfate	$R-O-\overset{\overset{O}{\|}}{\underset{\underset{O}{\|}}{S}}-O^-$	May be attached to carbohydrates, proteins, and lipids
Sulfhydryl	$R-SH$	Proteins that contain the amino acid cysteine

* This list contains many of the functional groups that are important in biology. However, many more functional groups have been identified by biochemists.
** A carbonyl group is C=O. When the carbon is linked to a free hydrogen atom, this is an aldehyde. In a ketone, the carbon forms covalent bonds with two other carbon atoms.

Carbon-Containing Molecules May Exist in Multiple Forms Called Isomers

When Wöhler did his famous experiment, he was surprised to discover that urea and ammonium cyanate apparently contained the exact same ratio of carbons, nitrogens, hydrogens, and oxygens, yet they were different molecules with distinct chemical and biological properties. Two structures with an identical molecular formula but different structures and characteristics are called **isomers**.

Figure 3.5 depicts three ways in which isomers may occur. **Structural isomers** contain the same atoms but in different

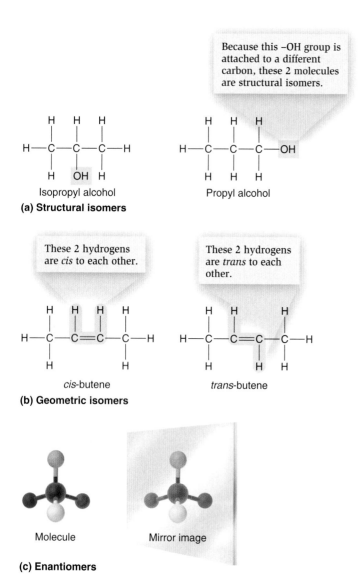

Because this –OH group is attached to a different carbon, these 2 molecules are structural isomers.

Isopropyl alcohol   Propyl alcohol

(a) Structural isomers

These 2 hydrogens are *cis* to each other.

These 2 hydrogens are *trans* to each other.

cis-butene   *trans*-butene

(b) Geometric isomers

Molecule   Mirror image

(c) Enantiomers

Figure 3.5   Types of isomers.   Isomers are compounds with the same molecular formula but different structures. The differences in structure, though small, are sufficient to result in very different biological properties.

bonding relationships. Wöhler's compounds fall into this category. **Stereoisomers** have identical bonding relationships, but the spatial positioning of the atoms differs in the two isomers. Two types of stereoisomers are geometric isomers and enantiomers. In **geometric isomers** like those shown in Figure 3.5b, the two hydrogen atoms linked to the two carbons of a C=C double bond may be on the same side of the carbons, in which case the C=C bond is called a *cis* double bond. If the hydrogens are on opposite sides, it is a *trans* double bond. *Cis-trans* stereoisomers may have very different chemical properties from each other, most notably their stability and sensitivity to heat and light. For instance, the light-sensitive region of your eye contains a molecule called retinal, which may exist in either a *cis* or *trans* form because of a pair of double-bonded carbons in its string of carbon atoms. In darkness, the *cis* form predominates. The energy of sunlight, however, causes retinal to isomerize to the *trans* form. The *trans*-retinal activates the light-capturing cells in the eye.

A second type of stereoisomer, called an **enantiomer**, exists as a pair of molecules that are mirror images. Four different atoms can bind to a single carbon atom in two possible ways, designated a left-handed and a right-handed structure. If the resulting structures are not identical, but instead are mirror images of each other, the molecules are enantiomers (Figure 3.5c). A given pair of enantiomers share identical chemical properties, such as solubility and melting point. However, due to the different orientation of atoms in space, their ability to noncovalently bind to other molecules can be strikingly different. For example, the right-handed form of glucose, called D-glucose, binds very well to certain enzymes in living cells, while the left-handed form, L-glucose, binds poorly. Most enzymes recognize only one type of enantiomer but not both.

3.2 Classes of Organic Molecules and Macromolecules

As we have seen, organic molecules have various shapes due to the bonding properties of carbon. During the past two centuries, biochemists have studied many organic molecules found in living organisms and determined their structures at the molecular level. Many of these compounds are relatively small molecules, containing a few or a few dozen atoms. However, some organic molecules are extremely large macromolecules, being composed of thousands or even millions of atoms. Such large molecules are formed by linking together many smaller molecules called monomers and are thus also known as **polymers** (meaning many small parts). The structure of macromolecules depends on the structure of their monomers, the number of monomers linked together, and the three-dimensional way in which the monomers are linked.

By analyzing the cells of many different species, researchers have determined that all forms of life have organic molecules that fall into four broad categories, based on their chemical and biological properties. The four major types of organic molecules and macromolecules found in all living organisms are carbohydrates, lipids, proteins, and nucleic acids. In this section, we will survey the structures of these organic compounds and begin to examine their biological functions.

Carbohydrates Exist as Sugars and Longer Polymers of Sugars

Carbohydrates are composed of carbon, hydrogen, and oxygen atoms in the proportions represented by the general formula $C_n(H_2O)_n$, where n is a whole number. This formula gives carbohydrates their name—carbon-containing compounds that are hydrated (that is, contain water). Most of the carbon atoms in a carbohydrate are linked to a hydrogen atom and a hydroxyl group. However, other functional groups, such as amino and carboxyl groups, are also found in certain carbohydrates. As discussed next, sugars are relatively small carbohydrates, while polysaccharides are large macromolecules.

Sugars Sugars are small carbohydrates that taste sweet. The simplest sugars are the **monosaccharides** (from the Greek, meaning single sugars). The most common types are molecules with five carbons, called pentoses, and six carbons, called hexoses. Important pentoses are ribose ($C_5H_{10}O_5$) and the closely related deoxyribose ($C_5H_{10}O_4$), which are part of RNA and DNA molecules, respectively. The most common hexose is glucose ($C_6H_{12}O_6$). Like other monosaccharides, glucose is very water-soluble and thus circulates in the blood of animals and the fluids of plants, where it can be transported across plasma membranes. Once inside a cell, glucose is broken down by enzymes. The energy released in this process is used to make many molecules of ATP (adenosine triphosphate), which powers a variety of cellular processes. In this way, sugar is often used as a source of energy by living organisms.

Figure 3.6a illustrates two traditional ways of depicting the bonds between atoms in a monosaccharide. The ring structure is a better approximation of the true shape of the molecule as it mostly exists in solution, with the carbon atoms numbered by convention as shown. The ring is made from the linear structure by an oxygen atom, which forms a bond that bridges two carbons. The hydrogen atoms and the hydroxyl groups may lie above or below the plane of the carbon ring structure.

Figure 3.6b compares different types of isomers of glucose. As mentioned earlier, glucose can exist as D- and L-glucose, which are mirror images of each other. These are enantiomers. Alternatively, other types of isomers are formed by changing the relative positions of the hydrogens and hydroxyl groups along the sugar ring. For example, glucose exists in two interconvertible forms, with the hydroxyl group attached to the number 1 carbon atom lying either above (the β form of glucose, Figure 3.6b) or below (the α form, Figure 3.6a) the plane of the ring. As discussed later, these different isoforms of glucose

have different biological properties. In another example, if the hydroxyl group on carbon atom number 4 of glucose is switched from below to above the plane of the ring, the sugar called galactose is created (Figure 3.6b).

Monosaccharides can join together to form larger carbohydrates. **Disaccharides** (meaning two sugars) are carbohydrates composed of two monosaccharides. A familiar disaccharide is sucrose, or table sugar, which is composed of glucose and fructose (**Figure 3.7**). The linking together of most monosaccharides involves the removal of a hydroxyl group from one monosaccharide and a hydrogen atom from the other, giving rise to a molecule of water and bonding the two sugars together through an oxygen atom. This occurs by a dehydration reaction, also known as a condensation reaction. The bond formed between two sugar molecules is a glycosidic bond. Conversely, hydrolysis of a glycosidic bond in a disaccharide breaks this linkage by adding back the water and thus uncouples the two monosaccharides. Other disaccharides frequently found in nature are maltose, formed in animals during the digestion of large carbohydrates in the intestinal tract, and lactose, present in the milk of mammals. Maltose is α-D-glucose linked to α-D-glucose, while lactose is β-D-galactose linked to β-D-glucose.

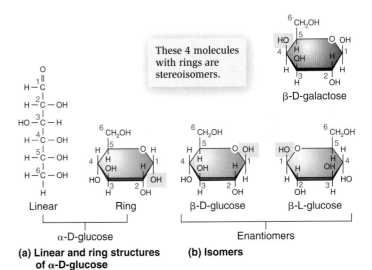

(a) Linear and ring structures of α-D-glucose

(b) Isomers

Figure 3.6 Monosaccharide structure. (a) A comparison of the linear and ring structures of glucose. In solution, such as the fluids of organisms, nearly all glucose is in the ring form. (b) Isomers of glucose. Glucose exists as stereoisomers designated α- and β-glucose, which differ in the position of the —OH group attached to carbon atom number 1. Glucose and galactose differ in the position of the —OH group attached to carbon atom number 4. Enantiomers of glucose, called D-glucose and L-glucose, are mirror images of each other. D-glucose is the form that is used by living cells. Note: The letters *D* and *L* are derived from dextrorotatory (rotating to the right) and levorotatory (rotating to the left).

Biological inquiry: With regard to their binding to enzymes, why do enantiomers such as D- and L-glucose have different biological properties?

Figure 3.7 **Formation of a disaccharide.** Two monosaccharides can bond to each other to form a disaccharide, such as sucrose, by a dehydration reaction.

Glucose   +   Fructose   ⟶   Sucrose   +   Water

Reactions resulting in the removal of 1 net molecule of water are called dehydration or condensation reactions.

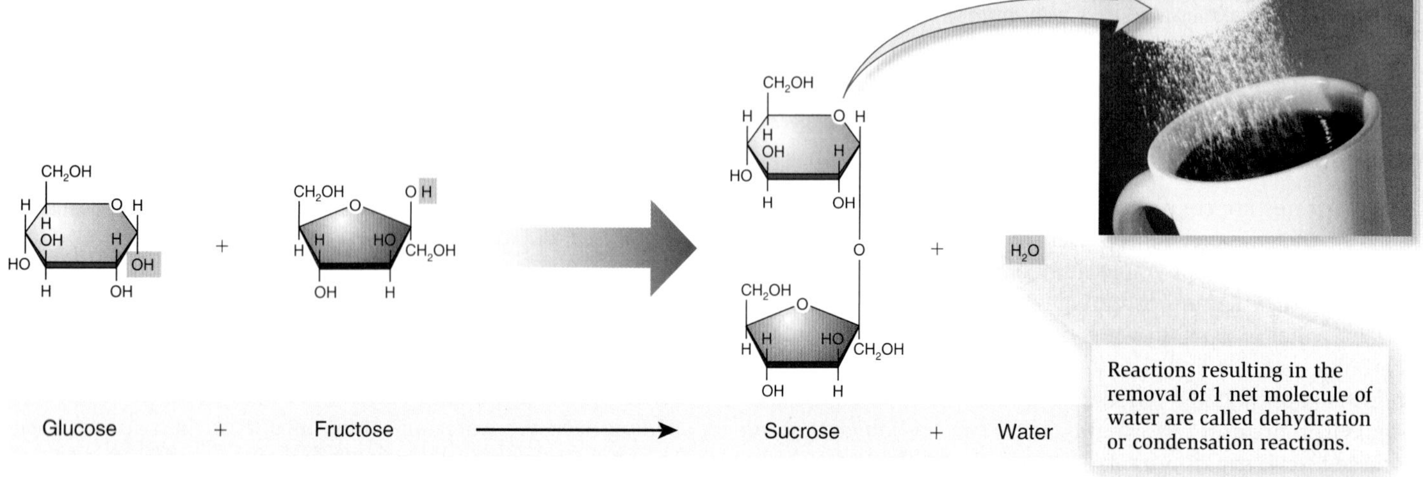

Polysaccharides When many monosaccharides are linked together to form long polymers, **polysaccharides** (meaning many sugars) are made. **Starch**, found in plant cells, and **glycogen**, present in animal cells and sometimes called animal starch, are examples of polysaccharides (**Figure 3.8**). Both of these polysaccharides are composed of thousands of α-D-glucose molecules linked together in long, branched chains, differing only in the extent of branching along the chain. As you can see from the numbering system of the carbon atoms, the bonds that form in polysaccharides are not random but instead form between specific carbon atoms of each molecule. The higher degree of branching in glycogen contributes to its solubility in animal tissues, such as muscle. Starch, because it is less branched, is less soluble and contributes to the properties of plant structures (think of a tough, insoluble kernel of corn).

Certain polysaccharides, such as starch and glycogen, are used to store energy in cells. Like disaccharides, polysaccharides can be hydrolyzed in the presence of water to yield monosaccharides, which are broken down to make ATP. Starch and glycogen, the polymers of α-glucose, provide efficient means of storing energy for those times when a plant or animal cannot obtain sufficient energy for its needs from its environment or diet.

Other polysaccharides provide a structural role, rather than storing energy. The plant polysaccharide **cellulose** is a polymer of β-glucose, with a linear arrangement of carbon-carbon bonds (Figure 3.8). The bond orientations in β-glucose prevent cellulose from being hydrolyzed for ATP production in most organisms. Instead, cellulose forms part of the rigid cell-wall structure characteristic of plants. Cellulose accounts for up to half of all the carbon contained within a typical plant, making it the most common organic compound on Earth. A simple change in bond orientation of glucose molecules, namely α versus β, dramatically alters the biological properties of the resultant polymers, in one case yielding a form of stored fuel and in the other case providing a rigid, protective feature of plant cells.

Some bacteria present in the gastrointestinal tracts of grass and wood eaters, such as cows and termites, can digest cellulose

into usable monosaccharides, because they contain an enzyme that can hydrolyze the β-glucose bonds. Humans lack this enzyme, and therefore we eliminate most of the cellulose ingested in our diet as fiber.

Other polysaccharides play structural roles. **Chitin**, a tough, structural polysaccharide, forms the external skeleton of many insects and the cell walls of fungi. The sugar monomers within chitin have nitrogen-containing groups attached to them. **Glycosaminoglycans** are large polysaccharides that play a structural role in animals. For example, glycosaminoglycans are abundantly found in cartilage. These polysaccharides tend to have sugar monomers with carboxyl and sulfate groups.

Lipids Store Energy and Form Membranes and Hormones

Lipids are molecules composed predominantly of hydrogen and carbon atoms. The defining feature of lipids is that they are nonpolar and therefore very insoluble in water. Lipids account for about 40% of the organic matter in the average human body and include fats, phospholipids, and steroids.

Fats Fats are a mixture of **triglycerides**, also known as triacylglycerols. Fats are formed by bonding glycerol to three fatty acids (**Figure 3.9**). A fatty acid is a chain of carbon and hydrogen atoms with a carboxyl group at the end. Because the carboxyl group (—COOH) releases an H^+ in water to become —COO^-, these molecules are called fatty acids. Each of the three hydroxyl groups (—OH) in glycerol is linked to the carboxyl group of a fatty acid by the removal of a molecule of water by a dehydration reaction. The resulting bond is called an ester bond.

The fatty acids found in fats and other lipids may differ with regard to their lengths and the presence of double bonds. Fatty acids are synthesized by the linking together of two-carbon fragments. Therefore, most fatty acids in nature have an even number of carbon atoms, with 16- and 18-carbon fatty acids being the most common in the cells of plants and animals. Fatty acids also differ with regard to the presence of double bonds.

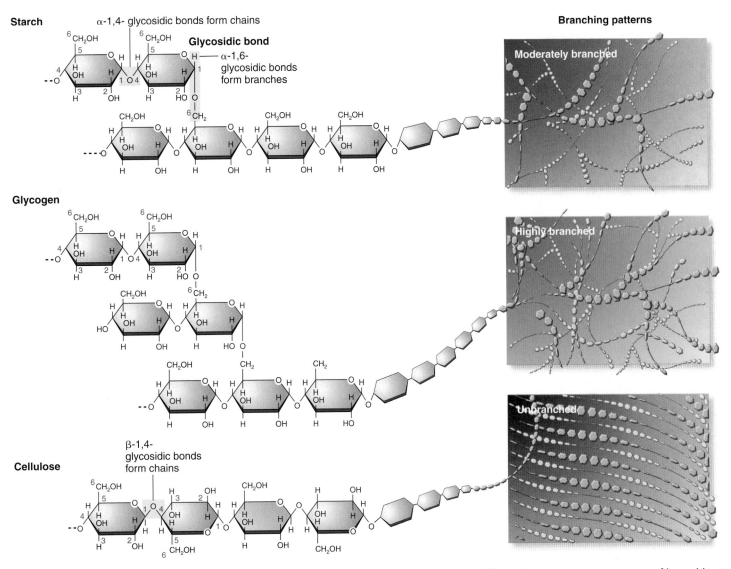

Figure 3.8 **Polysaccharides that are polymers of glucose.**   These polysaccharides differ in their arrangement, extent of branching, and type of glucose isomer.

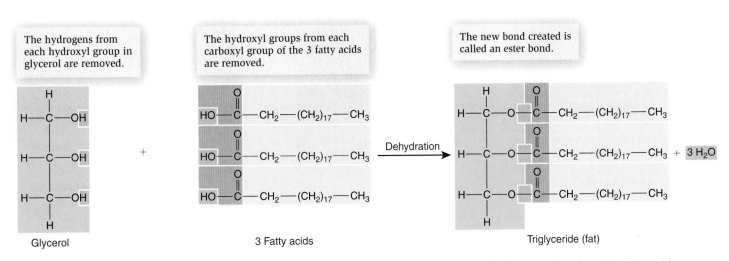

Figure 3.9   **The formation of a fat.**   The formation of a triglyceride requires three dehydration reactions in which fatty acids are bonded to glycerol.

When all the carbons in a fatty acid are linked by single covalent bonds, the fatty acid is said to be a **saturated fatty acid**, because all the carbons are saturated with covalently bound hydrogen. Alternatively, some fatty acids contain one or more C=C double bonds and are known as **unsaturated fatty acids**. A fatty acid with one C=C bond is a monounsaturated fatty

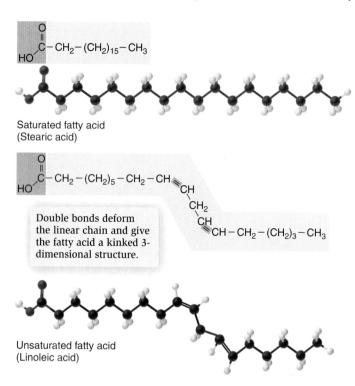

Saturated fatty acid
(Stearic acid)

Double bonds deform the linear chain and give the fatty acid a kinked 3-dimensional structure.

Unsaturated fatty acid
(Linoleic acid)

Figure 3.10 **Examples of fatty acids.** Fatty acids are hydrocarbon chains with a carboxyl functional group at one end and either no double-bonded carbons (saturated) or one or more double bonds (unsaturated). Stearic acid, for example, is an abundant saturated fatty acid in animals, while linoleic acid is an unsaturated fatty acid found in plants.

acid, while two or more C=C bonds constitutes a polyunsaturated fatty acid (**Figure 3.10**). In organisms such as mammals, some fatty acids are necessary for good health but cannot be synthesized by the body. Such fatty acids are called essential fatty acids, because they must be obtained in the diet.

Fats that contain high amounts of saturated fatty acids have high melting points, and therefore they tend to be solid at room temperature. Fats high in unsaturated fatty acids, on the other hand, usually have low melting points and thus are liquids at lower temperatures. Such fats are called oils. Animal fats generally contain a high proportion of saturated fatty acids, whereas vegetable oils contain more unsaturated fatty acids. When you heat a hamburger on the stove, the saturated animal fats melt, and liquid grease appears in the frying pan (**Figure 3.11**). When allowed to cool, however, the oily grease returns to its solid form. By comparison, oils derived from a plant, like olive oil, are liquid even at room temperature.

Like starch and glycogen, fats are important for storing energy. The hydrolysis of triglycerides releases the fatty acids from glycerol, and these products can then be metabolized to provide energy to make ATP. Certain organisms, most notably mammals, have the ability to store large amounts of energy by accumulating fats. One gram of fat stores twice as much energy as 1 g of glycogen or starch. For mobile animals, carrying around less weight is an advantage. In contrast, nonmobile organisms, such as plants, tend to store their energy in the form of polysaccharides. In animals, fats can also play a structural role by forming cushions that support organs. In addition, fats provide insulation under the skin that helps protect terrestrial animals during cold weather and marine mammals in cold water.

Phospholipids Another class of lipids, **phospholipids**, are similar in structure to triglycerides but with one important difference. The third hydroxyl group of glycerol is linked to a phosphate group instead of a fatty acid. In most phospholipids, a small polar or charged nitrogen-containing molecule is attached to this

High temperature converts solid, saturated fats to oil.

After cooling, saturated fats return to their solid form.

(a) Animal fats at high and low temperatures

Unsaturated fats are oils at room temperature and below.

(b) Vegetable fats at low temperature

Figure 3.11 **Fats at different temperatures.** Saturated fats found in animals tend to have high melting points compared to unsaturated fats found in plants.

Biological inquiry: Certain types of fats that are used in baking are called shortenings. They are solid at room temperature. Shortenings are often made from vegetable oils by a process called hydrogenation. What do you think happens to the structure of an oil when it is hydrogenated?

phosphate (**Figure 3.12**). These groups constitute a polar hydrophilic region at one end of the phospholipid, whereas the fatty acid chains provide a nonpolar hydrophobic region at the opposite end. Therefore, phospholipids are amphipathic.

In water, phospholipids become organized into bilayers, with their polar ends attracted to the water molecules and their nonpolar ends facing each other. As you will learn in Chapter 5, this bilayer arrangement of phospholipids is critical for determining the structure of plasma membranes.

Steroids **Steroids** have a distinctly different chemical structure from that of the other types of lipid molecules discussed thus far. Four fused rings of carbon atoms form the skeleton of all steroids (**Figure 3.13a**). A few polar hydroxyl groups may be attached to this ring structure, but they are not numerous enough to make a steroid highly water soluble. For example, steroids with a hydroxyl group are known as sterols—the most well known being cholesterol. Cholesterol is found in the blood of animals, where it can contribute to the formation of clots in major blood vessels.

In steroids, tiny differences in chemical structure can lead to profoundly different biological properties. For example, estrogen is a steroid found in high amounts in female vertebrates (**Figure 3.13b**). Estrogen differs from testosterone (**Figure 13.3c**), a steroid found largely in males, by having one less methyl group,

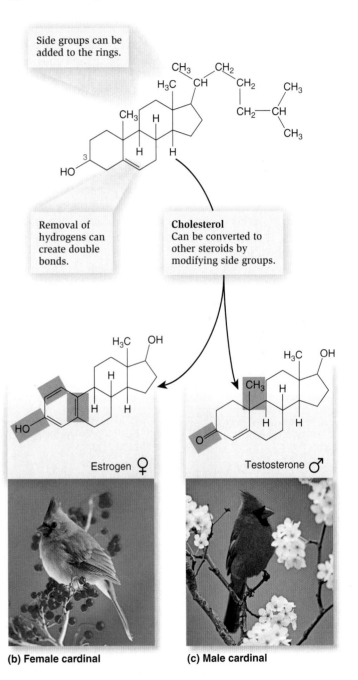

(a) The steroid ring structure

Figure 3.13 **Structure of cholesterol and steroid hormones derived from cholesterol.** (a) The structure of a steroid has four rings. Steroids include cholesterol and molecules derived from cholesterol, such as steroid hormones. These include the reproductive hormones **(b)** estradiol, a type of estrogen and **(c)** testosterone.

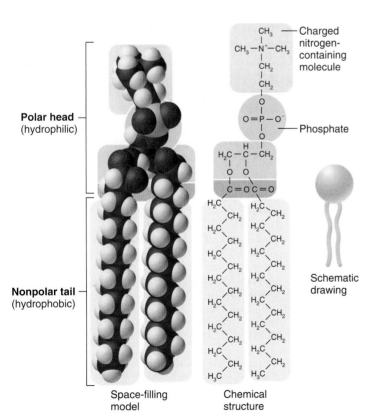

Figure 3.12 **Structure of phospholipids.** Phospholipids contain both polar and nonpolar regions, making them amphipathic. The fatty acyl tails, formed from fatty acids, are the nonpolar region. The rest of the molecule is polar.

a hydroxyl group instead of a ketone group, and additional double bonds in one of its rings. However, these seemingly small differences are sufficient to make these two molecules largely responsible for whether an animal exhibits male or female characteristics, and whether it is fertile.

Waxes Many plants and animals produce lipids called waxes that are typically secreted onto their surface, such as the leaves of plants and the cuticles of insects. Although any wax may contain hundreds of different compounds, all waxes contain one or more hydrocarbons, and long structures that resemble a fatty acid attached by its carboxyl group to another long hydrocarbon chain. Most waxes are very nonpolar and thus repel water, providing a barrier to water loss. They may also be used as structural elements in colonies like those of bees, where beeswax forms the honeycomb of the hive.

Proteins Are Composed of Amino Acids and Are Involved in Nearly All Life Processes

The word **protein** comes from the Greek *proteios* (meaning of the first rank), which aptly describes their importance. Proteins account for about 50% of the organic material in a typical animal's body, and they play critical roles in almost all life processes (**Table 3.2**).

Proteins are composed of carbon, hydrogen, oxygen, nitrogen, and small amounts of other elements, notably sulfur. The building blocks of proteins are **amino acids**. In other words, proteins are polymers of amino acids. Amino acids have a common structure in which a carbon atom, called the α-carbon, is linked to an amino group (NH_2) and a carboxyl group (COOH). The α-carbon also is linked to a hydrogen atom and a side chain, which is given a general designation R.

When dissolved in water at neutral pH, the amino group accepts a hydrogen ion and is positively charged, while the carboxyl group loses a hydrogen ion and is negatively charged. The term amino acid is the name given to such molecules because they have an amino group, and also a carboxyl group that behaves like an acid.

The 20 amino acids found in proteins differ with regard to the structures of their side chains (**Figure 3.14**). The amino acids are categorized as those that are nonpolar, polar and uncharged, and polar and charged. The varying structures of the side chains are critical features of protein structure and function. The arrangement and chemical features of the side chains cause proteins to fold and adopt their three-dimensional shapes. In addition, certain amino acids may be critical in protein function. For example, amino acid side chains found within the active sites of enzymes are important in catalyzing chemical reactions.

Table 3.2	Major Categories and Functions of Proteins	
Category	**Functions**	**Examples**
Proteins involved in gene expression and regulation	Make mRNA from a DNA template; synthesize polypeptides from mRNA; regulate genes	RNA polymerase transcribes genes; ribosomal proteins are needed for translation; transcription factor proteins are involved in gene regulation
Motor proteins	Initiate movement	Myosin is a motor protein that provides the contractile force of muscles; kinesin is a key protein that helps cells to sort their chromosomes
Defense proteins	Protect organisms against disease	Antibodies ward off infection due to bacteria or viruses
Metabolic enzymes	Increase rates of chemical reactions	Hexokinase is an enzyme involved in sugar metabolism
Cell signaling proteins	Enable cells to communicate with each other and with the environment	Taste receptors in the tongue allow animals to taste molecules in food
Structural proteins	Support and strengthen structures	Actin provides shape to the cytoplasm of cells such as plant and animal cells; collagen gives strength to tendons
Transporters	Promote movement of solutes across plasma membranes	Ion channels allow movement of charged molecules across plasma membranes; glucose transporters move glucose from outside cells to inside cells, where it can be used for energy

Amino acids are joined together by linking the carboxyl group of one amino acid to the amino group of another. A molecule of water is formed each time two amino acids are joined by a dehydration reaction (**Figure 3.15a**). The covalent bond formed between a carboxyl and amino group is called a **peptide bond**. When many amino acids are joined by peptide bonds, the resulting molecule is called a **polypeptide** (**Figure 3.15b**). The backbone of the polypeptide is highlighted in yellow. The amino acid side chains project from the backbone. When two or more amino acids are linked together, one end of the resulting molecule has a free amino group. This is the amino terminus, or N-terminus. The other end of the polypeptide, called the carboxyl terminus, or C-terminus, has a free carboxyl group. As shown in **Figure 3.15c**, amino acids within a polypeptide are numbered from the amino to the carboxyl terminus.

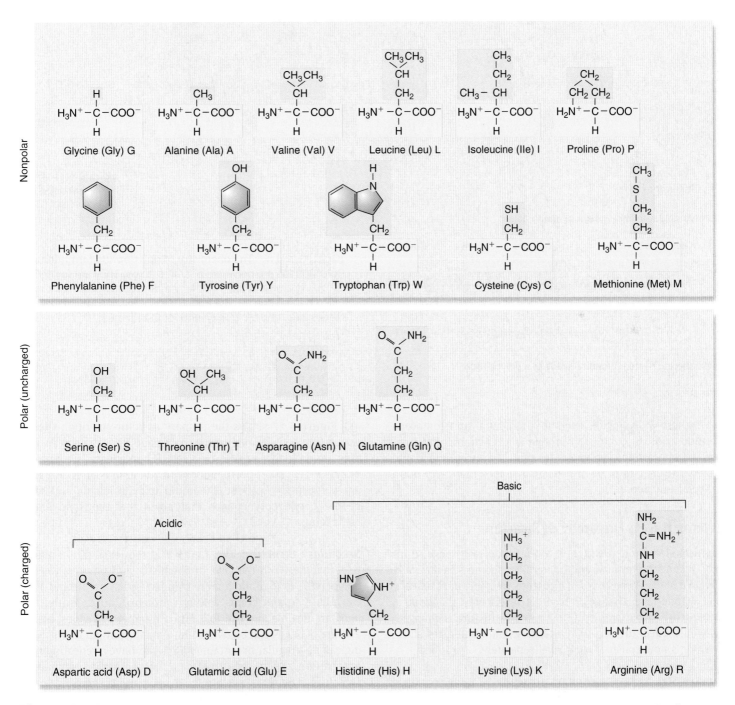

Figure 3.14 **The 20 amino acids found in living organisms.** The various amino acids have different chemical properties (for example, polar versus nonpolar). These properties contribute to the differences in the three-dimensional shapes of proteins, which in turn influence their biological functions.

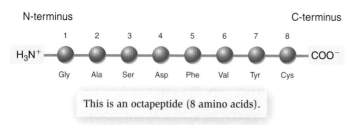

(a) Formation of a peptide bond between 2 amino acids

Free amino group

The amino end of a protein is called the N-terminus.

Free carboxyl group

The carboxyl end of a protein is called the C-terminus.

(b) Polypeptide—a linear chain of amino acids

N-terminus   C-terminus

1   2   3   4   5   6   7   8

H_3N^+ COO^-

Gly   Ala   Ser   Asp   Phe   Val   Tyr   Cys

This is an octapeptide (8 amino acids).

(c) Numbering system of amino acids in a polypeptide

Figure 3.15   The chemistry of polypeptide formation. Polypeptides are polymers of amino acids. They are formed by linking amino acids together via dehydration reactions to make peptide bonds. Every polypeptide has an amino end, or N-terminus, and a carboxyl end, or C-terminus.

Biological inquiry: How many water molecules would be produced in making a polypeptide that is 72 amino acids long by dehydration reactions?

The term polypeptide refers to a structural unit composed of amino acids. In contrast, a protein is a functional unit composed of one or more polypeptides that have been folded and twisted into precise three-dimensional shapes that carry out a particular function.

Proteins Have a Hierarchy of Structure

Scientists view protein structure at four progressive levels: primary, secondary, tertiary, and quaternary, shown schematically in **Figure 3.16**. These levels of structure are dependent on each other. If one level changes, the other levels may change as a consequence. For example, if the primary structure is changed, this would affect the secondary, tertiary, and quaternary structures. Let's now consider each level separately.

Primary Structure   The **primary structure** of a polypeptide is its amino acid sequence, from beginning to end. The primary structures of polypeptides are determined by genes. As discussed in Chapter 12, genes carry the information to make polypeptides with a defined amino acid sequence.

Figure 3.17 shows the primary structure of ribonuclease, which functions as an enzyme to degrade RNA molecules after they are no longer needed by a cell. Ribonuclease is composed of a relatively short polypeptide with 124 amino acids. An average polypeptide is about 300 amino acids in length, and some genes encode polypeptides that are a few thousand amino acids long.

Secondary Structure   The amino acid sequence of a polypeptide, together with the laws of chemistry and physics, cause a polypeptide to fold into a more compact structure. Amino acids can rotate around bonds within a protein. Consequently, proteins are flexible and can fold into a number of shapes, just as a string of beads can be twisted into many configurations. Folding can be irregular or certain regions can have a repeating folding pattern. Such repeating patterns are called **secondary structure**. The two types are the α helix and β sheet.

In an α helix, the polypeptide backbone forms a repeating helical structure that is stabilized by hydrogen bonds. As shown in Figure 3.16, the hydrogen linked to a nitrogen atom forms a hydrogen bond with an oxygen atom that is double-bonded to a

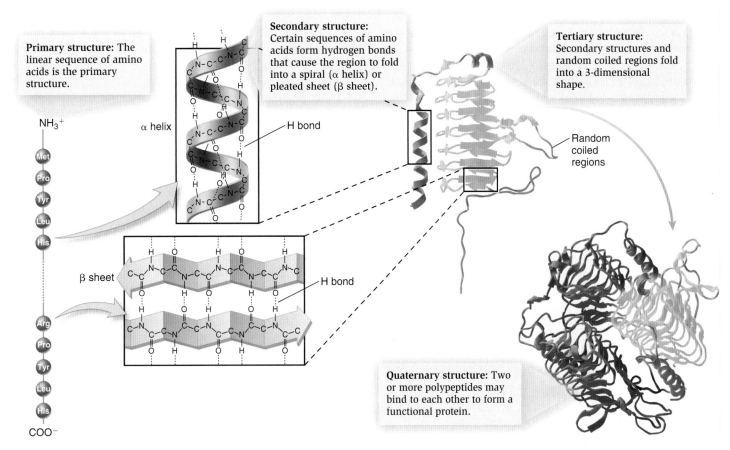

Figure 3.16 The hierarchy of protein structure.

carbon. These hydrogen bonds occur at regular intervals and cause the polypeptide backbone to form a helix. In a β sheet, regions of the polypeptide backbone come to lie parallel to each other. When these parallel regions form hydrogen bonds, again between the hydrogen linked to a nitrogen atom and a double-bonded oxygen, the polypeptide backbone adopts a repeating zigzag shape called a β pleated sheet.

α helices and β sheets are key determinants of a protein's characteristics. For example, α helices in certain proteins are composed primarily of nonpolar amino acids. Proteins containing many such regions with an α helix structure tend to anchor themselves into a lipid-rich environment, such as a cell's plasma membrane. In this way, a protein whose function is needed in a specific location such as a plasma membrane can be retained there. Secondary structure also contributes to the great strength of certain proteins, including the keratins found in hair and hooves, the proteins that make up the silk webs of spiders, and collagen, the chief component of cartilage in mammals.

Some regions along a polypeptide chain do not assume an α helix or β sheet conformation. In other words, they do not have secondary structure. These regions are sometimes called random coiled regions. However, this term is somewhat misleading because the shapes of random coiled regions are usually very specific and are important to the function of a protein.

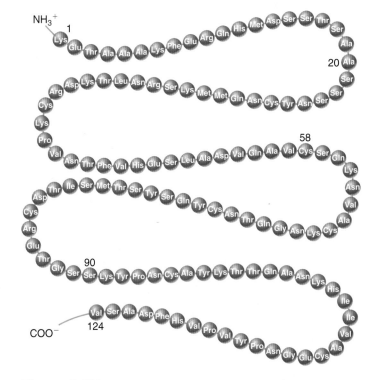

Figure 3.17 The primary structure of ribonuclease. The example shown here is ribonuclease from cows, which was studied by Anfinsen as described later in Figure 3.20.

Tertiary Structure As the secondary structure becomes established due to the particular primary structure, a polypeptide folds and refolds upon itself to assume a complex three-dimensional shape—its **tertiary structure** (see Figure 3.16). The tertiary structure is the three-dimensional shape of a single polypeptide. For some proteins, such as ribonuclease, the tertiary structure is the final structure of a functional protein. However, as described next, other proteins are composed of two or more polypeptides and adopt a quaternary structure.

Quaternary Structure Most functional proteins are composed of two or more polypeptides that each adopt a tertiary structure and then assemble with each other (see Figure 3.16). The individual polypeptides are called **protein subunits**. Subunits may be identical polypeptides or they may be different. When proteins consist of more than one polypeptide chain, they are said to have **quaternary structure** and are also known as **multimeric proteins** (meaning many parts).

Factors That Influence Protein Structure Several factors determine the way that polypeptides adopt their secondary, tertiary, and quaternary structures. The amino acid sequences of polypeptides are the defining features that distinguish the structure of one protein from another. As polypeptides are synthesized in a cell, they fold into secondary and tertiary structures, which assemble into quaternary structures for most proteins. As mentioned, the laws of chemistry and physics, together with the amino acid sequence, govern this process. As shown in **Figure 3.18**, five factors are critical for protein folding and stability:

1. *Hydrogen bonds*—The large number of hydrogen bonds within a polypeptide and between polypeptides adds up to a strong force that promotes protein folding and stability. As we have already learned, hydrogen bonding is a critical determinant of protein secondary structure, and also is important in tertiary and quaternary structure.
2. *Ionic bonds and other polar interactions*—Some amino acid side chains are positively charged while others are negatively charged. Positively charged side chains may bind to negatively charged side chains via ionic bonds. Similarly, uncharged polar side chains in a protein may interact with ionic amino acids. These ionic and polar interactions promote protein folding and stability.
3. *Hydrophobic effect*—Some amino acid side chains are nonpolar. These amino acids tend to avoid water. As a protein folds, the hydrophobic amino acids are likely to be

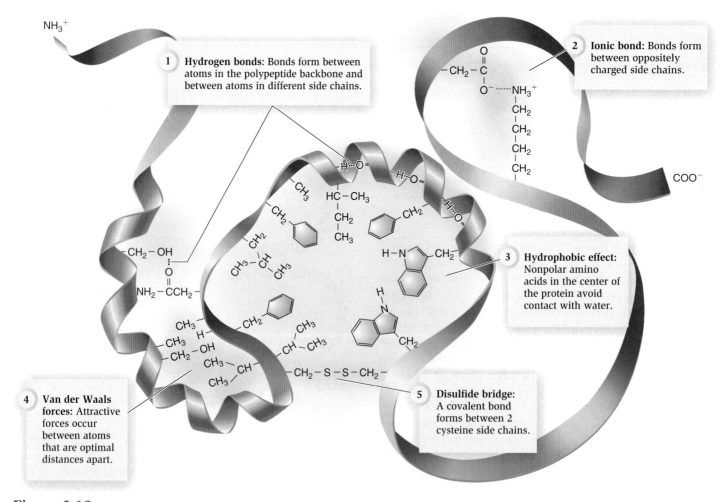

Figure 3.18 The factors that influence protein folding and stability.

found in the center of the protein to avoid contact with water. As mentioned, some proteins have stretches of nonpolar amino acids that anchor them in the hydrophobic portion of membranes.

4. *Van der Waals forces*—Atoms within molecules have weak attractions for each other if they are an optimal distance apart. This optimal distance is called the van der Waals radius, and the weak attraction is the van der Waals force. If two atoms are too close together, their electron clouds will repel each other. If they are too far apart, the van der Waals force will diminish. Similar to hydrogen bonds, many van der Waals forces can contribute to protein folding and stability.

5. *Disulfide bridges*—The side chain of the amino acid cysteine ($—CH_2—SH$) contains a sulfhydryl group, which can react with a sulfhydryl group in another cysteine side chain to produce a disulfide bridge or bond, which links the two amino acid side chains together ($—CH_2—S—S—CH_2—$). Disulfide bonds are covalent bonds that can occur within a single polypeptide or between different polypeptides. Though other forces are usually more important in protein folding, the covalent nature of disulfide bonds can help to stabilize the structure of a protein.

The first four factors just described are also important in the ability of different proteins to interact with each other. As discussed throughout Unit II and other parts of this textbook, many cellular processes involve steps in which two or more different proteins interact with each other. For this to occur, the surface of one protein must bind to the surface of the other. Such binding is usually very specific. The surface of one protein precisely fits into the surface of another (**Figure 3.19**). Such **protein-protein interactions** are critically important so that cellular processes can occur in a series of defined steps. In addition, protein-protein interactions are also important in building large cellular structures that provide shape and organization to cells.

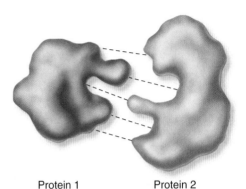

Protein 1   Protein 2

Figure 3.19 Protein-protein interaction. Two different proteins may interact with each other due to hydrogen bonding, ionic bonding, the hydrophobic effect, and van der Waals forces.

FEATURE INVESTIGATION

Anfinsen Showed That the Primary Structure of Ribonuclease Determines Its Three-Dimensional Structure

Prior to the 1960s, the mechanisms by which proteins assume their three-dimensional structures were not understood. Scientists believed that correct folding required unknown cellular factors, or that ribosomes, the site where polypeptides are synthesized, somehow shaped proteins as they were being made. Christian Anfinsen, however, postulated that proteins contain all the information necessary to fold into their proper conformation without the need for organelles or cellular factors. He hypothesized that proteins spontaneously assume their most stable conformation based on the laws of chemistry and physics (**Figure 3.20**).

To test this hypothesis, Anfinsen studied ribonuclease, which we discussed earlier (see Figure 3.17). Biochemists had already determined that ribonuclease has four disulfide bonds between eight cysteine amino acids. Anfinsen began with purified ribonuclease—this is called an *in vitro* experiment, meaning under glass, as in a test tube. The key point is that other cellular components were not present, only the purified protein. He exposed ribonuclease to a chemical called urea that disrupted the hydrogen and ionic bonds, and to another chemical called β-mercaptoethanol that broke the S—S bonds. Following this treatment, he measured the ability of the treated enzyme to degrade RNA. The enzyme had lost nearly all of its ability to degrade RNA. Therefore, Anfinsen concluded that when ribonuclease was unfolded or denatured, it was no longer functional.

The key step in this experiment came when Anfinsen removed the urea and β-mercaptoethanol from the solution. Because these molecules are much smaller than ribonuclease, removing them from the solution was accomplished with a technique called dialysis. In dialysis, solutions are placed in a synthetic bag with microscopic pores that permit small molecules to pass through and leave the bag but retain large macromolecules such as ribonuclease. Anfinsen placed the entire bag in a large beaker of water, into which the urea and β-mercaptoethanol diffused. Then he retested the ribonuclease. The result revolutionized our understanding of proteins. The activity of the ribonuclease was almost completely restored! This meant that even in the complete absence of any cellular factors or organelles, an unfolded protein can refold into its functional structure. This was later confirmed by chemical analyses that demonstrated that the disulfide bonds had re-formed at the proper locations.

Since Anfinsen's time, we have also learned that his experiments with ribonuclease are not representative of all proteins. Some proteins do require certain enzymes and other proteins to assist them in their proper folding. Nonetheless, Anfinsen's experiments provided compelling evidence that the primary structure of a polypeptide is the key determinant of a protein's tertiary structure, a correct observation that earned him a Nobel Prize in 1972.

Figure 3.20 Anfinsen's experiments with ribonuclease demonstrating that the primary structure of a polypeptide plays a key role in protein folding.

HYPOTHESIS Within their amino acid sequence, proteins contain all the information needed to fold into their correct, 3-dimensional shapes.

STARTING MATERIALS Purified ribonuclease and RNA.

Experimental level   Conceptual level

1 Incubate purified ribonuclease in test tube with RNA, and measure its ability to degrade RNA.

Numerous H bonds and 4 S—S bonds. Protein is properly folded.

2 Denature protein shape by adding urea (breaks H bonds and ionic bonds) and β-mercaptoethanol (breaks S—S bonds). Measure its ability to degrade RNA.

β-mercaptoethanol + Urea

No more H bonds, ionic bonds, or S—S bonds. Protein is unfolded.

3 Place into dialysis bag. Pores allow urea and β-mercaptoethanol to escape, but ribonuclease is trapped inside. After urea and β-mercaptoethanol have exited the bag, measure the ability of ribonuclease to degrade RNA.

Add mixture to dialysis bag.

Denatured ribonuclease + β-mercapto-ethanol + Urea

Seal end when filled.

Sealed end

Pores

Ribonuclease   Urea   β-Mercaptoethanol

4 THE DATA

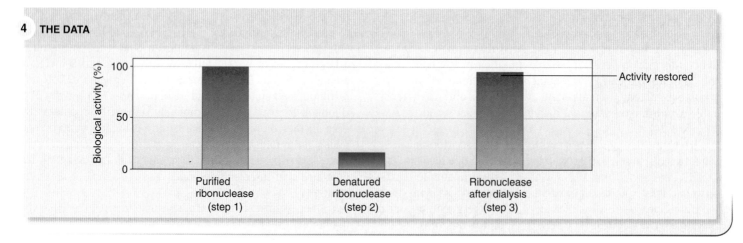

Purified ribonuclease (step 1)   Denatured ribonuclease (step 2)   Ribonuclease after dialysis (step 3)   Activity restored

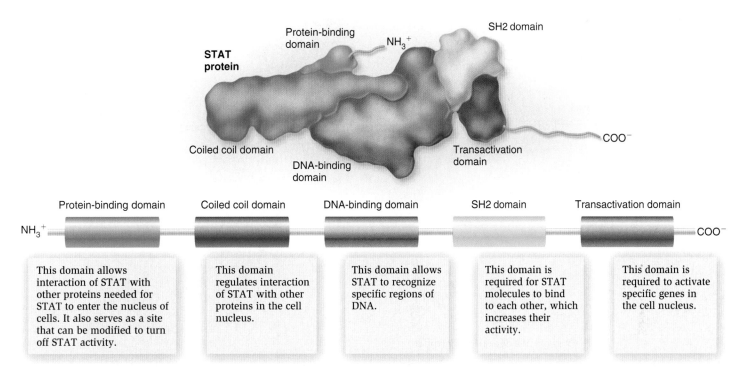

Figure 3.21   **The domain structure of a STAT protein.**   The boxes represent different domains, connected by chains of amino acids (the connecting lines in this figure).

GENOMES & PROTEOMES

Proteins Contain Functional Domains Within Their Structures

Modern research into the functions of proteins has revealed that many proteins have a modular design. This means that portions within proteins, called modules or **domains**, have distinct structures and functions. These units of amino acid sequences have been duplicated during evolution so that the same kind of domain may be found in several different proteins. When the same domain is found in different proteins, the domain has the same three-dimensional shape and performs a function that is characteristic of that domain.

As an example, **Figure 3.21** shows a protein that is known to play a critical role in regulating how certain genes are turned on and off in living cells. This protein bears the cumbersome name of *signal transducer and activator of transcription* (STAT) protein. In the primary structure, each domain of the STAT protein is shown as a separate box, linked to the next domain by a straight line. These boxes and lines represent strings of amino acids, which have secondary and tertiary structures.

Each domain of this protein is involved in a distinct biological function, a common occurrence in proteins with multiple domains. For example, one of the domains is labeled the SH2 domain (Figure 3.21). In many different proteins, this domain allows proteins to recognize other proteins in a very specific way. The function of SH2 domains is to bind to tyrosines that are phosphoryated by cellular enzymes. Many proteins contain SH2 domains, and as might be predicted, they all bind to phosphorylated tyrosines in the proteins they recognize.

As a second example, a STAT protein has another domain called a DNA-binding domain. This portion of the protein has a structure that specifically binds to DNA. Overall, the domain structure of proteins enables them to have multiple regions, each with its own structure and purpose in the functioning of the protein.

Nucleic Acids Are the Source of Genetic Information

Nucleic acids account for only about 2% of the weight of animals like ourselves, yet these molecules are extremely important because they are responsible for the storage, expression, and transmission of genetic information. The expression of genetic information in the form of specific proteins determines whether one is a human, a mouse, an onion, or a bacterium. Likewise, genetic information determines whether a cell is part of a muscle or a leaf.

The two classes of nucleic acids are **deoxyribonucleic acid (DNA)** and **ribonucleic acid (RNA)**. DNA molecules store genetic information coded in the sequence of their monomer building blocks. RNA molecules are involved in decoding this information into instructions for linking together a specific sequence of amino acids to form a polypeptide chain.

Like other macromolecules, both types of nucleic acids are polymers and consist of linear sequences of repeating monomers.

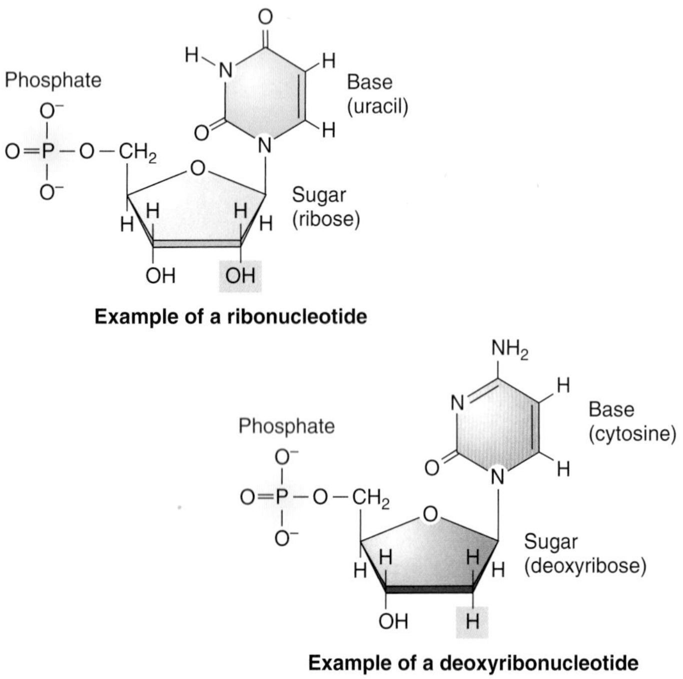

Example of a ribonucleotide

Example of a deoxyribonucleotide

Figure 3.22 Examples of two nucleotides. A nucleotide has a phosphate group, a five-carbon sugar, and a nitrogenous base.

Each monomer, known as a **nucleotide**, has three components: a phosphate group, a five-carbon sugar (either ribose or deoxyribose), and a single or double ring of carbon and nitrogen atoms known as a **base** (**Figure 3.22**). The phosphate group of one nucleotide is linked to the sugar of the adjacent nucleotide to form a polynucleotide strand with the bases protruding from the side of the phosphate-sugar backbone (**Figure 3.23**). This is a phosphoester bond.

DNA The nucleotides in DNA contain the five-carbon sugar **deoxyribose**. Four different nucleotides are present in DNA, corresponding to the four different bases that can be linked to deoxyribose. The **purine** bases, **adenine (A)** and **guanine (G)**, have double (fused) rings of nitrogen and carbon atoms, and the **pyrimidine** bases, **cytosine (C)** and **thymine (T)**, have only a single ring (see Figure 3.23).

A DNA molecule consists of two strands of nucleotides coiled around each other to form a double helix (**Figure 3.24**). The two strands are held together by hydrogen bonds between a purine base in one strand and a pyrimidine base in the opposite strand. The ring structure of each base lies in a flat plane perpendicular to the sugar-phosphate backbone, somewhat like steps on a spiral staircase. This base pairing maintains a constant distance between the sugar-phosphate backbones of the two strands as they coil around each other.

As we will see in Chapter 11, only certain bases can pair with others, due to the location of the hydrogen-bonding groups in the four bases (see Figure 3.24). Two hydrogen bonds can be formed between adenine and thymine (A-T pairing), while three hydrogen bonds are formed between guanine and cytosine (G-C pairing). In a DNA molecule, A is always paired with T,

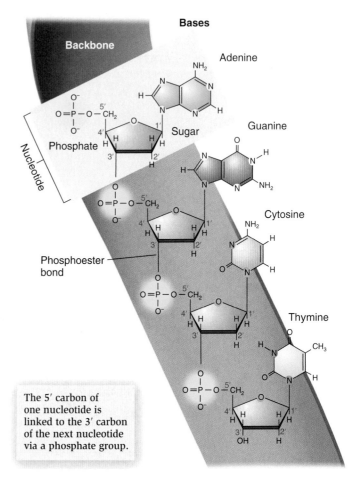

The 5' carbon of one nucleotide is linked to the 3' carbon of the next nucleotide via a phosphate group.

Figure 3.23 Structure of a DNA strand. Nucleotides are linked to each other to form a strand of DNA. The four bases found in DNA are shown. A strand of RNA would be similar except the sugar would be ribose and uracil would be substituted for thymine.

and G with C. If we know the amount of one type of base in a DNA molecule, we can predict the relative amounts of each of the other three bases. For example, if a DNA molecule were composed of 20% A bases, then there must also be 20% T bases. That leaves 60% of the bases that must be C and G combined. Because the amounts of C and G must be equal, this particular DNA molecule must be composed of 30% each of C and G. This specificity provides the mechanism for duplicating and transferring genetic information.

RNA RNA molecules differ in only a few respects from DNA. RNA consists of a single rather than double strand of nucleotides. In RNA, the sugar in each nucleotide is **ribose** rather than deoxyribose. Also, the pyrimidine base thymine in DNA is replaced in RNA with the pyrimidine base **uracil (U)** (see Figure 3.22). The other three bases—adenine, guanine, and cytosine—are found in both DNA and RNA. Certain forms of RNA called messenger RNA (mRNA) and transfer RNA (tRNA) are responsible for converting the information contained in DNA into the formation of a new polypeptide. This topic will be discussed in Chapter 12.

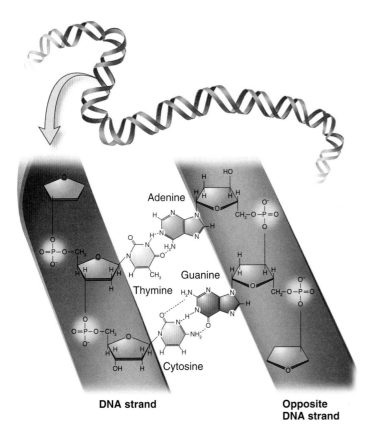

Figure 3.24   The double-stranded structure of DNA.   DNA consists of two strands coiled together into a double helix. The bases form hydrogen bonds in which A pairs with T, and G pairs with C.

CHAPTER SUMMARY

3.1   The Carbon Atom and the Study of Organic Molecules

- Organic chemistry is the science of studying carbon-containing molecules, which are found in living organisms. Wöhler's work with urea marked the birth of organic chemistry. (Figure 3.1)

- One property of the carbon atom that makes life possible is its ability to form four covalent bonds with other atoms. Carbon can form both polar and nonpolar bonds. The combination of different elements and different types of bonds allows a vast number of organic compounds to be formed from only a few chemical elements. (Figures 3.2, 3.3)

- Organic molecules may occur in various shapes. The structures of molecules determine their functions.

- Carbon bonds are stable at the different temperatures associated with life. (Figure 3.4)

- Organic compounds may contain functional groups. (Table 3.1)

- Carbon-containing molecules can exist as isomers, which have identical molecular composition but different structures and characteristics. Structural isomers contain the same atoms but in different bonding relationships. Stereoisomers have identical bonding relationships but different spatial positioning of their atoms. Enantiomers exist as mirror images of each other. (Figure 3.5)

3.2   Classes of Organic Molecules and Macromolecules

- The four major classes of organic molecules are carbohydrates, lipids, proteins, and nucleic acids. Macromolecules are large organic molecules that are composed of many thousands of atoms. Some macromolecules are polymers because they are formed by linking together many smaller molecules called monomers.

- Carbohydrates are composed of carbon, hydrogen, and oxygen atoms. Most cells can break down carbohydrates, releasing energy and storing it in newly created bonds in ATP.

- Carbohydrates include monosaccharides (the simplest sugars), disaccharides, and polysaccharides. The polysaccharides starch (in plant cells) and glycogen (in animal cells) provide an efficient means of storing energy. The plant polysaccharide cellulose serves a support or structural function. (Figures 3.6, 3.7, 3.8)

- Lipids, composed predominantly of hydrogen and carbon atoms, are nonpolar and very insoluble in water. Major classes of lipids include fats, phospholipids, steroids, and waxes.

- Fats, a mixture of triglycerides, are formed by bonding glycerol with three fatty acids. In a saturated fatty acid, all the carbons are linked by single covalent bonds. Unsaturated fatty acids contain one or more C=C double bonds. Animal fats generally contain a high proportion of saturated fatty acids, and vegetable fats contain more unsaturated fatty acids. (Figures 3.9, 3.10, 3.11)

- Phospholipids are similar in structure to triglycerides, except they are amphipathic because one fatty acid is replaced with a charged polar group. (Figure 3.12)

- Steroids are constructed of four fused rings of carbon atoms. Small differences in steroid structure can lead to profoundly different biological properties, such as the differences between estrogen and testosterone. (Figure 3.13)

- Waxes, another class of lipids, are nonpolar and repel water, and they are often found as protective coatings on the leaves of plants and the outer surfaces of animals' bodies.

- Proteins are composed of carbon, hydrogen, oxygen, nitrogen, and small amounts of other elements, such as sulfur. Proteins are macromolecules that play critical roles in almost all life processes. The proteins of living organisms are composed of the same set of 20 amino acids, corresponding to 20 different side chains. (Figure 3.14, Table 3.2)

- Amino acids are joined together by linking the carboxyl group of one amino acid to the amino group of another, forming a peptide bond. A polypeptide is a structural unit composed of amino acids, while a protein is a functional unit composed of one or more polypeptides that have been folded and twisted into precise three-dimensional shapes. (Figure 3.15)

- The four levels of protein structure are primary (its amino acid sequence), secondary (bending or twisting into helices or β sheets), tertiary (folding and refolding to assume a three-dimensional shape), and quaternary (multimeric proteins that consist of more than one polypeptide chain). If the primary structure of a protein changes, the other levels would change as a consequence. The three-dimensional structure of a protein determines its function, for example, by creating binding sites for other molecules. (Figures 3.16, 3.17, 3.18, 3.19, 3.20, 3.21)

- Nucleic acids are responsible for the storage, expression, and transmission of genetic information. The two types of nucleic acids are deoxyribonucleic acid (DNA) and ribonucleic acid (RNA). (Figures 3.22, 3.23)

- DNA molecules store genetic information coded in the sequence of their monomers. A DNA molecule consists of two strands of nucleotides coiled around each other to form a double helix, held together by hydrogen bonds between a purine base on one strand and a pyrimidine base on the opposite strand. (Figure 3.24)

- RNA molecules are involved in decoding this information into instructions for linking a specific sequence of amino acids to form a specific polypeptide chain. RNA consists of a single strand of nucleotides. The sugar in each nucleotide is ribose rather than deoxyribose, and the base uracil replaces thymine.

Test Yourself

1. Molecules that contain the element _____ are considered organic molecules.
   a. hydrogen   d. nitrogen
   b. carbon   e. calcium
   c. oxygen

2. _____ was the first scientist to synthesize an organic molecule. The organic molecule synthesized was _____.
   a. Kolbe, urea   d. Kolbe, acetic acid
   b. Wöhler, urea   e. Wöhler, glucose
   c. Wöhler, acetic acid

3. The versatility of carbon to serve as the backbone for a variety of different molecules is due to
   a. the ability of carbon atoms to form four covalent bonds.
   b. the fact that carbon usually forms ionic bonds with many different atoms.
   c. the abundance of carbon in the environment.
   d. the ability of carbon to form covalent bonds with many different types of atoms.
   e. both a and d.

4. _____ are molecules that have the same molecular composition but differ in structure and/or bonding association.
   a. Isotopes   d. Analogues
   b. Isomers   e. Ions
   c. Free radicals

5. _____ is a storage polysaccharide commonly found in the cells of animals.
   a. Glucose   d. Starch
   b. Sucrose   e. Cellulose
   c. Glycogen

6. In contrast to other fatty acids, essential fatty acids
   a. are always saturated fats.
   b. cannot be synthesized by the organism and are necessary for survival.
   c. can act as building blocks for large, more complex macromolecules.
   d. are the simplest form of lipids found in plant cells.
   e. are structural components of plasma membranes.

7. Phospholipids are said to be amphipathic, which means these molecules
   a. are partially hydrolyzed during cellular metabolism.
   b. are composed of a hydrophilic portion and hydrophobic portion.
   c. may be poisonous to organisms if in combination with certain other molecules.
   d. are molecules composed of lipids and proteins.
   e. all of the above.

8. The monomers of proteins are _____ and these are linked by polar covalent bonds commonly referred to as _____ bonds.
   a. nucleotides, peptide
   b. amino acids, ester
   c. hydroxyl groups, phosphodiester
   d. amino acids, peptide
   e. monosaccharides, glycosidic

9. The _____ of a nucleotide determines whether it is a component of DNA or a component of RNA.
   a. phosphate group   d. fatty acid
   b. five-carbon sugar   e. both b and d
   c. side chain

10. A _____ is a portion of protein with a particular structure and function.
    a. peptide bond   d. wax
    b. domain   e. monosaccharide
    c. phospholipid

Conceptual Questions

1. Define isomers.

2. List the four classes of organic molecules and give a function of each.

3. Explain the difference between saturated and unsaturated fatty acids.

Experimental Questions

1. Before the experiments conducted by Anfinsen, what were the common beliefs among scientists about protein folding?

2. Explain the hypothesis tested by Anfinsen.

3. Why did Anfinsen use urea and β-mercaptoethanol in his experiments? Explain the result that was crucial to the discovery that the tertiary structure of a protein is dependent on the primary structure.

Collaborative Questions

1. Discuss several types of carbohydrates.

2. Discuss some of the roles that proteins play in organisms.

www.brookerbiology.com
This website includes answers to the Biological Inquiry questions found in the figure legends and all end-of-chapter questions.

4
GENERAL FEATURES OF CELLS

CHAPTER OUTLINE

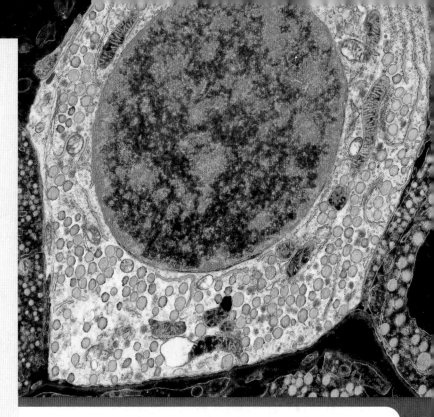

A cell from the pituitary gland. The cell in this micrograph was viewed by a technique called transmission electron microscopy, which is described in this chapter. The micrograph is artificially colored using a computer to enhance the visualization of certain cell structures.

When German botanist Matthias Schleiden studied plant material under the microscope, he was struck by certain consistent features. In particular, he noted the presence of many similar-looking compartments, each of which contained a dark area. (Today we call those compartments cells and the dark area is the nucleus.) In 1838, Schleiden speculated that cells are living entities and plants are aggregates of cells arranged according to definite laws.

Schleiden was a good friend of the German physiologist Theodor Schwann. Over dinner one evening, their conversation turned to the nuclei of plant cells, and Schwann remembered having seen similar structures in animal tissue. Schwann conducted additional studies that showed large numbers of nuclei in animal tissue, at regular intervals, and also located in cell-like compartments. In 1839, Schwann extended Schleiden's hypothesis to animals. In 1855, German biologist Rudolf Virchow proposed that *omnis cellula e cellula* ("every cell originates from another cell"). This idea arose from his research, which showed that diseased cells divide to produce more diseased cells.

According to the **cell theory** or **cell doctrine**, which is credited to both Schleiden and Schwann with contributions from Virchow:

1. all living things are composed of one or more cells;
2. cells are the smallest units of living organisms;
3. new cells come only from pre-existing cells by cell division.

Cell biology is the study of individual cells and their interactions with each other.

Most cells are so small that they cannot be seen with the naked eye. However, as cell biologists have begun to unravel

cell structure and function at the molecular level, the cell has emerged as a unit of wonderful complexity and adaptability. In this chapter, we will begin our examination of cells with an overview of their structures and functions. Later chapters in this unit will explore certain aspects of cell biology in greater detail. But first, let's look at the tools and techniques that allow us to observe these tiny entities.

4.1 Microscopy

The **microscope** is a magnification tool that enables researchers to study the structure and function of cells. The first compound microscope—a microscope with more than one lens—was invented in 1595 by Zacharias Jansen of Holland. In 1663 an English biologist, Robert Hooke, studied cork under a primitive compound microscope he had made. (He actually observed cell walls because cork cells are dead and have lost their internal components.) Hooke coined the word *cell* (from the Latin word *cellula*, meaning small compartment) to describe the structures he observed. Ten years later, the Dutch merchant Anton van Leeuwenhoek refined techniques of making lenses and was able to observe single-celled microorganisms such as bacteria. Among his many accomplishments, he discovered blood cells and was the first to see living sperm cells of animals.

Three important parameters in microscopy are magnification, resolution, and contrast. **Magnification** is the ratio between the size of an image produced by a microscope and its actual size. For example, if the image size is 100 times larger than its actual size, the magnification is designated 100×.

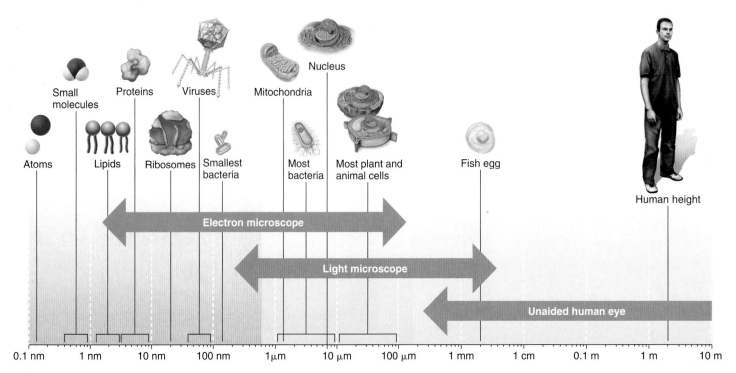

Figure 4.1 A comparison of the sizes of various chemical and biological structures, and the resolving power of the naked eye, light microscope, and electron microscope. The scale shown at the bottom is a logarithmic scale to accommodate the wide range of sizes shown in this drawing.

Depending on the quality of the lens and illumination source, every microscope has an optimal range of magnification before objects appear too blurry to be readily observed. **Resolution**, a measure of the clarity of an image, is the ability to observe two adjacent objects as distinct from one another. For example, a microscope with good resolution enables a researcher to distinguish two adjacent chromosomes as separate objects, which would appear as a single object under a microscope with poor resolution. The third important parameter in microscopy is **contrast**. The ability to visualize a particular cell structure may depend on how different it looks from an adjacent structure. If the object of interest, such as a particular protein, can be specifically stained with a colored dye, this makes viewing much easier. The application of stains, which selectively label individual components of the cell, greatly improves contrast. However, staining should not be confused with colorization. Many of the micrographs shown in this textbook are colorized to emphasize certain cellular structures (see the chapter opener, for example). In colorization, particular colors are added to micrographs with the aid of a computer. This is done for educational purposes. For example, colorization can help to emphasize different parts of a cell.

Microscopes are categorized into two groups based on the source of illumination. A **light microscope** utilizes light for illumination, while an **electron microscope** uses an electron beam. Very good light microscopes can resolve structures that are 0.2 μm (micron, or micrometer) apart or greater. The resolving power of a microscope depends on several factors including the wavelength of the source of illumination. Resolution is improved when the illumination source has a shorter wavelength.

A major advance in microscopy occurred in 1931 when Max Knoll and Ernst Ruska invented the first electron microscope. Because the wavelength of an electron beam is much shorter than visible light, the resolution of the electron microscope is far better than any light microscope. The limit is typically around 2 nm (nanometers), which is about 100 times better than the light microscope. **Figure 4.1** shows the range of resolving powers of the light and electron microscopes, and compares them to various cells and cell structures.

Over the past several decades, enormous technological advances have made light microscopy a powerful research tool. Improvements in lens technology, microscope organization, sample preparation, sample illumination, and computerized image processing have enabled researchers to create different types of light microscopes, each with its own advantages and disadvantages (**Figure 4.2**).

Similarly, improvements in electron microscopy occurred during the 1930s and 1940s, and by the 1950s the electron microscope was playing a major role in advancing our understanding of cell biology. During **transmission electron microscopy (TEM)**, a beam of electrons is transmitted through a biological sample. In preparation for TEM, a sample is treated with a chemical that binds to cellular molecules and fixes them in place. The sample is placed in a liquid resin and then the resin polymerizes to form a hardened block. The sample embedded within the block is sliced into very thin sections, typically 0.1–1.0 μm in thickness. To provide contrast, the sample is stained with a heavy metal. During staining, the metal binds to certain cellular structures such as membranes. The thin sections of the sample that have been stained with heavy metal are then adhered to a

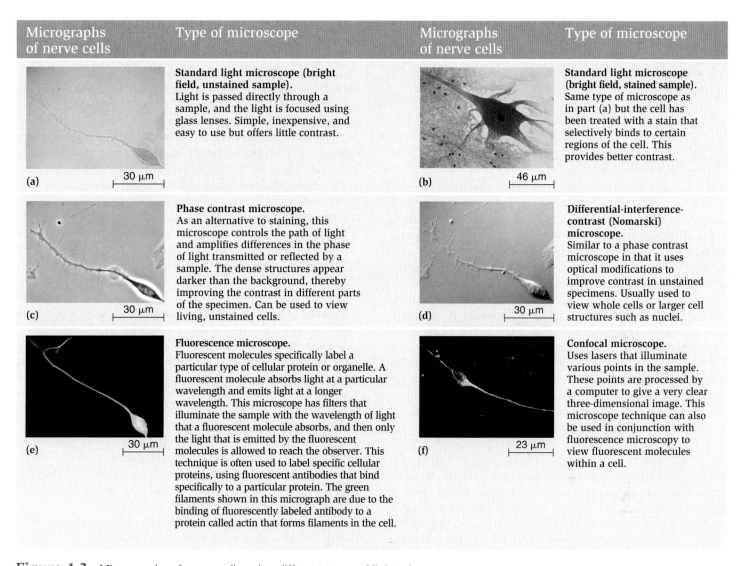

Micrographs of nerve cells	Type of microscope	Micrographs of nerve cells	Type of microscope
(a) 30 μm	**Standard light microscope (bright field, unstained sample).** Light is passed directly through a sample, and the light is focused using glass lenses. Simple, inexpensive, and easy to use but offers little contrast.	(b) 46 μm	**Standard light microscope (bright field, stained sample).** Same type of microscope as in part (a) but the cell has been treated with a stain that selectively binds to certain regions of the cell. This provides better contrast.
(c) 30 μm	**Phase contrast microscope.** As an alternative to staining, this microscope controls the path of light and amplifies differences in the phase of light transmitted or reflected by a sample. The dense structures appear darker than the background, thereby improving the contrast in different parts of the specimen. Can be used to view living, unstained cells.	(d) 30 μm	**Differential-interference-contrast (Nomarski) microscope.** Similar to a phase contrast microscope in that it uses optical modifications to improve contrast in unstained specimens. Usually used to view whole cells or larger cell structures such as nuclei.
(e) 30 μm	**Fluorescence microscope.** Fluorescent molecules specifically label a particular type of cellular protein or organelle. A fluorescent molecule absorbs light at a particular wavelength and emits light at a longer wavelength. This microscope has filters that illuminate the sample with the wavelength of light that a fluorescent molecule absorbs, and then only the light that is emitted by the fluorescent molecules is allowed to reach the observer. This technique is often used to label specific cellular proteins, using fluorescent antibodies that bind specifically to a particular protein. The green filaments shown in this micrograph are due to the binding of fluorescently labeled antibody to a protein called actin that forms filaments in the cell.	(f) 23 μm	**Confocal microscope.** Uses lasers that illuminate various points in the sample. These points are processed by a computer to give a very clear three-dimensional image. This microscope technique can also be used in conjunction with fluorescence microscopy to view fluorescent molecules within a cell.

Figure 4.2   Micrographs of nerve cells using different types of light microscopes.

copper grid and placed in a transmission electron microscope. When the beam of electrons strikes the sample, some of them hit the heavy metal and are scattered, while those that pass through without being scattered are focused to form an image on a photographic plate or screen (**Figure 4.3a**). Because the scattered electrons are lost from the beam, the metal-stained regions of the sample that scatter electrons appear as areas of reduced electron penetration. These areas are darker than those that allow electrons to pass through them. Compared with other forms of microscopy, TEM has the best resolution of any microscope. TEM provides the greatest resolution of organelles and other cellular structures. However, such microscopes are expensive and are not commonly used to view living cells.

Scanning electron microscopy (SEM) is another type of electron microscopy that utilizes an electron beam to produce an image of the three-dimensional surface of biological samples (**Figure 4.3b**). A biological sample is coated with a thin layer of heavy metal such as gold or palladium and then exposed to an electron beam that scans the surface of the specimen.

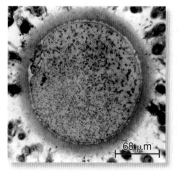

(a) Transmission electron micrograph

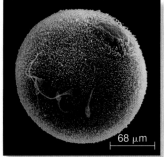

(b) Scanning electron micrograph

Figure 4.3   A comparison of transmission and scanning electron microscopy.   (a) A developing human egg cell, observed by TEM, shortly before it was released from an ovary. (b) An egg cell, with a few attached sperm, was coated with heavy metal and observed via SEM. This SEM is colorized.

Biological inquiry: What is the primary advantage of SEM?

The electrons that are scattered from the surface of the sample are detected and create an image on a computer screen. SEM provides a three-dimensional image of the surface of a sample.

And now, let's turn our attention to what microscopes show us about cells.

4.2 Overview of Cell Structure

Cell structure relies on four critical phenomena: (1) matter, (2) energy, (3) organization, and (4) information. In Chapters 2 and 3, we considered the first factor. The matter that is found in living organisms is composed of atoms, molecules, and macromolecules. We will discuss the second factor, energy, throughout this unit, particularly in Chapters 7 and 8. Energy is needed to create molecules and macromolecules, and to carry out many cellular functions. Cells also need energy to become organized, the third phenomenon that underlies cell structure. As discussed throughout this chapter and Unit II, a cell is not a haphazard bag of components. The molecules and macromolecules that constitute cells have specific sites where they are found. For instance, if we compare the structure of a nerve cell in two different humans, or two nerve cells within the same individual, we would see striking similarities in their overall structures. Thus, a key attribute of all living cells is the ability to maintain a particular type of internal structure and organization.

Finally, a fourth critical issue is information. Cell organization requires instructions. These instructions are found in the blueprint of life, namely the genetic material, which is discussed in Unit III. Each living organism has a **genome**, which is defined as the entire complement of its genetic material. Every living cell has a copy of the genome; the **genes** within each species' genome contain the information to create cells with particular structures and functions. This information is passed from cell to cell and from parent to offspring to yield new generations of cells and new generations of life. In this section, we will explore the general structure of cells and examine how the genome contributes to cell structure and function.

Prokaryotic Cells Have a Simple Structure

All forms of life can be placed into two categories based on cell structure—prokaryotes and eukaryotes. We will first consider the **prokaryotes**, which have a relatively simple structure. The term comes from the Greek *pro* and *karyon*, which means "before a kernel"—a reference to the kernel-like appearance of what would later be named the cell nucleus. Prokaryotic cells lack a membrane-enclosed nucleus.

From an evolutionary perspective, the two categories of prokaryotes are **bacteria** and **archaea**. Both types are microorganisms that are relatively small. Bacteria are abundant throughout the world, being found in soil, water, and even our digestive tracts. Most bacterial species are not harmful to humans, but some species are pathogenic—they cause disease. Examples of

pathogenic bacteria include *Vibrio cholerae*, the source of cholera, and *Bacillus anthracis*, which causes anthrax. Archaea are less common than bacteria and often occupy extreme environments such as hot springs and deep-sea vents. In this chapter, we will discuss the structure of bacterial cells. We will examine the genetics of bacteria in Chapter 18 and the evolutionary origins of bacteria and archaea in Chapter 22.

Figure 4.4 shows a typical bacterial cell. The **plasma membrane**—a double layer of phospholipids and embedded proteins—forms an important barrier between the cell and its external environment. The **cytoplasm** is the region of the cell that is contained within the plasma membrane. Certain structures in the bacterial cytoplasm are visible via microscopy. These include the **nucleoid**, which is the region of the cell where its genetic material (DNA) is located, and **ribosomes**, which are involved in polypeptide synthesis. We will examine the functions of ribosomes later in this chapter.

Many bacterial structures are located outside the plasma membrane. Nearly all species of prokaryotes have a relatively rigid **cell wall** that supports and protects the plasma membrane and cytoplasm. The cell wall is porous, so it does not prevent most nutrients in the environment from reaching the plasma membrane. Many bacteria also secrete a **glycocalyx**, an outer viscous covering surrounding the bacterium. The glycocalyx traps water and helps protect bacteria from drying out. Certain strains of bacteria that invade animals' bodies produce a very thick, gelatinous glycocalyx called a **capsule** that may help them avoid being destroyed by the animal's immune (defense) system. Finally, many prokaryotes have appendages such as **pili** and **flagella**. Pili allow prokaryotes to attach to surfaces and to each other. Flagella provide a way for prokaryotes to swim.

For many decades, the cytoplasm of bacterial cells was thought to be a fluid-filled space with relatively little defined organization, other than the nucleoid. The cell wall was believed to be solely involved with forming cell shape. During the past decade, however, these notions have been challenged by a molecular analysis of bacterial cells. Researchers have discovered that bacteria possess an architecture inside their cytoplasm that bears striking similarities to the cytoskeleton found in eukaryotic cells (described later in this chapter). **Figure 4.5** illustrates the functions of three proteins in the organization of bacterial cells. FtsZ, which is important in cell division, is found at the site where a cell divides into two cells. MreB plays a role in cell polarity. In many bacteria such as *Caulobacter crescentus*—an aquatic bacterium that survives in nutrient-poor water—cellular components are asymmetrically distributed throughout the cell. As suggested in Figure 4.5, the concentrations of components at one pole are different compared to the other pole. MreB forms a spiral structure in the cell, and evidence suggests it is necessary for this polarity. Finally, the localization of CreS in certain regions of the cell is critical for cell shape. Interestingly, the bacterial proteins described in Figure 4.5 are evolutionarily related to eukaryotic proteins described later in this chapter. In particular, FtsZ, MreB, and CreS are related to tubulin, actin, and intermediate filament proteins, respectively.

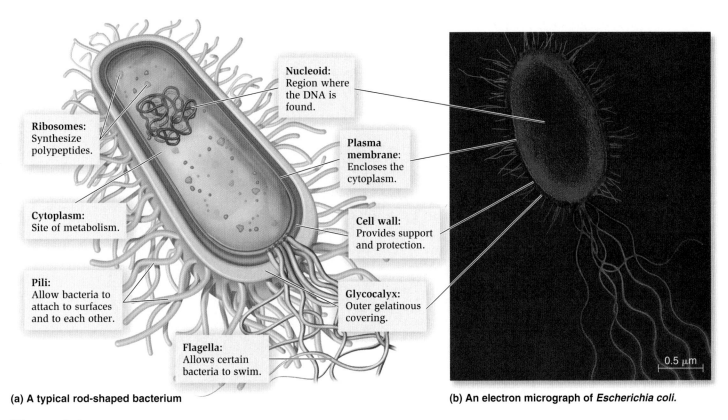

Nucleoid:
Region where
the DNA is
found.

Ribosomes:
Synthesize
polypeptides.

Plasma
membrane:
Encloses the
cytoplasm.

Cytoplasm:
Site of metabolism.

Cell wall:
Provides support
and protection.

Pili:
Allow bacteria to
attach to surfaces
and to each other.

Glycocalyx:
Outer gelatinous
covering.

Flagella:
Allows certain
bacteria to swim.

0.5 μm

(a) A typical rod-shaped bacterium

(b) An electron micrograph of *Escherichia coli.*

Figure 4.4   Structure of a typical prokaryotic cell.   Prokaryotic cells, which include bacteria and archaea, lack internal compartmentalization.

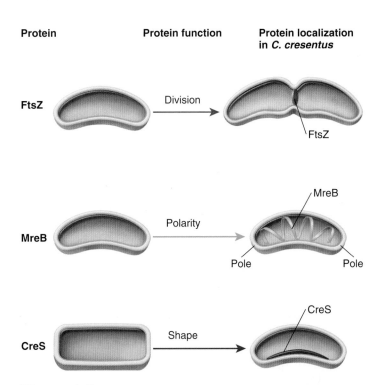

Protein	Protein function	Protein localization in *C. cresentus*
FtsZ	Division	FtsZ
MreB	Polarity	MreB Pole Pole
CreS	Shape	CreS

Figure 4.5   Proteins that play a role in the architecture of bacterial cells.   FtsZ plays a role in cell division, MreB is involved in cell polarity, and CreS influences cell shape.

Eukaryotic Cells Are Compartmentalized into Organelles

Aside from prokaryotes, all other species are **eukaryotes** (meaning "true nucleus"), which include protists, fungi, plants, and animals. Paramecia and algae are types of protists, while yeasts and molds are types of fungi. The DNA of all eukaryotic cells is housed in a distinct compartment called a **nucleus**, which is an example of an **organelle**—a subcellular structure or membrane-bounded compartment with its own unique structure and function. In contrast to prokaryotes, eukaryotic cells exhibit **compartmentalization**, which means that they have many organelles that separate the cell into different regions. Cellular compartmentalization allows a cell to carry out specialized chemical reactions in different places. For example, protein synthesis and protein breakdown occur in different compartments in the cell.

Figures 4.6 and **4.7** describe the morphology (form and structure) of typical animal and plant cells. Some general features of cell organization, such as a nucleus, are found in nearly all eukaryotic cells. Even so, be aware that the shape, size, and organization of cells vary considerably among different species and even among different cell types of the same species. Micrographs of a human skin cell and a human nerve cell show that, although these cells contain the same types of organelles, their overall morphologies are quite different (see Figure 4.6b).

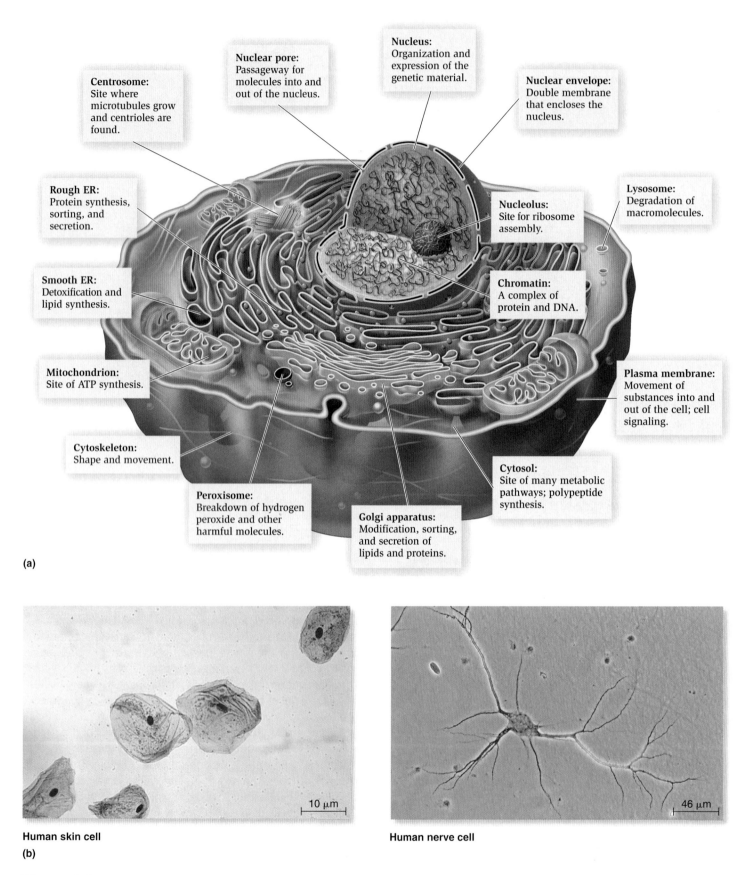

Centrosome:
Site where microtubules grow and centrioles are found.

Nuclear pore:
Passageway for molecules into and out of the nucleus.

Nucleus:
Organization and expression of the genetic material.

Nuclear envelope:
Double membrane that encloses the nucleus.

Rough ER:
Protein synthesis, sorting, and secretion.

Nucleolus:
Site for ribosome assembly.

Lysosome:
Degradation of macromolecules.

Smooth ER:
Detoxification and lipid synthesis.

Chromatin:
A complex of protein and DNA.

Mitochondrion:
Site of ATP synthesis.

Plasma membrane:
Movement of substances into and out of the cell; cell signaling.

Cytoskeleton:
Shape and movement.

Cytosol:
Site of many metabolic pathways; polypeptide synthesis.

Peroxisome:
Breakdown of hydrogen peroxide and other harmful molecules.

Golgi apparatus:
Modification, sorting, and secretion of lipids and proteins.

(a)

10 μm

46 μm

Human skin cell

Human nerve cell

(b)

Figure 4.6   General structure of an animal cell.   (a) A schematic drawing of a typical animal cell. (b) Micrographs of a human skin cell (*left*) and a human nerve cell (*right*). Although these cells have the same types of organelles, note that their general morphologies are quite different.

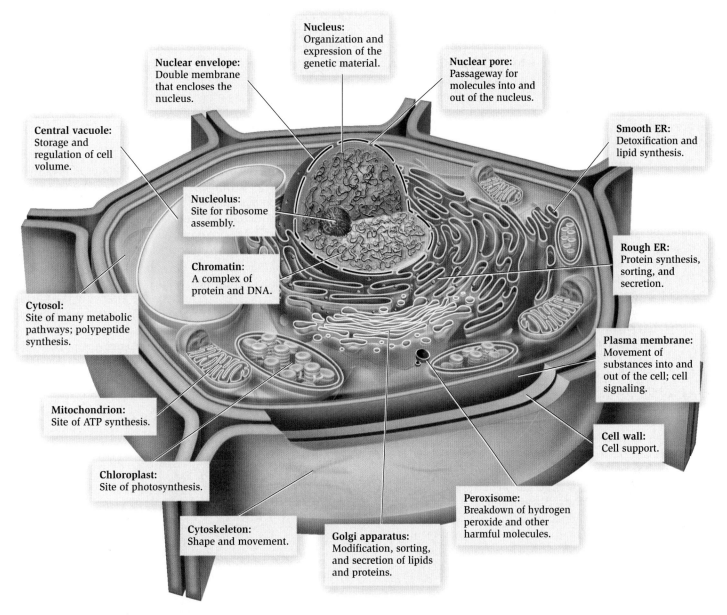

Nucleus:
Organization and expression of the genetic material.

Nuclear envelope:
Double membrane that encloses the nucleus.

Nuclear pore:
Passageway for molecules into and out of the nucleus.

Central vacuole:
Storage and regulation of cell volume.

Smooth ER:
Detoxification and lipid synthesis.

Nucleolus:
Site for ribosome assembly.

Rough ER:
Protein synthesis, sorting, and secretion.

Chromatin:
A complex of protein and DNA.

Cytosol:
Site of many metabolic pathways; polypeptide synthesis.

Plasma membrane:
Movement of substances into and out of the cell; cell signaling.

Mitochondrion:
Site of ATP synthesis.

Cell wall:
Cell support.

Chloroplast:
Site of photosynthesis.

Peroxisome:
Breakdown of hydrogen peroxide and other harmful molecules.

Cytoskeleton:
Shape and movement.

Golgi apparatus:
Modification, sorting, and secretion of lipids and proteins.

Figure 4.7   General structure of a plant cell. Plant cells lack lysosomes and centrioles. Unlike animal cells, plant cells have an outer cell wall; a large central vacuole that functions in storage, digestion, and cell volume; and chloroplasts, which carry out photosynthesis.

GENOMES & PROTEOMES

The Proteome Determines the Characteristics of a Cell

Many organisms, such as plants and animals, are multicellular, meaning that the body of a single organism is composed of many cells. However, the cells of a multicellular organism are not all identical. For example, your body contains nerve cells, muscle cells, skin cells, etcetera. An intriguing question, therefore, is, How does a single organism produce different types of cells?

To answer this question, we need to consider the distinction between genomes and proteomes. Recall that the genome constitutes all types of genetic material that an organism has. Most genes encode the production of polypeptides, which assemble into functional proteins. An emerging theme discussed in this unit is that the structures and functions of proteins are primarily responsible for the structures and functions of cells. A typical eukaryotic cell produces thousands of different types of proteins. For example, researchers estimate that one skeletal muscle cell in your arm produces about 15,000 different types of proteins; the total number of proteins in one cell is far more than 15,000 because many copies of some proteins are made. The **proteome** is defined as all of the types and relative amounts of proteins that are made in a particular cell at a particular time and under specific conditions.

As an example, let's consider muscle cells and nerve cells—two cell types that have dramatically different organization and structure. Actually, the genes in a human muscle cell of a particular individual are identical to those in a human nerve cell. However, their proteomes are different. An important principle in cell biology is that *the proteome of a cell determines its structure and function*. Several phenomena underlie the differences that are observed in the proteomes of different cell types. If we compare muscle and nerve cells, these phenomena include:

1. *Certain proteins that are found in muscle cells are not found in nerve cells, and vice versa.* For a protein to be expressed in a particular cell, the gene that corresponds to that protein must be "turned on," that is, actively expressing that protein. Due to gene regulation, which is described in Chapter 13, certain genes that are turned on in muscle cells are not turned on in nerve cells and vice versa.

2. *The relative amounts of certain proteins are different in muscle and nerve cells.* The amount of a given protein depends on many factors including how strongly the corresponding gene is turned on, how efficiently the protein is synthesized, and how long the protein lasts within a cell. Some proteins are found in both nerve and muscle cells, but in greatly different amounts. For example, a protein called actin, which is discussed later in this chapter, occurs abundantly in muscle cells—where it plays a key role in muscle contraction—but to a much lesser extent in nerve cells.

3. *The amino acid sequences of particular proteins can vary in different cell types.* As discussed in Chapter 13, the mRNA from a single gene can produce two or more polypeptides with slightly different amino acid sequences via a process called alternative splicing. For example, tropomyosin is a protein that regulates cell movement. The form of tropomyosin in muscle cells has a slightly different amino acid sequence from the type in nerve cells.

4. *Nerve and muscle cells may alter their proteins in different ways.* After a protein is made, its structure may be changed in a variety of ways. These include the covalent attachment of molecules such as phosphate and carbohydrate, and the cleavage of a protein to a smaller size.

These four phenomena enable nerve and muscle cells to produce different proteomes, and thus different structures and functions. Likewise, the proteomes of muscle and nerve cells differ from those of other cell types—skin, liver, etcetera.

During the last decade or so, researchers have also discovered an association between proteome changes and disease. For example, the proteomes of healthy cells are different from the proteomes of cancer cells. Furthermore, the proteomes of cancer cells change as the disease progresses. One reason for studying cancer-cell proteomes is to improve the early detection of cancer by identifying proteins that are made in the early stages, when the disease is most treatable. In addition, information

about the ways that the proteomes of cancer cells change may help researchers uncover new treatment options. A key challenge for biologists is to understand the synthesis and function of proteomes in different cell types, and how proteome changes may lead to disease conditions.

4.3 The Cytosol

Thus far, we have focused on the general features of prokaryotic and eukaryotic cells. In the rest of this chapter we will survey the various compartments of eukaryotic cells with a greater emphasis on structure and function. **Figure 4.8** highlights a plant and animal cell according to four different regions. We will start with the **cytosol** (shown in yellow), the region of a eukaryotic cell that is outside the cell organelles but inside the plasma membrane. The other regions of the cell, which we will examine later in this chapter, include the interior of the nucleus (blue), the endomembrane system (purple/pink), and semiautonomous organelles (green). As in prokaryotes, the term cytoplasm refers to the region inside the plasma membrane. This includes the cytosol, the endomembrane system inside the plasma membrane, and the semiautonomous organelles.

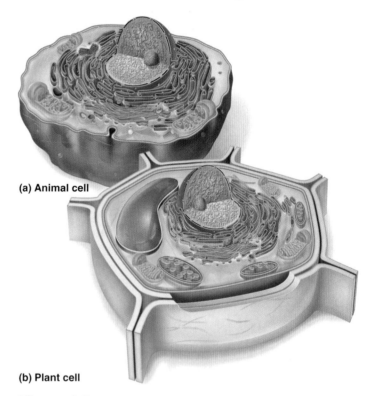

(a) Animal cell

(b) Plant cell

Figure 4.8 Compartments within (a) animal and (b) plant cells.   The cytosol, which is outside the organelles but inside the plasma membrane, is shown in yellow. The membranes of the endomembrane system are shown in purple, while the fluid filled interiors are pink. The interior of the nucleus is blue. Semiautonomous organelles, which include mitochondria, chloroplasts, and peroxisomes, are green.

Though the amount varies among different types of cells, the cytosol typically occupies about 50% of the total cell volume. In this section, we will consider the primary functions of the cytosol. First, it is the site of many chemical reactions that produce the materials and energy necessary for life, such as breaking down food molecules into smaller components. Such reactions release energy, and the components can be used as building blocks to create new cellular molecules and macromolecules. For example, we will explore a particularly important activity of the cytosol, which is the synthesis of cellular proteins. In addition, we will examine the structure and function of large protein filaments, found in the cytosol, that provide organization to the cell and allow cells to move.

Synthesis and Breakdown of Molecules Occur in the Cytosol

Metabolism is defined as the sum of the chemical reactions by which cells produce the materials and energy that are necessary to sustain life. Although specific steps of metabolism also occur in cell organelles, the cytosol is a central coordinating region for many metabolic activities of eukaryotic cells. Metabolism often involves a series of steps called a metabolic pathway. A specific **enzyme** is responsible for speeding up each step in a metabolic pathway. In Chapter 7, we will examine the functional properties of enzymes and consider a few metabolic pathways that occur in the cytosol and cellular organelles.

Some pathways involve the breakdown of a molecule into smaller components, a process termed **catabolism**. Such pathways are needed to capture energy for use by the cell, and also to generate molecules that provide the building blocks to construct cellular macromolecules. Conversely, other metabolic pathways are involved in **anabolism**, the synthesis of cellular molecules and macromolecules. For example, polysaccharides are made by linking together sugar molecules. To create proteins, amino acids are covalently connected to form a polypeptide. This process is described next.

Translation Is the Process of Polypeptide Synthesis

A **polypeptide** is composed of a linear sequence of amino acids. The term polypeptide describes a unit of structure. By comparison, the term **protein** is a unit of function. One or more polypeptides assemble into a three-dimensional protein that performs a particular function. A critical activity of all cells is the synthesis of polypeptides. This process is called **translation** because the information within a gene is ultimately translated into the sequence of amino acids in a polypeptide. Chapter 12 describes the details of the process. In this chapter, we will briefly consider the general features of translation to help us appreciate how cells make proteins, which are vital to cell structure and function.

Translation requires many cellular components including a ribosome and two types of RNA molecules (**Figure 4.9**). The ribosome is the site where polypeptide synthesis occurs. Messenger RNA (mRNA) is produced from a gene and provides the information to make a polypeptide. Transfer RNA (tRNA) molecules, which carry amino acids, bind to the mRNA so that a polypeptide can be made, one amino acid at a time. The role of the ribosome is to facilitate the binding between the mRNA and tRNA molecules, and to catalyze the formation of covalent bonds between adjacent amino acids. Once the entire polypeptide is made, it is released from the ribosome.

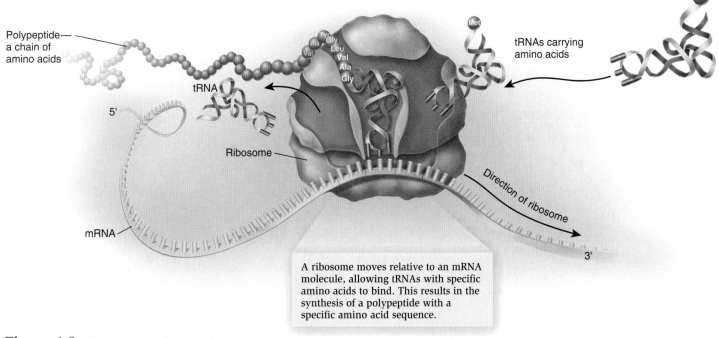

A ribosome moves relative to an mRNA molecule, allowing tRNAs with specific amino acids to bind. This results in the synthesis of a polypeptide with a specific amino acid sequence.

Figure 4.9   The process of translation.

The Cytoskeleton Provides Cell Organization, Shape, and Movement

The **cytoskeleton** is a network of three different types of protein filaments: **microtubules, intermediate filaments**, and **actin filaments** (Table 4.1). Let's first consider the structure of these protein filaments and their roles in the construction and organization of cells. Later, we will examine how they are involved in cell movement.

Microtubules Microtubules are long, hollow, cylindrical structures about 25 nm in diameter composed of the protein tubulin. The assembly of tubulin to form a microtubule results in a polar structure with a plus end and a minus end (Table 4.1). Growth of microtubules occurs at the plus end, while shortening of microtubules can occur at either the plus or minus end. A single microtubule can oscillate between growing and shortening phases, a phenomenon termed **dynamic instability**. Dynamic instability is important in many cellular activities including the sorting of chromosomes during cell division.

The sites where microtubules form within a cell can vary among different types of organisms. Animal cells that are not preparing to divide contain a single structure near their nucleus called the **centrosome** or **microtubule-organizing center** (Table 4.1). Within the centrosome are the **centrioles**, a conspicuous pair of structures arranged perpendicular to each other. In animal cells, microtubule growth starts at the centrosome such that the minus end is anchored there. In contrast, most plant cells and many protists lack centrosomes and centrioles. Microtubules are created at many sites that are scattered throughout a plant cell.

Microtubules are important for cell shape and organization. Organelles such as the Golgi apparatus often are attached to microtubules. In addition, microtubules are involved in the organization of chromosomes during mitosis and in the orientation of cells during cell division. We will examine these events in Chapter 15.

Intermediate Filaments Intermediate filaments are another class of cytoskeletal filament found in the cells of many but not all animal species. Their name is derived from the observation

Table 4.1	Properties of Cytoskeletal Filaments		
Characteristic	Microtubules	Intermediate filaments	Actin filaments
Diameter	25 nm	10 nm	7 nm
Structure	Hollow tubule	Twisted filament	Spiral filament
Protein composition	Tubule wall composed of the protein tubulin	Can be composed of different proteins including desmin, keratin, lamin, and others	Two intertwined strands composed of the protein actin
Cellular location			
Common functions	Cell shape Organization of cell organelles Chromosome sorting Intracellular movement of cargo Cell motility (cilia and flagella)	Cell shape Provide cells with mechanical strength Anchorage of cell and nuclear membranes	Cell shape Muscle contraction Cell movement (amoeboid movement) Animal cell division Intracellular movement of cargo

that they are intermediate in diameter between actin filaments and myosin filaments. (Myosin filaments are described in Chapter 46.) Intermediate filament proteins bind to each other in a staggered array to form a twisted, ropelike structure with a diameter of approximately 10 nm (Table 4.1). Intermediate filaments tend to be more stable than microtubules and actin filaments, which readily polymerize and depolymerize. They function as tension-bearing fibers that help maintain cell shape and rigidity.

Several types of related proteins can assemble into intermediate filaments. Desmins form intermediate filaments in muscle cells and provide mechanical strength. Keratins form intermediate filaments in skin, intestinal, and kidney cells, where they are important for mechanical strength and cell shape. They are also a major constituent of hair and nails. In addition, intermediate filaments are found inside the cell nucleus. As discussed later in this chapter, nuclear lamins form a network of intermediate filaments that line the inner nuclear membrane and provide anchorage points for the nuclear pores.

Actin Filaments Actin filaments—also known as **microfilaments** because they are the thinnest cytoskeletal filaments—are long, thin fibers approximately 7 nm in diameter (Table 4.1).

Each fiber is composed of two strands of actin monomers that spiral around each other. Like microtubules, actin filaments have plus and minus ends, and they are very dynamic structures that grow at the plus end.

Despite their thinness, actin filaments play a key role in cell strength and shape. Although actin filaments are dispersed throughout the cytosol, they tend to be highly concentrated near the plasma membrane. In many types of cells, actin filaments support the plasma membrane and provide strength and shape to the cell. The minus ends of actin filaments are usually anchored at the plasma membrane, which explains why actin filaments are typically found there.

Motor Proteins Interact with Microtubules or Actin Filaments to Promote Cellular Movements

Motor proteins are a category of cellular proteins that use ATP as a source of energy to promote movement. As shown in **Figure 4.10a**, a motor protein consists of three domains called the head, hinge, and tail. The head is the site where ATP binds and is hydrolyzed to ADP and P$_i$. ATP binding and hydrolysis cause a bend in the hinge, which results in movement. The tail region is attached to other proteins, or to other kinds of cellular molecules.

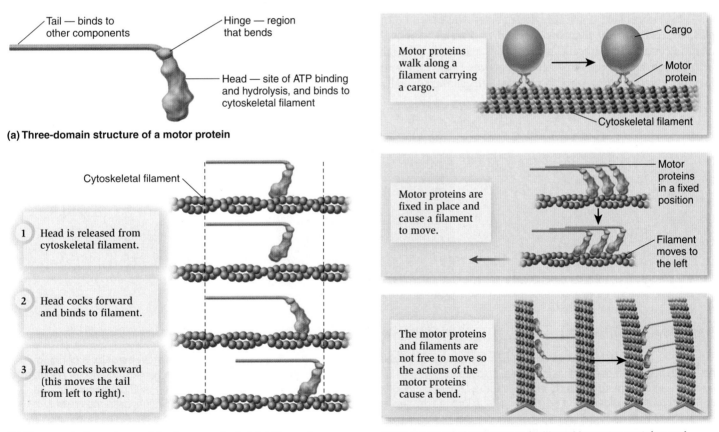

(a) **Three-domain structure of a motor protein**

(b) **Movement of a motor protein along a cytoskeletal filament**

(c) **Three types of movements facilitated by motor proteins and cytoskeletal filaments**

Figure 4.10   **Motor proteins and their interactions with cytoskeletal filaments.**   (a) Three-domain structure of a motor protein. Note: The protein subunits of motor proteins often associate with each other along their tails, such that the motor has two tails, two hinges, and two heads. (b) Conformational changes in a motor protein that allow it to walk along a cytoskeletal filament. (c) Three ways that motor proteins and cytoskeletal filaments can cause movement.

To promote cellular movement, the head region of a motor protein interacts with a cytoskeletal filament (**Figure 4.10b**). When ATP binds and is hydrolyzed, the motor protein attempts to "walk" along the filament. The head of the motor protein is initially attached to a filament. To move forward, the head detaches from the filament, cocks forward, binds to the filament, and cocks backward. To imagine how this works, consider the act of walking in which the ground is a cytoskeletal filament, your leg is the head of the motor protein, and your hip is the hinge. To walk, you lift your leg up, you move it forward, you place it on the ground, and then you cock it backward (which propels you forward). This series of events is analogous to how a motor protein walks along a cytoskeletal filament.

Interestingly, cells have utilized the actions of motor proteins to promote three different kinds of movements. In the first example shown in **Figure 4.10c** (top), the tail region is attached to a cargo, so that the motor protein moves the cargo from one location to another. Alternatively, a motor protein can remain in place and cause the filament to move (Figure 4.10c, middle). As discussed in Chapter 46, this occurs during muscle contraction. A third possibility is that both the motor protein and filament are restricted in their movement. In this case, when the motor protein attempts to walk, it exerts a force that causes the filament to bend (Figure 4.10c, bottom). As described next, this occurs during the bending of cilia and flagella.

Let's now consider some specific examples where motor proteins and cytoskeletal filaments interact and result in movement. In certain kinds of cells, microtubules and motor proteins facilitate movement involving cell appendages called **cilia** and **flagella** (singular, *cilium* and *flagellum*). Flagella are usually longer than cilia and present singly or in pairs. A single flagellum may propel a cell such as a sperm cell with a whiplike motion (**Figure 4.11a**). Alternatively, a pair of flagella may move in a synchronized manner to pull a microorganism through the water (think of a human swimmer doing the breaststroke). Certain unicellular algae swim in this manner (**Figure 4.11b**). By comparison, cilia are often shorter than flagella and tend to cover all or part of the surface of a cell. Protists such as paramecia may have hundreds of adjacent cilia that beat in a coordinated fashion to propel the organism through water (**Figure 4.11c**).

Despite their differences in length, cilia and flagella share the same internal structure (**Figure 4.12**). This arrangement containing microtubules, the motor protein dynein, and linking proteins is called an **axoneme**. In the cilia and flagella of most eukaryotic organisms, the microtubules form an arrangement called a 9 + 2 array. Each of the two central microtubules consists of a single microtubule, while the outer nine are doublet microtubules, which are two merged microtubules. The microtubules in cilia and flagella emanate from **basal bodies**, which are anchored to the cytoplasmic side of the plasma membrane. Much like the centrosome of animal cells, the basal bodies provide a site for microtubules to grow. In addition to microtubules, the core structure of a cilium and flagellum also has motor proteins, namely dynein, and linking proteins such as nexin, that hold the axoneme together.

The movement of both cilia and flagella involves the propagation of a bend, which begins at the base of the structure and proceeds toward the tip (see Figure 4.11a). The bending occurs because dynein is activated to walk toward the basal body of the microtubules. ATP hydrolysis is required for this process.

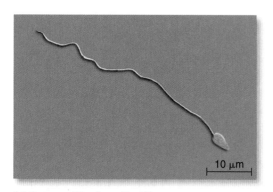
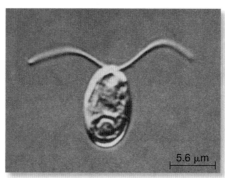

(a) Sperm with a long flagellum   **(b) *Chlamydomonas* with 2 flagella**   **(c) Paramecium with many cilia**

Figure 4.11 Cellular movements due to the actions of flagella and cilia. Both flagella and cilia cause movement by a bending motion. In flagella, movement occurs by a whiplike motion that is due to the propagation of a bend from the base to the tip. In addition, the nature of swimming depends on the length of the appendage and whether it involves coordination among multiple flagella or cilia. **(a)** Sperm swim by means of a single, long flagellum that moves in a whiplike motion. **(b)** The swimming of *Chlamydomonas reinhardtii* also involves a whiplike motion at the base, but the motion is precisely coordinated between two flagella. This results in swimming behavior that resembles a breaststroke. **(c)** Ciliated protozoa swim via many shorter cilia. The bending motion is coordinated among multiple adjacent cilia.

Biological inquiry: During the movement of a cilium or flagellum, describe the type of movements that are occurring in dynein and microtubules.

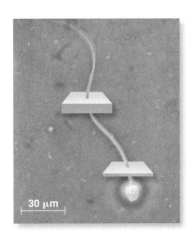

(a) Human sperm cell

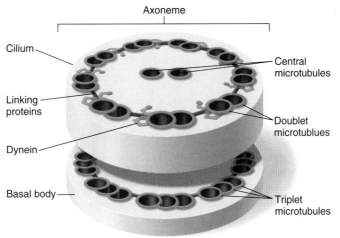

Axoneme

Cilium

Linking proteins

Dynein

Basal body

Central microtubules

Doublet microtublues

Triplet microtubules

(b) Molecular structure of a flagellum

Figure 4.12   Structure of a eukaryotic flagellum.   (a) SEM of a human sperm cell. (b) Drawing of the axoneme. The core structure consists of a 9 + 2 arrangement of nine outer doublet microtubules and two central microtubules. This structure is anchored to the basal body, which has nine triplet microtubules, in which three microtubules are fused together. Note: The structure of the basal body is very similar to centrioles in animal cells.

However, the microtubules and dynein are not free to move relative to each other because of linking proteins. Therefore, instead of dyneins freely walking along the microtubules, they exert a force that bends the microtubules (see Figure 4.10c, bottom). The dyneins at the base of the structure are activated first, followed by dyneins that are progressively closer to the tip of the appendage. The resulting movement propels the organism.

As a second example, let's consider how motor proteins interact with actin. As discussed in Chapter 46, actin and a motor protein called myosin are responsible for the movement observed in muscle cells. In protists such as the amoeba, movement occurs via the dynamic rearrangement of the actin cytoskeleton (**Figure 4.13**). Actin filaments are formed near the leading edge to create a projection called a lamellipodium. The cell is pulled toward the leading edge using motor proteins such as myosin, which tugs on actin filaments and promotes cellular movement. Actin filaments and myosin motors are also involved in other types of movement, as we will see next in our Feature Investigation.

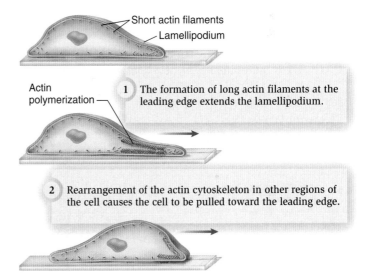

Short actin filaments

Lamellipodium

Actin polymerization

1   The formation of long actin filaments at the leading edge extends the lamellipodium.

2   Rearrangement of the actin cytoskeleton in other regions of the cell causes the cell to be pulled toward the leading edge.

Figure 4.13   Amoeboid movement promoted by changes in the locations of actin filaments.

FEATURE INVESTIGATION

Sheetz and Spudich Showed That Myosin Walks Along Actin Filaments

Cell biologists often gain clues to protein function from studying living cells. In the early 1950s, Hugh Huxley, Andrew F. Huxley, and their colleagues studied muscle contraction via microscopy and other techniques. They proposed the sliding-filament model for muscle contraction, in which actin filaments slide past thicker filaments composed of myosin. This model was based on observations involving intact muscle cells. Research at that time and during subsequent decades indicated that actin and myosin were necessary for muscle movement.

Biologists want to understand how a process, such as muscle contraction, works at the molecular level. However, studying living cells has its drawbacks. Recall that the proteome of every living cell is composed of thousands of different proteins, making it difficult to establish the function of any one protein. As an alternative to studying a process in living cells, another approach is to isolate and purify cellular components and study their functions outside the cell. This is an *in vitro* approach (literally "in glass," such as in a glass test tube). By comparison, studying living cells is termed *in vivo*, meaning "in life."

In 1983, approximately 30 years after the sliding-filament model was proposed, Michael Sheetz and James Spudich devised a clever approach to study myosin function *in vitro*.

Prior to their work, researchers had learned how to purify myosin protein from muscle cells. A fragment of myosin could be attached to a fluorescently labeled bead, making it possible to follow myosin movement using a fluorescence microscope. However, to study movement, Sheetz and Spudich also needed actin filaments. Although actin filaments can be purified from cells, they become a tangled mess during the purification process. As an alternative, the researchers were aware that the alga *Nitella axillaris* has arrays of actin filaments that lie inside the cell and parallel to the plasma membrane. These parallel arrays function in the phenomenon known as **cytoplasmic streaming**, in which the cytoplasm circulates throughout the cell to distribute resources efficiently in large cells. Along these lines, another advantage of *Nitella* for this experiment was that the cells are relatively large—several hundred microns in diameter and several centimeters in length.

Figure 4.14 illustrates the *in vitro* approach of Sheetz and Spudich. Their procedure involved cutting open *Nitella* cells and pinning down the plasma membrane to expose the actin filaments. Except for chloroplasts, which are found between the plasma membrane and the actin filaments, the rest of the cellular contents were washed away. Next, a solution containing purified myosin attached to fluorescent beads was added and observed via fluorescence microscopy. Sheetz and Spudich conducted their experiments with and without ATP, which is needed for muscle cell movement. In addition, the researchers tested the effects of N-ethylmaleimide (NEM), a chemical that was already known to bind to myosin and inhibit its function. As shown in the data, myosin was able to move along actin filaments in the presence of ATP. Furthermore, when myosin was treated with NEM, the movement was inhibited.

Taken together, these *in vitro* experiments confirmed that myosin is a motor protein that uses ATP to walk along actin filaments. Furthermore, this purified system provided evidence that all that is needed for movement are actin, myosin, and ATP. In addition, the results are consistent with the idea that different types of movement, such as cytoplasmic streaming in algae and muscle contraction in animals, use the same underlying molecular mechanism—in this case, an interaction between the motor protein myosin and actin filaments.

Figure 4.14   Movement of myosin-coated beads along actin filaments.

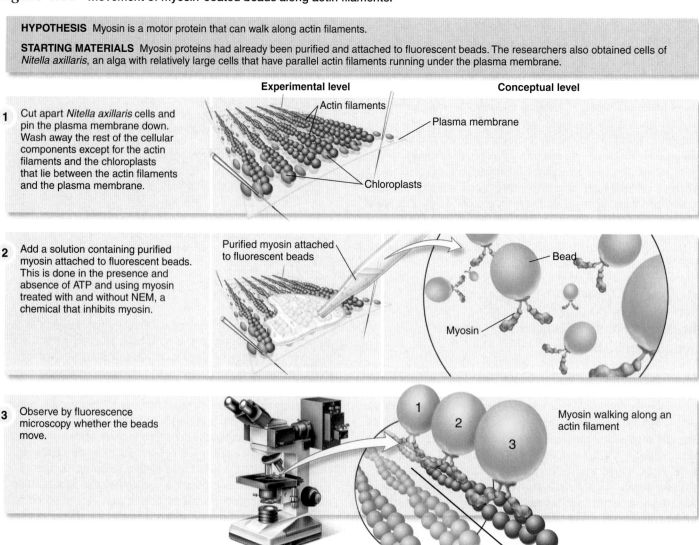

HYPOTHESIS Myosin is a motor protein that can walk along actin filaments.

STARTING MATERIALS Myosin proteins had already been purified and attached to fluorescent beads. The researchers also obtained cells of *Nitella axillaris*, an alga with relatively large cells that have parallel actin filaments running under the plasma membrane.

Experimental level   Conceptual level

1 Cut apart *Nitella axillaris* cells and pin the plasma membrane down. Wash away the rest of the cellular components except for the actin filaments and the chloroplasts that lie between the actin filaments and the plasma membrane.

Actin filaments
Plasma membrane
Chloroplasts

2 Add a solution containing purified myosin attached to fluorescent beads. This is done in the presence and absence of ATP and using myosin treated with and without NEM, a chemical that inhibits myosin.

Purified myosin attached to fluorescent beads
Bead
Myosin

3 Observe by fluorescence microscopy whether the beads move.

Myosin walking along an actin filament

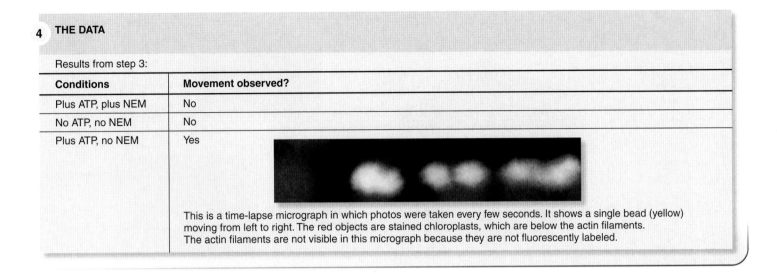

4 **THE DATA**

Results from step 3:

Conditions	Movement observed?
Plus ATP, plus NEM	No
No ATP, no NEM	No
Plus ATP, no NEM	Yes

This is a time-lapse micrograph in which photos were taken every few seconds. It shows a single bead (yellow) moving from left to right. The red objects are stained chloroplasts, which are below the actin filaments. The actin filaments are not visible in this micrograph because they are not fluorescently labeled.

4.4 The Nucleus and Endomembrane System

In Chapter 2, we learned that the nucleus of an atom contains protons and neutrons. In cell biology, the term **nucleus** has a different meaning. It is an organelle found in eukaryotic cells that contains most of the cell's genetic material. A small amount of genetic material is also found in mitochondria and chloroplasts.

The membranes that enclose the nucleus are part of a larger network of membranes called the **endomembrane system**. These include not only the nuclear envelope, which encloses the nucleus, but also the endoplasmic reticulum, Golgi apparatus, lysosomes, and vacuoles. The prefix *endo*—meaning "inside"—originally referred only to these organelles and internal membranes. However, we now know that the plasma membrane is also part of this integrated membrane system (**Figure 4.15**). Some of these membranes, such as the nuclear envelope and the membrane of the endoplasmic reticulum, have direct connections to one another. Other organelles of the endomembrane system pass materials to each other via **vesicles**—small membrane-enclosed spheres. The movement of vesicles occurs in both directions. For example, vesicles that are formed from the endoplasmic reticulum can fuse with the Golgi apparatus and vesicles from the Golgi apparatus can fuse with the endoplasmic reticulum. Therefore, the endomembrane system forms a dynamic, integrated network of membranes that requires constant sorting to maintain the functional properties of each organelle.

In this section, we will survey the structures and functions of the organelles of the endomembrane system. We will also examine the plasma membrane, which is formed from the endomembrane system.

The Eukaryotic Nucleus Contains Chromosomes

The nucleus is the internal compartment that is enclosed by a double-membrane structure termed the **nuclear envelope** (**Figure 4.16**). In most cells, the nucleus is a relatively large organelle

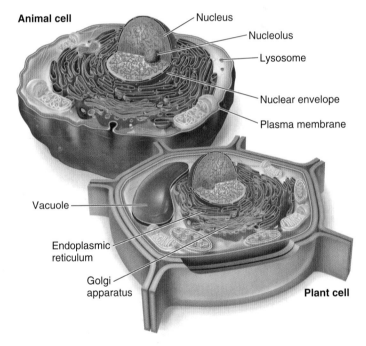

Figure 4.15 **The nucleus and endomembrane system.** This figure highlights the internal compartment of the nucleus (blue), the membranes of the endomembrane system (purple), and the fluid-filled interiors of the endomembrane system (pink). The nuclear envelope is considered part of the endomembrane system, but the interior of the nucleus is not.

that typically occupies 10–20% of the total cell volume. The outer membrane of the nuclear envelope is continuous with the endoplasmic reticulum membrane. **Nuclear pores** are formed where the inner and outer nuclear membranes make contact with each other. The pores provide a passageway for the movement of molecules and macromolecules into and out of the nucleus. Although cell biologists view the nuclear envelope as part of the endomembrane system, the materials within the nucleus are not (see Figure 4.15).

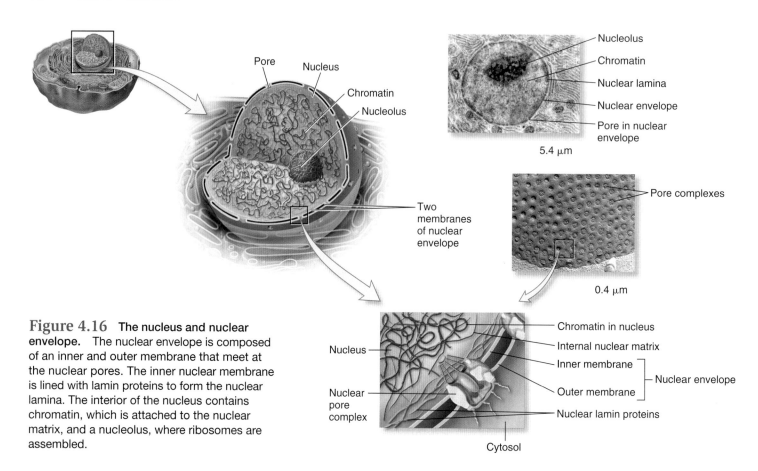

Figure 4.16   The nucleus and nuclear envelope.   The nuclear envelope is composed of an inner and outer membrane that meet at the nuclear pores. The inner nuclear membrane is lined with lamin proteins to form the nuclear lamina. The interior of the nucleus contains chromatin, which is attached to the nuclear matrix, and a nucleolus, where ribosomes are assembled.

Inside the nucleus are the **chromosomes** and a filamentous network of proteins called the **nuclear matrix**. Each chromosome is composed of genetic material, namely DNA, and many types of proteins that help to compact the chromosome to fit inside the nucleus. The complex formed by DNA and such proteins is termed **chromatin**. The nuclear matrix consists of two parts: the nuclear lamina, which is composed of intermediate filaments that line the inner nuclear membrane, and an internal nuclear matrix, which is connected to the lamina and fills the interior of the nucleus. The nuclear matrix serves to organize the chromosomes within the nucleus. Each chromosome is located in a distinct, nonoverlapping **chromosome territory,** which is visible when cells are exposed to dyes that label each type of chromosome (**Figure 4.17**).

The primary function of the nucleus involves the protection, organization, and expression of the genetic material. Another important function is the assembly of ribosomes. Ribosome assembly occurs in the **nucleolus** (plural, *nucleoli*), a prominent region in the nucleus of nondividing cells. A ribosome is composed of two subunits, one small and one large; each subunit contains one or more RNA molecules and several types of proteins. The RNA molecules that are components of ribosomes are made at the nucleolus because the genes that encode these RNA molecules are located there. The ribosomal

proteins are produced in the cytosol, imported into the nucleus through the nuclear pores, and assembled with the RNA molecules to form the ribosomal subunits. The subunits then exit through the nuclear pores into the cytosol, where they are needed for protein synthesis.

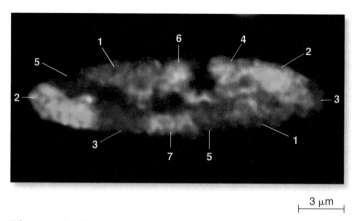

Figure 4.17   Chromosome territories in the cell nucleus. Chromosomes from a chicken were labeled with chromosome-specific probes. Each of the seven types of chicken chromosomes is colored with a different dye. Each chromosome occupies its own distinct, nonoverlapping territory within the cell nucleus.

The Endoplasmic Reticulum Initiates Protein Sorting and Carries Out Certain Metabolic Functions

The **endoplasmic reticulum (ER)** is a convoluted network of membranes that form flattened, fluid-filled tubules or **cisternae** (**Figure 4.18**). The terms endoplasmic (which means "in the cytoplasm") and reticulum ("little net") refer to the location and shape of this organelle when viewed under a microscope. The term **lumen** describes the internal space of an organelle. The ER membrane encloses a single compartment called the **ER lumen**. In some cells, the ER membrane makes up more than half of the total membrane in the cell. The rough ER has its outer surface studded with ribosomes, giving it a bumpy appearance. Once bound to the ER membrane, the ribosomes actively synthesize proteins through the ER membrane. The smooth ER lacks ribosomes.

Rough ER The **rough endoplasmic reticulum (rough ER)** plays a key role in the initial synthesis and sorting of proteins that are destined for the ER, Golgi apparatus, lysosomes, vacuoles, plasma membrane, or outside of the cell. To reach any of these locations, a protein must first be directed to the ER membrane. In conjunction with protein sorting, a second function of the rough ER is the insertion of certain newly made proteins into the membrane. A third important function of the rough ER is the attachment of carbohydrate to proteins and lipids. This process is called **glycosylation**. The topics of protein sorting, membrane protein insertion, and protein glycosylation will be discussed in Chapter 6, because they are important in the maintenance of cell organization.

Smooth ER The **smooth endoplasmic reticulum (smooth ER)**, which is continuous with the rough ER, functions in diverse metabolic processes. The extensive network of smooth ER membranes allows increased surface area for key enzymes that play important metabolic roles. In liver cells, enzymes in the smooth ER detoxify many potentially harmful organic molecules including barbiturate drugs and ethanol. These enzymes convert hydrophobic toxic molecules into more hydrophilic molecules, which are easily excreted from the body. Chronic alcohol consumption, as in alcoholics, leads to a greater amount of smooth ER in liver cells, which increases the rate of alcohol breakdown. This explains why people who consume alcohol regularly must ingest more alcohol to experience its effects.

The smooth ER of liver cells also plays a role in carbohydrate metabolism. The liver cells of animals store energy in the form of glycogen, which is a polymer of glucose. Glycogen granules, which are in the cytosol, sit very close to the smooth ER membrane. When chemical energy is needed, enzymes are activated that break down the glycogen to glucose-6-phosphate. Then, an enzyme in the smooth ER called glucose-6-phosphatase removes the phosphate group, and glucose is released into the bloodstream.

Another important function of the smooth ER in all eukaryotes is the accumulation of calcium ions. The smooth ER contains calcium pumps that transport Ca^{2+} into the ER lumen. The regulated release of Ca^{2+} into the cytosol is involved in many vital cellular processes, including muscle contraction in animals.

Finally, enzymes in the smooth ER are critical in the synthesis and modification of lipids. For example, steroid hormones such as estrogen and testosterone are derived from the lipid

Figure 4.18   **Structure of the endoplasmic reticulum.**   The ER is composed of a network of flattened tubules called cisternae that enclose a continuous ER lumen. The rough ER is studded with ribosomes, while the smooth ER lacks ribosomes. The rough ER is continuous with the outer nuclear membrane.

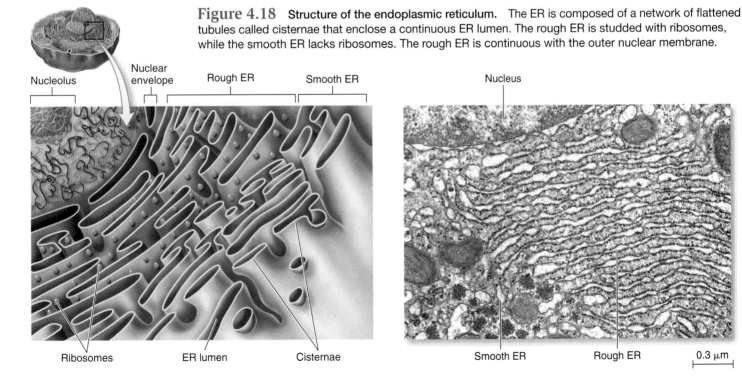

Nucleolus   Nuclear envelope   Rough ER   Smooth ER   Nucleus

Ribosomes   ER lumen   Cisternae   Smooth ER   Rough ER   0.3 μm

cholesterol. Enzymes in the smooth ER are necessary for certain modifications that are needed to produce these hormones. In addition, the smooth ER is the primary site for the synthesis of phospholipids, which are the main lipid component of eukaryotic cell membranes.

The Golgi Apparatus Directs the Secretion, Processing, and Sorting of Cellular Molecules

The **Golgi apparatus** (also called the Golgi body, Golgi complex, or simply Golgi) was discovered by the Italian microscopist Camillo Golgi in 1898. It consists of a stack of flattened, membranes; each flattened membrane encloses a single compartment (**Figure 4.19**). The Golgi stacks are named according to their orientation in the cell. The *cis* Golgi is close to the ER membrane, the *trans* Golgi is near the plasma membrane, and the *medial* Golgi is found in the middle. Materials are transported between the Golgi stacks via membrane vesicles that bud from one compartment in the Golgi (for example, the *cis* Golgi) and fuse with another compartment (for example, the *medial* Golgi).

The Golgi apparatus performs three overlapping functions: (1) secretion, (2) processing, and (3) protein sorting. The Golgi apparatus packages different types of materials into **secretory vesicles** that later fuse with the plasma membrane, thereby releasing their contents outside the plasma membrane (Figure 4.19). Proteins that are destined for secretion are synthesized into the ER, travel to the Golgi, and then to the plasma membrane for secretion. This route, called the secretory pathway, is described in Chapter 6.

Enzymes in the Golgi apparatus process, or modify, certain proteins and lipids. As mentioned earlier, carbohydrates can be attached to proteins and lipids in the endoplasmic reticulum. Glycosylation continues in the Golgi. For this to occur, a protein or lipid is transported via vesicles from the ER to the *cis* Golgi. Most of the glycosylation occurs in the *medial* Golgi. A second type of processing event is **proteolysis**—enzymes called **proteases** cut proteins into smaller polypeptides. For example, the hormone insulin is first made as a large precursor protein termed proinsulin. In the Golgi apparatus, proinsulin is packaged with proteases into vesicles. Prior to secretion, the proteases cut out a portion of the proinsulin to create a smaller insulin molecule that is a functional hormone.

The third function of the Golgi is protein sorting. After a protein enters the Golgi from the ER, it will be directed to one of six locations. Either it will stay in the Golgi, or it will be transported via vesicles to the ER, a lysosome (in animal cells), a vacuole (in plant cells), the plasma membrane, or the exterior of the cell.

Lysosomes Are Involved in Degrading Macromolecules

Lysosomes are small organelles found in animal cells that are able to lyse macromolecules, hence their name. Lysosomes contain many **acid hydrolases**, which are hydrolytic enzymes that use a molecule of water to break a covalent bond. This type of chemical reaction is called hydrolysis. The hydrolases found in a lysosome function optimally at an acidic pH. The fluid-filled

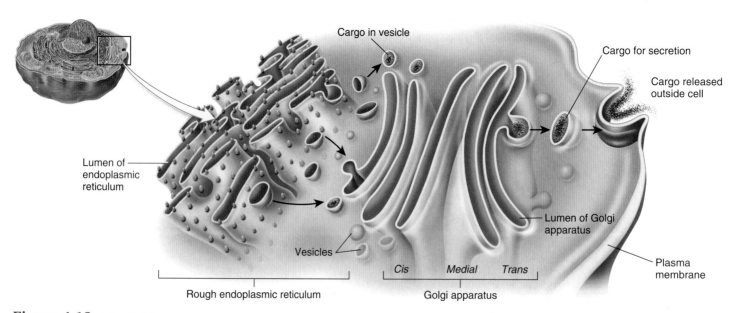

Figure 4.19   **The Golgi apparatus and secretory pathway.**   The Golgi is composed of stacks of membranes that enclose separate compartments. Transport to and from the Golgi compartments occurs via membrane vesicles. Vesicles can bud from the ER and go to the Golgi, and vesicles from the Golgi can fuse with the plasma membrane to release cargo to the outside. The pathway from the ER to the Golgi to the plasma membrane is termed the secretory pathway.

Biological inquiry: If we consider the Golgi apparatus as three compartments (cis, medial, and trans), describe the compartments that a protein will travel through to be secreted.

interior of a lysosome has a pH of approximately 4.8. If a lysosomal membrane breaks, releasing acid hydrolases into the cytosol, the enzymes are not very active because the cytosolic pH is neutral (approximately pH 7.0). This prevents significant damage to the cell from accidental leakage.

Lysosomes contain many different types of acid hydrolases that can break down proteins, carbohydrates, nucleic acids, and lipids. This enzymatic function enables lysosomes to break down complex materials. One function of lysosomes involves the digestion of substances that are taken up from outside the cell. This process, called endocytosis, is described in Chapter 5. In addition, lysosomes help digest intracellular materials. In a process known as **autophagy** (meaning the eating of one's self), cellular material, such as a worn-out organelle, becomes enclosed in a double membrane (**Figure 4.20**). This **autophagosome** then fuses with a lysosome, and the material inside the autophagosome is digested. The small molecules that are released from this digestion are recycled back into the cytosol.

Vacuoles Are Specialized Compartments That Function in Storage, the Regulation of Cell Volume, and Degradation

The term **vacuole** (literally, "empty space") came from early microscopic observations of these compartments. We now know that vacuoles are not empty but instead contain fluid and sometimes even solid substances. Most vacuoles are made from the fusion of many smaller membrane vesicles. Vacuoles are prominent organelles in plant cells, fungal cells, and certain protists. In animal cells, vacuoles tend to be smaller and are more commonly used to temporarily store materials or transport substances. In animals, such vacuoles are sometimes called storage vesicles.

The functions of vacuoles are extremely varied, and they differ among cell types and even environmental conditions. The best way to appreciate vacuole function is to consider a few examples. Mature plant cells often have a large **central vacuole** that occupies 80% or more of the cell volume (**Figure 4.21a**).

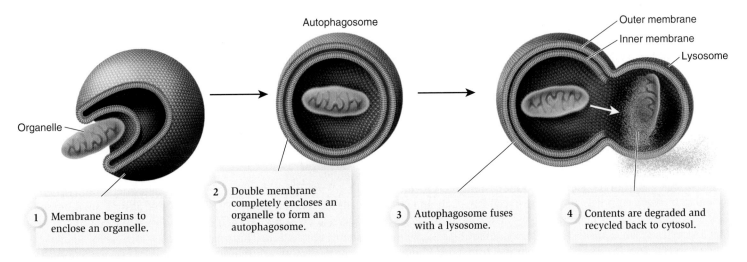

1 Membrane begins to enclose an organelle.

2 Double membrane completely encloses an organelle to form an autophagosome.

3 Autophagosome fuses with a lysosome.

4 Contents are degraded and recycled back to cytosol.

Figure 4.20   **Autophagy.**   In the example shown here, a double membrane surrounds a mitochondrion to form an autophagosome, which fuses with a lysosome. The contents of the autophagosome are degraded and released back into the cytosol.

Biological inquiry: Why do you think autophagy is useful to a cell?

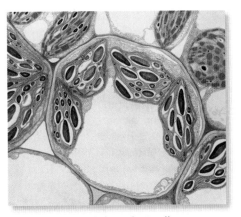

(a) Central vacuole in a plant cell

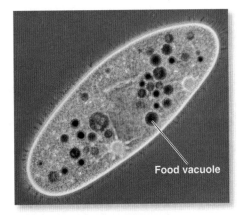

(b) Contractile vacuoles in an algal cell

(c) Food vacuoles in a paramecium

Figure 4.21   **Examples of vacuoles.**

The membrane of this vacuole is called the **tonoplast**. The central vacuole serves two important purposes. First, it stores a large amount of water, enzymes, and inorganic ions such as calcium; it also stores other materials including proteins and pigments. Second, it performs a space-filling function. The large size of the vacuole exerts a pressure on the cell wall called turgor pressure. If a plant becomes dehydrated and this pressure is lost, a plant will wilt. Turgor pressure is important in maintaining the structure of plant cells and the plant itself, and it helps to drive the expansion of the cell wall, which is necessary for growth.

Certain species of protists also use vacuoles to maintain cell volume. Freshwater organisms such as the alga *Chlamydomonas reinhardtii* have small, water-filled **contractile vacuoles** that expand as water enters the cell (**Figure 4.21b**). Once they reach a certain size, the vacuoles suddenly contract, expelling their contents to the exterior of the cell. This mechanism is necessary to remove the excess water that continually enters the cell by diffusing across the plasma membrane.

Another function of vacuoles is degradation. Some protists engulf their food into large **phagocytic vacuoles** or **food vacuoles** (**Figure 4.21c**). As in the lysosomes of animal cells, food vacuoles contain digestive enzymes to break down the macromolecules within the food. Macrophages, a type of cell found in animals' immune systems, engulf bacterial cells into phagocytic vacuoles, where the bacteria are destroyed.

The Plasma Membrane Is the Interface Between a Cell and Its Environment

The cytoplasm of all cells is surrounded by a plasma membrane, which is part of the endomembrane system and provides a boundary between a cell and the extracellular environment. Proteins in the plasma membrane play many important roles that affect the activities inside the cell. First, many plasma membrane proteins are involved in **membrane transport** (**Figure 4.22**). Some of these proteins function to transport essential nutrients or ions into the cell, while others are involved in the export of substances. Due to the functioning of these transporters, the plasma membrane is selectively permeable; it allows only certain substances in and out. We will examine the structures and functions of a variety of transporters in Chapter 5.

A second vital function of the plasma membrane is **cell signaling**. To survive and adapt to changing conditions, cells must be able to sense changes in their environment. In addition, the cells of a multicellular organism need to communicate with each other to coordinate their activities. The plasma membrane of all cells contains receptors that recognize signaling molecules—either environmental agents or molecules secreted by other cells. Once signaling molecules bind to a receptor, this elicits a series of steps known as a signal cascade that causes the cell to respond to the signal (Figure 4.22). For example, when you eat a meal, the hormone insulin is secreted into your bloodstream. This hormone binds to receptors in the plasma membrane of your cells, which results in a cellular response that allows your cells to take up the glucose from the food into the cytosol.

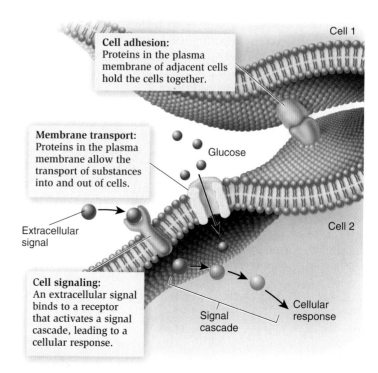

Figure 4.22 Major functions of the plasma membrane. These include membrane transport, cell signaling, and cell adhesion.

We will explore the details of receptors and signal cascades in Chapter 9.

A third important role of the plasma membrane in animal cells is **cell adhesion**. Proteins in the plasma membranes of adjacent cells bind to each other and promote cell-to-cell adhesion (Figure 4.22). This phenomenon is critical for animal cells to properly interact to form a multicellular organism and allows cells to recognize each other. The structures and functions of proteins that are involved in cell adhesion will be examined in Chapter 10.

4.5 Semiautonomous Organelles

In the rest of this chapter, we will examine those organelles in eukaryotic cells that are considered semiautonomous: mitochondria, chloroplasts, and peroxisomes. These organelles can grow and divide to reproduce themselves, but they are not completely autonomous because they depend on other parts of the cell for their internal components (**Figure 4.23**). For example, most of the proteins that are found in mitochondria are imported from the cytosol. In this section, we will survey the structures and functions of the semiautonomous organelles in eukaryotic cells. In Chapter 6 we will consider the evolutionary origins of these organelles, and in Chapters 7 and 8 we will explore the functions of mitochondria and chloroplasts in greater depth.

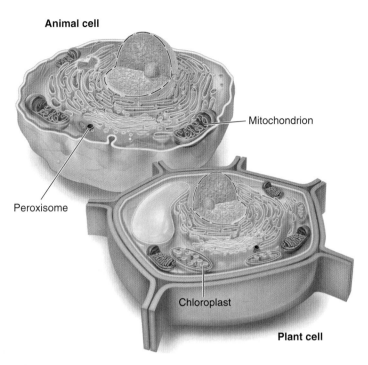

Figure 4.23 **Semiautonomous organelles.** These are the mitochondria, chloroplasts, and peroxisomes.

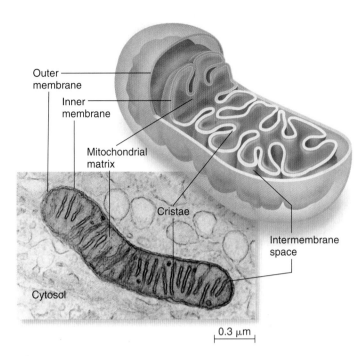

Figure 4.24 **Structure of a mitochondrion.** This organelle is enclosed in two membranes. Numerous cristae in the inner membrane increase the membrane's surface area. The mitochondrial matrix lies inside the inner membrane. The micrograph is a colorized TEM.

Mitochondria Supply Cells with Most of Their ATP

Mitochondrion (plural, *mitochondria*) literally means "thread granule," which is what mitochondria look like under a light microscope. They are similar in size to bacteria. Depending on its function, a cell may contain a few hundred to a few thousand mitochondria—cells with particularly heavy energy demands, such as muscle cells, have more mitochondria than other cells. Indeed, research has shown that regular exercise increases the number and size of mitochondria in human muscle cells to meet the expanded demand for energy.

A mitochondrion has an outer membrane and an inner membrane separated by a region called the intermembrane space (**Figure 4.24**). The inner membrane is highly invaginated (folded) to form projections called **cristae**. These invaginations greatly increase the surface area of the inner membrane, which is the site where ATP is made. The compartment inside the inner membrane is the **mitochondrial matrix**.

The primary role of mitochondria is to make ATP. Even though mitochondria produce most of a cell's ATP, it is incorrect to think that mitochondria create energy. Rather, their primary function is to convert chemical energy that is stored within the covalent bonds in organic molecules into a form that can be readily used by cells. Covalent bonds in sugars, fats, and amino acids store a large amount of energy. The breakdown of these molecules into simpler molecules releases energy that is used to make ATP. Many proteins in living cells utilize ATP to carry out their functions, such as muscle contraction, uptake of nutrients, cell division, and many other cellular processes.

Mitochondria perform other functions as well. They are involved in the synthesis, modification, and breakdown of several types of cellular molecules. For example, the synthesis of certain hormones requires enzymes that are found in mitochondria. Therefore, if mitochondria do not function properly, this affects not only ATP synthesis but the synthesis of other products as well. Another interesting role of mitochondria is to generate heat in specialized fat cells known as brown fat cells. Groups of brown fat cells serve as "heating pads" that help to revive hibernating animals and protect sensitive areas of young animals from the cold.

Chloroplasts Carry Out Photosynthesis

Chloroplasts are organelles that can capture light energy and use some of that energy to synthesize organic molecules such as glucose. This process, called **photosynthesis**, is described in Chapter 8. Chloroplasts are found in nearly all species of plants and algae. **Figure 4.25** shows the structure of a typical chloroplast. Like the mitochondrion, a chloroplast contains an outer and inner membrane. An intermembrane space lies between these two membranes. A third membrane, the **thylakoid membrane**, forms many flattened, fluid-filled tubules that enclose a single, convoluted compartment. These tubules tend to stack on top of each other to form a structure called a **granum** (plural, *grana*). The **stroma** is the compartment of the chloroplast that is inside the inner membrane but outside the thylakoid membrane.

The **thylakoid lumen** is enclosed by the thylakoid membrane. This organization facilitates the process of photosynthesis.

Chloroplasts are a specialized version of plant organelles that are more generally known as **plastids**. All plastids are derived from unspecialized **proplastids**. The various types of plastids are distinguished by their synthetic abilities and the types of pigments they contain. Chloroplasts, which carry out photosynthesis, contain the green pigment chlorophyll. The abundant number of chloroplasts in the leaves of plants gives them their green color (**Figure 4.26a**). Chromoplasts, a second type of plastid, function in synthesizing and storing yellow, orange, and red pigments. Chromoplasts give many fruits and flowers their colors (**Figure 4.26b**). In autumn, the chromoplasts also give many leaves their yellow, orange, and red colors. A third type of plastid, leucoplasts, typically lacks pigment molecules. An amyloplast is a leucoplast that synthesizes and stores starch. Amyloplasts are common in underground structures such as roots and tubers (**Figure 4.26c**).

Peroxisomes Catalyze Detoxifying Reactions

Peroxisomes, which were discovered by Christian de Duve in 1965, are relatively small organelles found in all eukaryotic cells. Peroxisomes consist of a single membrane that encloses a fluid-filled lumen (**Figure 4.27**). A typical eukaryotic cell contains several hundred of them. Peroxisomes are viewed as semi-autonomous because peroxisomal proteins are imported into the peroxisome in a manner that is very similar to the targeting of proteins to the mitochondria and chloroplasts. Another similarity is that new peroxisomes are produced by the division of pre-existing peroxisomes. However, the origin of peroxisomes remains controversial. As discussed in Chapter 6, mitochondria and chloroplasts have DNA because they are evolutionarily derived from bacteria that took up residence in a primordial eukaryotic cell. Likewise, some researchers speculate that peroxisomes could also have originated in this manner and lost their DNA during evolution. Alternatively, other scientists postulate that peroxisomes are derived from an invagination of cellular membranes around cytosolic enzymes. Further research is needed to resolve this controversy.

The general function of peroxisomes is to catalyze certain chemical reactions, typically those that break down molecules by removing hydrogen or adding oxygen. In mammals, for example, large numbers of peroxisomes can be found in the cells of the liver, where toxic molecules accumulate and are broken down. A by-product of this type of chemical reaction is hydrogen peroxide, H_2O_2, which is also broken down in this organelle (hence the name peroxisome). Hydrogen peroxide has the potential to be highly toxic. In the presence of metals such as iron (Fe^{2+}) that are found naturally in living cells, one way that hydrogen peroxide can be broken down causes the formation of a hydroxide ion (OH^-) and a molecule called a hydroxide free radical ($OH\bullet^-$).

$$Fe^{2+} + H_2O_2 \rightarrow Fe^{3+} + OH^- + OH\bullet^- \text{ (hydroxide free radical)}$$

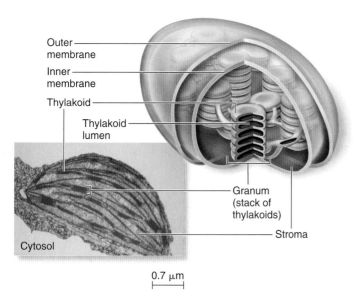

Outer membrane
Inner membrane
Thylakoid
Thylakoid lumen
Cytosol
Granum (stack of thylakoids)
Stroma

0.7 μm

Figure 4.25   Structure of a chloroplast.   Like a mitochondrion, a chloroplast is enclosed in a double membrane. In addition, it has an internal thylakoid membrane system that forms flattened compartments. These compartments stack on each other to form grana. The stroma is located inside the inner membrane but outside the thylakoid membrane. The micrograph is a colorized TEM.

(a) Leaves, which contain chloroplasts

(b) Fruit, which contain chromoplasts

(c) Roots, which contain amyloplasts

Figure 4.26   Types of plastids.   (a) Chloroplasts are involved in photosynthesis and give plants their green color. **(b)** Chromoplasts store yellow, orange, and red pigments, typically found in fruit and flowers. **(c)** Amyloplasts are colorless plastids that store starch in roots.

The hydroxide free radical is highly reactive and can damage proteins, lipids, and DNA. Therefore, it is beneficial for cells to break down hydrogen peroxide in an alternative manner that does not form a hydroxide free radical. Peroxisomes contain an enzyme called **catalase** that breaks down hydrogen peroxide to make water and oxygen gas.

$$2\ H_2O_2 \xrightarrow{\text{Catalase}} 2\ H_2O + O_2$$

Depending on the cell type, peroxisomes also contain enzymes that detoxify other molecules. These reactions may generate hydrogen peroxide, which is broken down via catalase.

Aside from detoxification, peroxisomes usually contain enzymes involved in the metabolism of fats and amino acids. For instance, plant seeds contain specialized organelles called **glyoxysomes** that are similar to peroxisomes. Glyoxysomes contain enzymes that are needed to convert fats to sugars. These enzymes become active when a seed germinates and the seedling begins to grow.

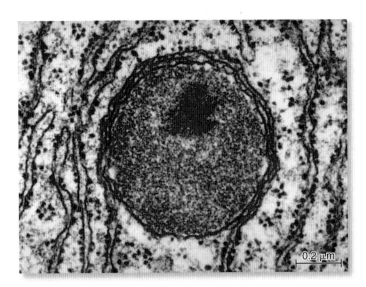

Figure 4.27   Structure of a peroxisome.   This micrograph is a TEM.

Chapter Summary

4.1 Microscopy

- Three important parameters in microscopy are magnification, resolution, and contrast. A light microscope utilizes light for illumination, while an electron microscope uses an electron beam.

- Transmission electron microscopy (TEM) provides the best resolution of any form of microscopy, and scanning electron microscopy (SEM) produces an image of a three-dimensional surface. (Figures 4.1, 4.2, 4.3)

4.2 Overview of Cell Structure

- Cell structure relies on four phenomena: matter, energy, organization, and information. Every living organism has a genome. The genes within the genome contain the information to create cells with particular structures and functions.

- We can classify all forms of life into two categories based on cell structure: prokaryotes and eukaryotes.

- The prokaryotes have a relatively simple structure and lack a membrane-enclosed nucleus. The two categories of prokaryotes are bacteria and archaea. Structures in prokaryotic cells include the plasma membrane, cytoplasm, nucleoid, and ribosomes. Many prokaryotes also have a cell wall and a glycocalyx. (Figures 4.4, 4.5)

- Eukaryotic cells are compartmentalized into organelles and contain a nucleus that houses most of their DNA. (Figures 4.6, 4.7, 4.8)

- The proteome of a cell determines its structure and function.

4.3 The Cytosol

- The cytosol is a central coordinating region for many metabolic activities of eukaryotic cells. A critical activity of all cells is translation, the synthesis of polypeptides. (Figure 4.9)

- The cytoskeleton is a network of three different types of protein filaments: microtubules, intermediate filaments, and actin filaments. Microtubules are important for cell organization, shape, and movement.

Intermediate filaments help maintain cell shape and rigidity. Actin filaments support the plasma membrane and play a key role in cell strength, shape, and movement. (Table 4.1, Figures 4.10, 4.11, 4.12, 4.13, 4.14)

4.4 The Nucleus and Endomembrane System

- The primary function of the nucleus involves the organization and expression of the cell's genetic material. A second important function is the assembly of ribosomes. (Figures 4.15, 4.16, 4.17)

- The endomembrane system includes the nuclear envelope, endoplasmic reticulum, Golgi apparatus, lysosomes, vacuoles, and plasma membrane. The rough endoplasmic reticulum (rough ER) plays a key role in the initial sorting of proteins. The smooth endoplasmic reticulum (smooth ER) functions in metabolic processes such as detoxification, carbohydrate metabolism, accumulation of calcium ions, and synthesis and modification of lipids. The Golgi apparatus performs three overlapping functions: secretion, processing, and protein sorting. Lysosomes degrade macromolecules and help digest substances taken up from outside the cell (endocytosis) and inside the cell (autophagy). (Figures 4.18, 4.19, 4.20)

- Types and functions of vacuoles include central vacuoles, contractile vacuoles, and phagocytic or food vacuoles. (Figure 4.21)

- Proteins in the plasma membrane perform many important roles that affect activities inside the cell, including membrane transport, cell signaling, and cell adhesion. (Figure 4.22)

4.5 Semiautonomous Organelles

- Mitochondria, chloroplasts, and peroxisomes are considered semiautonomous because they can grow and divide, but they still depend on other parts of the cell for their internal components. (Figure 4.23)

- Mitochondria produce most of a cell's ATP, which is utilized by many proteins to carry out their functions. Other mitochondrial functions include the synthesis, modification, and breakdown of cellular molecules and the generation of heat in specialized fat cells. (Figure 4.24)

- Chloroplasts, which are found in nearly all species of plants and algae, carry out photosynthesis. (Figure 4.25)
- Plastids, such as chloroplasts, chromoplasts, and amyloplasts differ in their function and the pigments they store. (Figure 4.26)
- Peroxisomes catalyze certain chemical reactions, typically those that break down molecules by removing hydrogen or adding oxygen. Peroxisomes usually contain enzymes involved in the metabolism of fats and amino acids. (Figure 4.27)

TEST YOURSELF

1. The cell doctrine states that
   a. any living organism is composed of one or more cells.
   b. new cells are derived from organic molecules from the environment.
   c. the smallest units of living organisms are atoms.
   d. the function of cells depends on the shape of the cell.
   e. all of the above.

2. When using microscopes, the resolution refers to
   a. the ratio between the size of the image produced by the microscope and the actual size of the object.
   b. the degree to which a particular structure looks different from other structures around it.
   c. how well a structure takes up certain dyes.
   d. the clarity of an image.
   e. the degree to which the image is magnified.

3. A bacterial cell may possess a _____, which may protect it from the immune system of other multicellular organisms that it may infect.
   a. cell wall
   b. flagellum
   c. pili
   d. nucleoid
   e. capsule

4. Different cells of the same multicellular individual have different proteomes due to all of the following except
   a. differences in the types of proteins made in different cell types.
   b. differences in the genomes of the different cell types.
   c. the abundance of certain proteins may not be the same in different cell types.
   d. the amino acid sequences of proteins may be different in different cell types.
   e. different cell types may alter the proteins in different ways.

5. The process of polypeptide synthesis is called
   a. metabolism.
   b. transcription.
   c. translation.
   d. hydrolysis.
   e. both c and d.

6. Each of the following is part of the endomembrane system except
   a. the nuclear envelope.
   b. the endoplasmic reticulum.
   c. the Golgi apparatus.
   d. lysosomes.
   e. peroxisomes.

7. Molecules move into and out of the nucleus by
   a. diffusing through the nuclear membrane.
   b. transport proteins.
   c. moving through nuclear pores.
   d. attaching to the nucleolus.
   e. all of the above.

8. Functions of the smooth endoplasmic reticulum include
   a. detoxification of harmful organic molecules.
   b. metabolism of carbohydrates.
   c. protein sorting.
   d. all of the above.
   e. a and b only.

9. The central vacuole in many plant cells is important for
   a. storage.
   b. photosynthesis.
   c. structural support.
   d. all of the above.
   e. a and c only.

10. Peroxisomes
    a. are vesicles similar to lysosomes that break down different classes of macromolecules.
    b. play an important role in the synthesis of ATP.
    c. are vesicles that contain enzymes necessary for manufacturing complex sugars.
    d. are the organelles primarily involved in protein synthesis.
    e. contain the enzyme catalase, which breaks down hydrogen peroxide to water and oxygen.

CONCEPTUAL QUESTIONS

1. Define organelle.
2. Explain how actin filaments are involved in movement.
3. Explain the function of the Golgi apparatus.

EXPERIMENTAL QUESTIONS

1. What hypothesis was tested in the experiment of Figure 4.14? What observations led to the proposal of this hypothesis?
2. What is the benefit of purifying cellular components and studying them *in vitro* instead of in intact cells? What was the benefit of using *Nitella axillaris* to determine the function of myosin? What was the purpose of using the fluorescent beads in the experiment? What was the purpose of NEM in the experiment?
3. Explain the results of the experiment of Figure 4.14.

COLLABORATIVE QUESTIONS

1. Discuss several differences between plant and animal cells.
2. Discuss the relationship between the nucleus, the rough endoplasmic reticulum, and the Golgi apparatus.

www.brookerbiology.com

This website includes answers to the Biological Inquiry questions found in the figure legends and all end-of-chapter questions.

5

MEMBRANE STRUCTURE AND TRANSPORT

CHAPTER OUTLINE

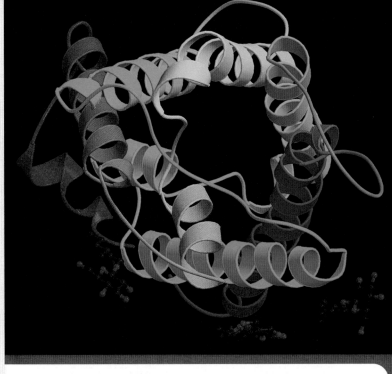

A model for the structure of aquaporin. This protein, found in the plasma membrane of many cell types, such as red blood cells and plant cells, allows the rapid movement of water molecules across the membrane.

Cellular membranes, also known as biological membranes or biomembranes, are an essential characteristic of all living cells. The **plasma membrane** is the biomembrane that separates the internal contents of a cell from its external environment. With such a role, you might imagine that the plasma membrane would be thick and rigid. Remarkably, the opposite is true. Cellular membranes are thin, typically 5–10 nm thick, and somewhat fluid. It would take 5,000 to 10,000 membranes stacked on top of each other to equal the thickness of the page you are reading. Despite their thinness, cellular membranes are impressively dynamic structures that effectively maintain the separation between a cell and its surroundings, and they provide an interface to carry out many vital cellular activities. Table 5.1 lists some of their key roles.

In this chapter, we will begin by considering the components that provide the structure of membranes. Then, we examine one of a membrane's primary functions, **membrane transport**.

Table 5.1	Important Functions of Cellular Membranes
Function	
Selective uptake and export of ions and molecules	
Cell compartmentalization	
Protein sorting	
Anchoring of the cytoskeleton	
Production of energy intermediates such as ATP and NADPH	
Cell signaling	
Cell and nuclear division	
Adhesion of cells to each other and to the extracellular matrix	

Biomembranes regulate the traffic of substances into and out of the cell and its organelles. In the second part of this chapter, we will focus on the various ways to transport ions, small molecules, and large macromolecules across membranes. Chapters 6 through 10 will examine other functions of membranes.

5.1 Membrane Structure

As we progress through this textbook, a theme that will emerge is "structure determines function." This paradigm is particularly interesting when we consider how the structure of cellular membranes enables them to compartmentalize the cell while selectively importing and exporting vital substances. The two primary components are lipids, which form the basic matrix of a membrane, and proteins, which are embedded in the membrane or loosely attached to its surface. A third component is carbohydrate, which may be attached to membrane lipids and proteins. In this section, we are mainly concerned with the organization of these components to form a biological membrane, and how they are important in the overall function of membranes. We also consider several interesting experiments that provided insight into the dynamic properties of membranes.

Biological Membranes Are a Mosaic of Lipids, Proteins, and Carbohydrates

Figure 5.1 shows the biochemical organization of cellular membranes, which are similar in composition among all living organisms. The framework of the membrane is the **phospholipid bilayer**, which consists of two layers of lipids. The most abundant lipids found in membranes are the phospholipids. Recall

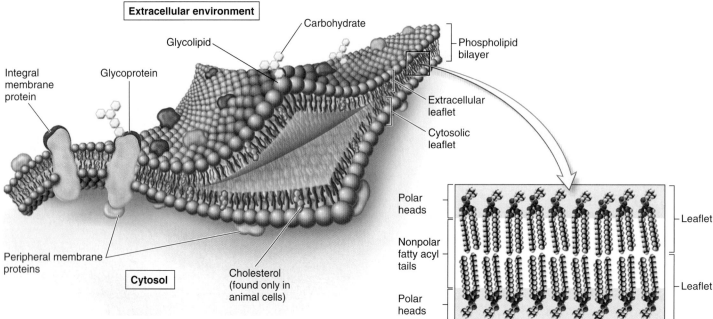

Figure 5.1 Fluid-mosaic model of membrane structure. The basic framework of a plasma membrane is a phospholipid bilayer. Proteins are inserted into the membrane and may be bound on the surface to other proteins or to lipids. Proteins and lipids, which have covalently bound carbohydrate, are called glycoproteins and glycolipids, respectively.

from Chapter 3 that phospholipids are **amphipathic** molecules, meaning they have a hydrophobic (water-fearing) region and a hydrophilic (water-loving) region. The hydrophobic tails of the lipids, referred to as fatty acyl tails, form the interior of the membrane and the hydrophilic head groups are on the surface. Experimentally, artificial membranes can be made from lipid alone.

Cellular membranes contain proteins, and most membranes also have carbohydrates attached to lipids and proteins. The relative amounts of lipids, proteins, and carbohydrates vary among different membranes. Some membranes, such as the inner mitochondrial membrane, have no carbohydrate while the plasma membrane of eukaryotic cells can have a large amount. A typical membrane found in cell organelles contains 50% protein by mass; the remainder is mostly lipids. However, the smaller lipid molecules outnumber the proteins by about 50 to 1 because the mass of one lipid molecule is much less than the mass of a protein.

Overall, the membrane is considered a mosaic of lipid, protein, and carbohydrate molecules. The membrane structure illustrated in Figure 5.1 is referred to as the **fluid-mosaic model**, originally proposed by Jonathan Singer and Garth Nicolson in 1972. As discussed later, the membrane exhibits properties that resemble a fluid because lipids and proteins can move relative to each other within the membrane. **Table 5.2** summarizes some of the historical experiments that led to the formulation of the fluid-mosaic model.

Table 5.2	Historical Developments That Led to the Formulation of the Fluid-Mosaic Model
Date	**Description**
1917	Irving Langmuir made artificial membranes experimentally by creating a monolayer of lipids on the surface of water. The polar heads interacted with water, and nonpolar tails projected into the air.
1925	Evert Gorter and F. Grendel proposed that lipids form bilayers around cells. This was based on careful measurements of lipid content enclosing red blood cells that showed there was just enough lipid to surround the cell with two layers.
1935	Because proteins were also found in membranes, Hugh Davson and James Danielli proposed incorrectly that a phospholipid bilayer was sandwiched between two layers of protein.
1950s	Electron microscopy revealed that membranes look like a train track—two dark lines separated by a light space. Initially, these results were misinterpreted. Researchers thought the two dark lines were layers of proteins and the light area was the phospholipids bilayer. Later, it was correctly determined that the dark lines in these experiments are the phospholipid heads, which were heavily stained, while the light region between them is their phospholipid tails.
1966	Using freeze fraction electron microscopy (described later in this chapter), Daniel Branton concluded that membranes are bilayers, because the freeze fracture procedure splits membranes in half, thus revealing proteins in the two membrane leaflets.
1972	Jonathan Singer and Garth Nicolson proposed the fluid-mosaic model described in Figure 5.1. Their model was consistent with the observation that membrane proteins are globular, and some are known to span the phospholipid bilayer and project from both sides.

Half of a phospholipid bilayer is termed a **leaflet**. Each leaflet faces a different region. For example, the plasma membrane contains a cytosolic leaflet and an extracellular leaflet (Figure 5.1). With regard to lipid composition, the two leaflets of cellular membranes are highly asymmetrical. The most striking asymmetry occurs with glycolipids—lipids with carbohydrate attached. These are found primarily in the extracellular leaflet so that the carbohydrate portion of a glycolipid protrudes into the extracellular medium.

Membrane Proteins Are Attached to or Embedded in the Phospholipid Bilayer

Although the phospholipid bilayer forms the basic foundation of cellular membranes, the protein component carries out most other functions (see Table 5.1). Proteins can bind to membranes in three different ways (**Figure 5.2**). **Transmembrane proteins** have one or more regions that are physically embedded in the hydrophobic region of the phospholipid bilayer. These regions, the **transmembrane segments**, are stretches of hydrophobic amino acids that span or traverse the membrane from one leaflet to the other. In most transmembrane proteins, the transmembrane segment is folded into an α-helix structure that is stabilized by hydrogen bonds. Such a segment is stable in a membrane because the nonpolar amino acids can interact favorably with the hydrophobic fatty acyl tails of the lipid molecules.

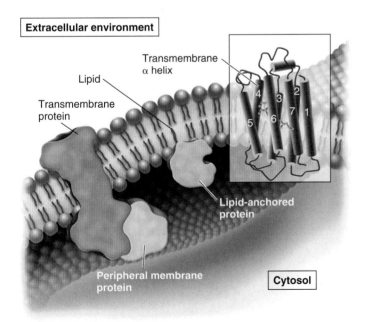

Figure 5.2 **Three types of membrane proteins.** Integral membrane proteins may have transmembrane segments that traverse the phospholipid bilayer or they may contain lipid anchors. Peripheral membrane proteins are noncovalently bound to the hydrophilic regions of integral membrane proteins or to the polar head groups of lipids. Inset: The protein shown here contains seven transmembrane segments in an α-helix structure. The transmembrane α helices are depicted as cylinders. This particular protein, bacteriorhodopsin, functions as an ion pump in halophilic (salt-loving) archaea.

A second way for proteins to associate with the membrane is via **lipid anchors**. A lipid anchor involves the covalent attachment of a lipid to an amino acid side chain within a protein. The fatty acyl tails keep the protein firmly bound to the membrane. Both transmembrane proteins and lipid-anchored proteins are classified as **integral membrane proteins**, also called intrinic membrane proteins, because they cannot be released from the membrane unless the membranes are dissolved with an organic solvent or detergent—in other words, you would have to disrupt the integrity of the membrane to remove them.

Peripheral membrane proteins, also called extrinsic proteins, are a third class of membrane proteins. These proteins do not interact with the hydrophobic interior of the phospholipid bilayer. Instead, they are noncovalently bound to regions of integral membrane proteins that project out from the membrane, or they are bound to the polar head groups of phospholipids. Peripheral membrane proteins are typically bound to the membrane by hydrogen and/or ionic bonds. For this reason, they usually can be removed from the membrane experimentally by exposing the membrane to high salt concentrations. Researchers can use this treatment to distinguish between peripheral and integral membrane proteins.

GENOMES & PROTEOMES

Approximately 25% of All Genes Encode Membrane Proteins

Membrane proteins participate in some of the most important and interesting cellular processes. These include transport, energy transduction, cell signaling, secretion, cell recognition, and cell-to-cell contact. Research studies have revealed that cells devote a sizeable fraction of their energy and metabolic machinery to the synthesis of membrane proteins. These proteins are particularly important in human medicine—approximately 70% of all medications exert their effects by binding to membrane proteins. Examples include the drugs aspirin, ibuprofen, and acetaminophen, which are widely used to relieve pain and inflammatory conditions such as arthritis. These drugs bind to cyclooxygenase, a protein in the ER membrane that is necessary for the synthesis of chemicals that play a role in inflammation and pain sensation.

Because membrane proteins are so important biologically and medically, researchers have analyzed the genomes of many species and asked the question, What percentage of genes encodes membrane proteins? They have developed tools to predict the likelihood that a gene encodes a protein that is a membrane protein. For example, the occurrence of transmembrane α helices can be predicted from the amino acid sequence of a protein. All 20 amino acids can be ranked according to their preference for a hydrophobic or hydrophilic environment. With these values, the amino acid sequence of a protein can be analyzed using computer software to determine the average hydrophobicity of short amino acid sequences within the protein. A stretch of 18 to 20 amino acids in an α helix is long enough to span the membrane.

If such a stretch contains a high percentage of hydrophobic amino acids, it is predicted to be a transmembrane α helix. However, such computer predictions must eventually be verified by experimentation.

Using a computer approach, many research groups have attempted to calculate the percentage of genes that encode membrane proteins in various species. **Table 5.3** shows the results of one such study. Note that the estimated percentage

Table 5.3	Estimated Percentage of Genes That Encode Membrane Proteins*
Organism	**Percentage of genes that encode membrane proteins**
Archaea	
Archaeoglobus fulgidus	24.2
Methanococcus jannaschii	20.4
Pyrococcus horikoshii	29.9
Bacteria	
Escherichia coli	29.9
Bacillus subtilis	29.2
Haemophilus influenzae	25.3
Eukaryotes	
Homo sapiens	29.7
Drosophila melanogaster	24.9
Arabidopsis thaliana	30.5
Saccharomyces cerevisiae	28.2

* Data from Stevens and Arkin (2000) *Proteins: Structure, Function, and Genetics* 39: 417–420. While the numbers may vary due to different computer programs and estimation techniques, the same general trends have been observed in other similar studies.

of membrane proteins is substantial: 20–30% of all genes may encode membrane proteins. This trend is found throughout all domains of life including archaea, bacteria, and eukaryotes. For example, in *E. coli*, approximately 30% of its genes encode membrane proteins. The genome of this bacterium contains about 4,300 genes, so roughly 1,290 genes may encode different membrane proteins. The human genome also has about 30% of genes that encode membrane proteins. However, the human genome is larger, containing 20,000 to 25,000 different genes, so the total number of genes that encode different membrane proteins is estimated at 6,000 to 7,500. The functions of many of them have yet to be determined. Identifying their functions will help researchers gain a better understanding of human biology. Likewise, medical researchers and pharmaceutical companies are interested in the identification of new membrane proteins that could be targets for effective new medications.

Membranes Are Semifluid

Let's now turn our attention to the dynamic properties of membranes. Although a membrane provides a critical interface between a cell and its environment, it is not a solid, rigid structure. Rather, biomembranes exhibit properties of **fluidity**, which means that individual molecules remain in close association yet have the ability to readily move within the membrane. Though membranes are often described as fluid, it is more appropriate to say they are **semifluid**. In a fluid substance, molecules can move in three dimensions. By comparison, most lipids can rotate freely around their long axes and move laterally within the membrane leaflet (**Figure 5.3**). This type of motion is considered two-dimensional, which means that it occurs within the

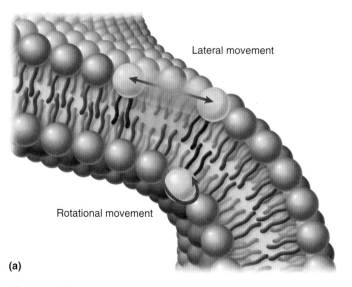

Lateral movement

Rotational movement

(a)

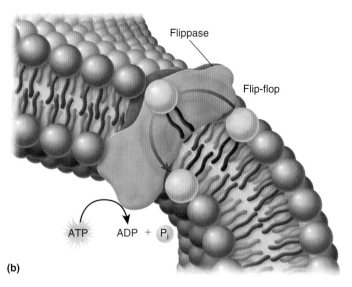

Flippase

Flip-flop

ATP   ADP + P$_i$

(b)

Figure 5.3 **Semifluidity of the lipid bilayer.** **(a)** Spontaneous movements in the bilayer. Lipids can rotate (that is, move 360°) and move laterally (for example, from left to right in the plane of the bilayer). **(b)** Flip-flop does not happen spontaneously because the polar head group would pass through the hydrophobic region of the bilayer. Instead, the enzyme flippase uses ATP to flip phospholipids from one leaflet to the other.

plane of the membrane. Because rotational and lateral movements keep the fatty acyl tails within the hydrophobic interior, such movements are energetically favorable. In fact, the movements of lipids within cellular membranes are quite pronounced. At 37°C, a typical lipid molecule exchanges places with its neighbors about 10^7 times per second, and it can move several micrometers per second. At this rate, a lipid could traverse the length of a bacterial cell (approximately 1 μm) in only 1 second and the length of a typical animal cell in 10–20 seconds.

In contrast to rotational and lateral movements, the "flip-flop" of lipids from one leaflet to the opposite leaflet does not occur spontaneously (Figure 5.3). Energetically, such movements are extremely unfavorable because the polar head of a phospholipid would have to be transported through the hydrophobic interior of the membrane. For this reason, the transport of lipids from one leaflet to another requires the action of the enzyme flippase, which uses energy from the hydrolysis of ATP to flip a lipid from one leaflet to the other.

The biochemical properties of phospholipids have a profound effect on the fluidity of the phospholipid bilayer. One key

factor is the length of their fatty acyl tails, which range from 14 to 24 carbon atoms with 18 to 20 carbons being the most common. Shorter acyl tails are less likely to interact, which makes the membrane more fluid. A second important factor is the presence of double bonds in the acyl tails. When a double bond is found, the lipid is said to be **unsaturated** with respect to the number of hydrogens that can be bound to the carbon atoms. A double bond creates a kink in the fatty acyl tail, making it more difficult for neighboring tails to interact and making the bilayer more fluid.

A third factor is the presence of cholesterol, which is a short and fairly rigid molecule that is produced by animal cells (refer back to Figure 3.13a). Cholesterol tends to stabilize membranes; its effects depend on temperature. At higher temperatures, such as those observed in mammals that maintain a constant body temperature, cholesterol makes the membrane less fluid. At lower temperatures, such as in icy water, cholesterol has the opposite effect. It makes the membrane more fluid and prevents it from freezing.

An optimal level of bilayer fluidity is essential for normal cell function, growth, and division. If a membrane is too fluid, which may occur at higher temperatures, it can become leaky. On the other hand, if a membrane becomes too solid, which may occur at lower temperatures, the functioning of membrane proteins will be inhibited. Cells adapt to changes in temperature by altering the lipid composition of their membranes. For example, when the water temperature drops, certain fish incorporate more cholesterol in their membranes. If a plant cell is exposed to high temperatures for many hours or days, it alters its lipid composition to have longer fatty acyl tails and fewer double bonds.

Like lipids, many integral membrane proteins may rotate and laterally move throughout the plane of a membrane. Because membrane proteins are larger than lipids, they move through the membrane at a much slower rate. Flip-flop of integral membrane proteins does not occur because the proteins also contain hydrophilic regions that project out from the phospholipid bilayer. It would be energetically unfavorable for the hydrophilic regions of membrane proteins to pass through the hydrophobic portion of the phospholipid bilayer.

Researchers can examine the lateral movements of lipids and integral membrane proteins by a variety of methods. In 1970, Larry Frye and Michael Edidin conducted an experiment that verified the lateral movement of membrane proteins (**Figure 5.4**). Mouse and human cells were mixed together and exposed to agents that caused them to fuse with each other. Some cells were cooled to 0°C while others were incubated at 37°C before being cooled. Both sets of cells were then exposed to fluorescently labeled antibodies that became specifically bound to a mouse membrane protein called H-2. The fluorescent label was observed with a fluorescence microscope. If the cells were maintained at 0°C, a temperature that greatly inhibits lateral movement, the fluorescence was seen on only one side of the fused cell. However, if the cells were incubated for several hours at 37°C

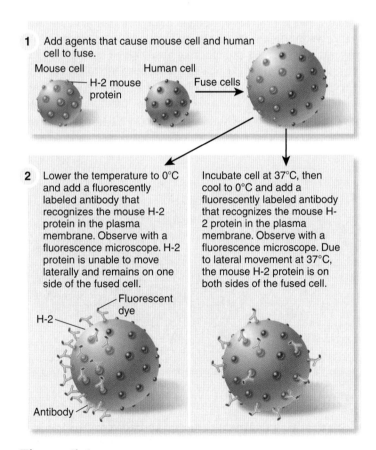

1 Add agents that cause mouse cell and human cell to fuse.

Mouse cell   Human cell

H-2 mouse protein   Fuse cells

2 Lower the temperature to 0°C and add a fluorescently labeled antibody that recognizes the mouse H-2 protein in the plasma membrane. Observe with a fluorescence microscope. H-2 protein is unable to move laterally and remains on one side of the fused cell.

Incubate cell at 37°C, then cool to 0°C and add a fluorescently labeled antibody that recognizes the mouse H-2 protein in the plasma membrane. Observe with a fluorescence microscope. Due to lateral movement at 37°C, the mouse H-2 protein is on both sides of the fused cell.

Fluorescent dye

H-2

Antibody

Figure 5.4 A method to measure the lateral movement of membrane proteins.

Biological inquiry: Explain why the H-2 proteins are found only on one side of the cell when the cells were incubated at 0°C.

and then cooled to 0°C, the fluorescence was distributed throughout the fused cell. This occurred because the higher temperature allowed the lateral movement of the H-2 protein throughout the plasma membrane.

A second approach to studying lateral movement, fluorescence recovery after photobleaching (FRAP), was developed in 1976 by Watt Webb and colleagues (**Figure 5.5**). In the experiment shown here, proteins on the surface of a cell were covalently labeled with a fluorescent molecule. In this example, the molecule emitted a red color so the entire surface of the cell appeared red. A laser beam was then focused on a small region of the cell surface. The energy of the laser beam altered the structure of the fluorescent molecules and eliminated the red color, a phenomenon called photobleaching. Immediately after photobleaching, a small region of the cell surface appeared white. Over time, bleached molecules within the white spot spread outward, and the white region filled in with red fluorescent molecules. These results indicate that proteins can laterally move in the membrane.

Unlike the examples shown in Figures 5.4 and 5.5, not all integral membrane proteins are capable of rotational and lateral movement. Depending on the cell type, 10–70% of membrane proteins may be restricted in their movement. Integral membrane proteins may be bound to components of the cytoskeleton, which restricts the proteins from moving laterally (**Figure 5.6**). Also, membrane proteins may be attached to molecules that are outside the cell, such as the interconnected network of proteins that forms the extracellular matrix of animal cells.

Glycosylation of Lipids and Proteins Serves a Variety of Cellular Functions

As mentioned earlier, the third constituent of biomembranes is carbohydrate. **Glycosylation** refers to the process of covalently attaching a carbohydrate to a protein or lipid. When a carbohydrate is attached to a lipid, this creates a **glycolipid**, while attachment to a protein produces a **glycoprotein**. We will discuss the mechanism of protein glycosylation in Chapter 6.

Though the roles of carbohydrate in cell structure and function are not entirely understood, some functional consequences of glycosylation are beginning to emerge. The carbohydrates that are attached to proteins and lipids have well-defined structures that serve in some cases as recognition signals for other cellular proteins. For example, proteins that are destined for the lysosome are glycosylated and have a sugar—mannose-6-phosphate—that is recognized by other proteins in the cell that target the glycosylated protein to the lysosome. Similarly, membrane glycolipids and glycoproteins often play a role in cell surface recognition.

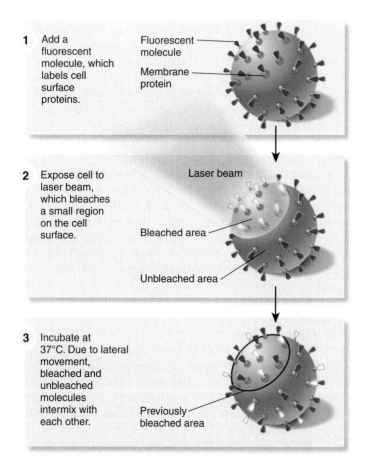

Figure 5.5 Fluorescence recovery after photobleaching (FRAP). In this method, the surface of cells was coated with fluorescent molecules. A laser beam bleached a small section shown in white. Over time, bleached molecules left the area and unbleached molecules invaded the bleached area by lateral movement.

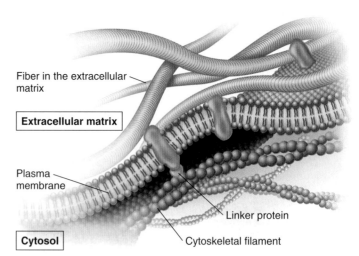

Figure 5.6 Attachment of transmembrane proteins to the cytoskeleton and extracellular matrix. Some membrane proteins have regions that project into the cytosol and are anchored to large cytoskeletal filaments (via linker proteins). The binding to these large filaments restricts lateral movement. Similarly, some integral membrane proteins may bind to large, immobile components in the extracellular matrix that also restrict the movement of the proteins.

During embryonic development in animals, significant cell movement occurs. Layers of cells slide over each other to create body structures such as the spinal cord and internal organs. The proper migration of individual cells and cell layers relies on the recognition of cell types via the carbohydrates on their cell surfaces.

In addition to its role as a recognition marker, carbohydrate can have a protective effect. The term **cell coat** or **glycocalyx** is used to describe the carbohydrate-rich zone on the cell surface that shields the cell from mechanical and physical damage (**Figure 5.7**). The carbohydrate portion of glycosylated proteins protects them from the harsh conditions of the extracellular environment and degradation by extracellular proteases, which are enzymes that digest proteins.

Membrane Structure Can Be Viewed with an Electron Microscope

Electron microscopy, discussed in Chapter 4, is a valuable tool to probe membrane structure and function. In transmission electron microscopy (TEM), a biological sample is thin sectioned and stained with heavy-metal dyes such as osmium tetroxide. This compound binds tightly to the polar head groups of phospholipids, but it does not bind well to the fatty acyl tails.

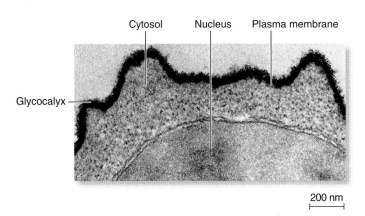

Cytosol   Nucleus   Plasma membrane

Glycocalyx

200 nm

Figure 5.7   **A micrograph of the cell coat or glycocalyx.** This figure shows a lymphocyte—a type of white blood cell—stained with ethidium red, which emphasizes the thick carbohydrate layer that surrounds the cell.

As shown in **Figure 5.8a**, membranes stained with osmium tetroxide resemble a railroad track. Two thin dark lines, which are the stained polar head groups, are separated by a uniform light space about 2 nm thick. This railroad track morphology is seen consistently when cell membranes are subjected to electron microscopy.

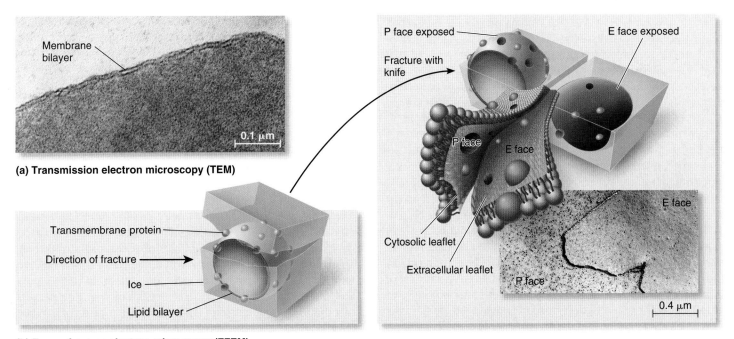

Membrane bilayer

0.1 μm

(a) Transmission electron microscopy (TEM)

Transmembrane protein

Direction of fracture

Ice

Lipid bilayer

(b) Freeze fracture electron microscopy (FFEM)

P face exposed

E face exposed

Fracture with knife

P face

E face

Cytosolic leaflet

Extracellular leaflet

E face

P face

0.4 μm

Figure 5.8   **Electron micrographs of a cellular membrane.**   (a) In the standard form of TEM, the membrane appears as two dark parallel lines. These lines are the lipid head groups, which stain darkly with osmium tetroxide. The fatty acyl tails do not stain well and appear as a light region sandwiched between the dark lines. (b) In the technique of freeze fracture electron microscopy, a sample is frozen in liquid nitrogen, split, and fractured. The sample is then coated with metal and viewed under the electron microscope. Note: The knife does not actually cut the two leaflets of the membrane apart. It simply separates the sample into two parts, and membranes that happen to be located at the fractured region will split along their bilayers.

Biological inquiry: If a heavy metal labeled the hydrophobic tails rather than the polar head groups (as osmium tetroxide does), do you think you would see a bilayer (that is, a railroad track) under TEM?

Due to the incredibly small size of biological membranes, scientists have not been able to invent instruments small enough to dissect them. However, a specialized form of TEM, freeze fracture electron microscopy (FFEM), can be used to analyze the interiors of phospholipid bilayers. Russell Steere invented this method in 1957. In FFEM, a sample is frozen in liquid nitrogen and split with a knife (**Figure 5.8b**). The knife does not actually cut through the bilayer, but it fractures the frozen sample. Due to the weakness of the central membrane region, the leaflets separate into a P face (the protoplasmic face that was next to the cytosol) and the E face (the extracellular face). Most transmembrane proteins do not break in half. They remain embedded within one of the leaflets, usually in the P face. The samples, which are under a vacuum, are then sprayed with a heavy metal such as platinum that coats the sample and reveals architectural features within each leaflet. When viewed with an electron microscope, membrane proteins are visible as bumps that provide significant three-dimensional detail about their form and shape.

5.2 Membrane Transport

If plasma membranes consisted of only a phospholipid bilayer, they would not permit the uptake of most nutrients and the export of waste products. However, the plasma membrane is a **selectively permeable** barrier between the cell and its external environment. As a protective envelope, its structure ensures that essential molecules such as glucose and amino acids enter the cell, metabolic intermediates remain in the cell, and waste products exit. The selective permeability of the plasma membrane allows the cell to maintain a favorable internal environment.

In this section, we begin with a discussion of the phospholipid bilayer, how it presents a barrier to the movement of ions and molecules across membranes, and the concept of gradients across membranes. We will then focus on **transport proteins**, which are embedded within the phospholipid bilayer. Transport proteins allow membranes to be selectively permeable by providing a passageway for the movement of some but not all substances across the membrane. Because different cells require various mixtures of ions and low-molecular-weight molecules, the plasma membrane of each cell type contains a specific set of transport proteins that allow only certain ions and molecules to cross. We will examine how transport proteins play a key role in the selective uptake and export of materials, and consider a mechanism found in eukaryotic cells for the transport of substances across membranes via membrane vesicles.

The Phospholipid Bilayer Is a Barrier to the Diffusion of Hydrophilic Substances

Because of their hydrophobic interiors, phospholipid bilayers present a formidable barrier to the movement of ions and hydrophilic molecules. **Diffusion** occurs when a solute (that is,

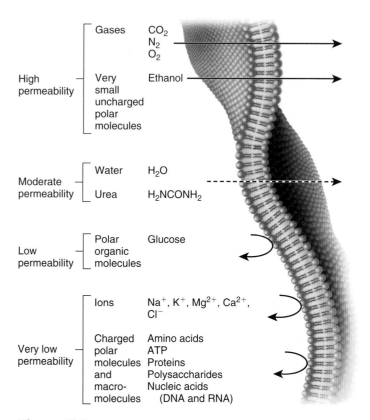

Figure 5.9 Relative permeability of an artificial phospholipid bilayer to a variety of solutes. Solutes that easily penetrate are shown with a *straight arrow* that passes through the bilayer. The *dotted line* indicates solutes that have moderate permeability. The remaining solutes shown at the bottom are relatively impermeable. Note: Permeability is also related to solute concentration. At high concentrations, solutes are more likely to pass through a membrane.

a dissolved substance) moves from a region of high concentration to a region of lower concentration. When diffusion occurs through a membrane without the aid of a transport protein, it is called **passive diffusion**. The rate of passive diffusion depends on the chemistry of the solute and its concentration. **Figure 5.9** compares the relative permeabilities of various solutes through an artificial phospholipid bilayer that does not contain any proteins or carbohydrates. Gases and a few small, uncharged polar molecules can passively diffuse across the bilayer. However, the rate of diffusion of ions and larger polar molecules such as sugars and amino acids is relatively slow. Similarly, macromolecules, such as proteins and large carbohydrates, do not readily cross a lipid bilayer.

When we consider the steps of passive diffusion among different solutes, the greatest variation occurs in the ability of solutes to enter the hydrophobic interior of the bilayer. As an example, let's compare urea and diethylurea. Diethylurea is much more hydrophobic because it contains two nonpolar ethyl groups ($-CH_2CH_3$) (**Figure 5.10**). For this reason, it can more readily pass through the hydrophobic region of the phospholipid

Urea

Diethylurea

Figure 5.10 Structures of urea and diethylurea.

Biological inquiry: Which molecule would you expect to pass through a phospholipid bilayer more quickly, methanol (CH₃OH) or methane (CH₄)?

bilayer. The rate of passive diffusion of diethylurea through a phospholipid bilayer is about 50 times faster than urea.

Cells Maintain Gradients Across Their Membranes

As we have just seen, phospholipid bilayers are quite impermeable to ions and most hydrophilic molecules. A hallmark of living cells is their ability to maintain a relatively constant internal environment that is distinctively different from their external environment. This involves establishing gradients of solutes across the plasma membrane and organellar membranes. When we speak of a **transmembrane gradient**, we mean that the concentration of a solute is higher on one side of a membrane than the other. For example, immediately after you eat a meal, a higher concentration of glucose is found outside your cells compared to inside. Gradients involving ions have two components—electrical and chemical. An **ion electrochemical gradient** is a dual gradient that has both an electrical gradient and chemical gradient. For example, let's consider a gradient involving Na^+. An electrical gradient could exist in which the amount of net positive charge outside a cell is greater than inside. At the same time, a chemical gradient could exist in which the concentration of Na^+ outside is greater than inside. These two gradients together constitute a Na^+ electrochemical gradient. Transmembrane gradients of ions and other solutes are a universal feature of all living cells.

One way to view the transport of solutes across membranes is to consider how the transport process affects the pre-existing gradients across membranes. **Passive transport** refers to the diffusion of a solute across a membrane in a process that is energetically favorable and does not require an input of energy. Passive transport tends to dissipate a pre-existing gradient. (Note: The adjective *passive* can have different meanings in biology. It can mean without an input of energy, as in passive transport, or without the aid of a transport protein, as in passive diffusion.)

Passive transport can occur in two ways, via passive diffusion or facilitated diffusion. As mentioned earlier, passive diffusion is the diffusion of a solute directly through the phospholipid bilayer to move across the membrane (**Figure 5.11a**). This is not a common way for most solutes to move. The second pathway for passive transport is **facilitated diffusion**, which involves the aid of transport proteins (**Figure 5.11b**). Transport proteins facilitate the movement of various nutrients and—in some types of cells—water across the membrane.

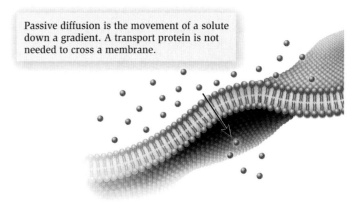

Passive diffusion is the movement of a solute down a gradient. A transport protein is not needed to cross a membrane.

(a) Passive diffusion

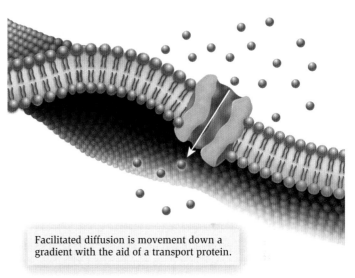

Facilitated diffusion is movement down a gradient with the aid of a transport protein.

(b) Facilitated diffusion

Figure 5.11 Types of passive transport. (a) Passive diffusion. (b) Facilitated diffusion.

Osmosis Is the Movement of Water Across Membranes to Balance Solute Concentrations

Lipid bilayers are relatively impermeable to many solutes, yet somewhat permeable to water. When the solute concentrations on both sides of the plasma membrane are equal, the two solutions are said to be **isotonic**. However, we have also seen that transmembrane gradients commonly exist across membranes. When the solute concentration inside the cell is higher, it is said to be **hypertonic** relative to the outside of the cell, which is **hypotonic**. If the solutes cannot move across the membrane, water will move and tend to balance the solute concentrations. In this process, called **osmosis**, water diffuses through a membrane from the hypotonic compartment into the hypertonic compartment.

Cells generally have a high internal concentration of a variety of solutes including ions, sugars, amino acids, etc. Animal cells,

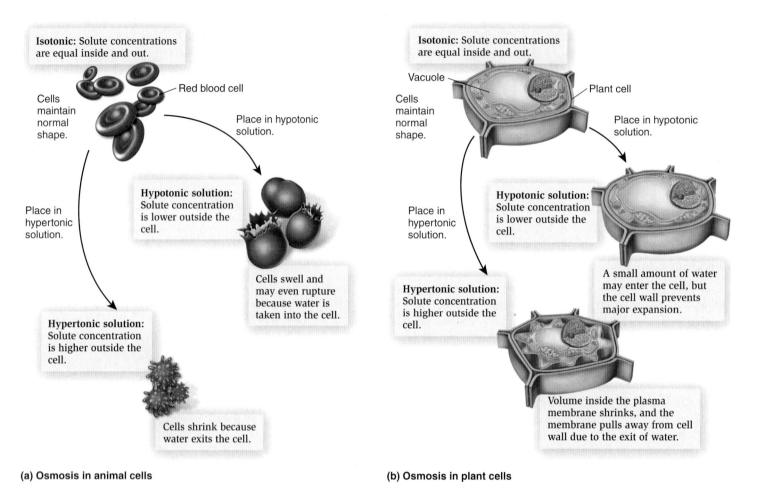

(a) Osmosis in animal cells

(b) Osmosis in plant cells

Figure 5.12   **The phenomenon of osmosis.**   **(a)** In animal cells that lack a cell wall, osmosis may promote cell shrinkage (crenation) or swelling. **(b)** In plant cells that have a rigid cell wall, a hypertonic medium causes the plasma membrane to pull away from the cell wall, while a hypotonic medium causes only a minor amount of expansion.

Biological inquiry: The inside of a cell has 100 mM KCl, while the outside has 10 mM KCl. If the membrane is impermeable to KCl, which direction will water move?

which are not surrounded by a rigid cell wall, must maintain a balance between the extracellular and intracellular solute concentrations. As discussed later, animal cells contain a variety of transport proteins that can sense changes in cell volume and allow the necessary movements of solutes across the membrane to prevent osmotic changes and maintain normal cell shape. However, if animal cells are placed in a hypertonic medium, water will exit the cells via osmosis and equalize solute concentrations on both sides of the membrane, causing them to shrink in a process called **crenation** (**Figure 5.12a**). Alternatively, if cells are placed in a hypotonic medium, water will diffuse into them to equalize solute concentrations on both sides of the membrane. In extreme cases, a cell may take up so much water that it bursts, a phenomenon called osmotic lysis.

Osmosis can also affect cells with a rigid cell wall, such as bacteria, fungi, algae, and plant cells. If the extracellular fluid surrounding a plant cell is hypertonic, water will exit the cell and the plasma membrane will pull away from the cell wall (**Figure 5.12b**). Alternatively, if the extracellular fluid is hypotonic, a plant cell will take up a small amount of water, but the cell wall prevents major changes in cell size. The tendency

of water to move into any cell creates an **osmotic pressure**, which is defined as the hydrostatic pressure required to stop the net flow of water across a membrane due to osmosis. In plant cells, osmotic pressure is also called **turgor pressure** or simply cell turgor. The turgor pressure pushes the plasma membrane against the rigid cell wall. An appropriate level of turgor is needed for cells to maintain their proper structure (**Figure 5.13**). If a plant has insufficient water, the extracellular fluid surrounding plant cells becomes hypertonic, the plasma membrane pulls away from the cell wall, and the osmotic pressure drops. The result is plasmolysis, which is associated with wilting.

Some freshwater organisms, such as amoebae and paramecia, can exist in extremely hypotonic environments where the external solute concentration is always much lower than the concentration of solutes in their cytosol. Because of the great tendency for water to move into the cell by osmosis, some organisms contain a contractile vacuole to prevent osmotic lysis. A contractile vacuole takes up water from the cytosol and periodically discharges it by fusing the vacuole with the plasma membrane (**Figure 5.14**).

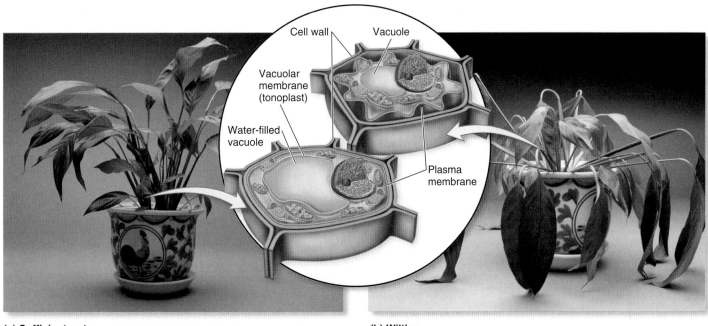

(a) Sufficient water   **(b) Wilting**

Figure 5.13   Wilting in plants.   (a) When a plant has plenty of water, the slightly hypotonic surroundings cause the vacuole to store water. The increased size of the vacuole influences the volume of the cytosol, thereby exerting a turgor pressure against the cell wall. **(b)** Under dry conditions, water is released from the cytosol into the extracellular medium. The vacuole also shrinks, because it loses water to the cytosol. Turgor pressure is lost. This causes the plant to wilt.

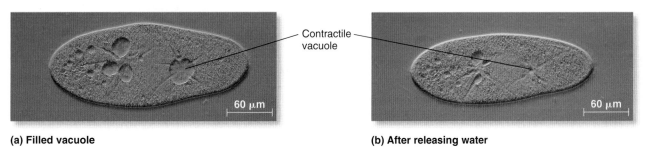

(a) Filled vacuole   **(b) After releasing water**

Figure 5.14   The contractile vacuole in *Paramecium caudatum*.   (a) A contractile vacuole is filled with water from radiating canals that collect fluid from the cytosol. **(b)** The contractile vacuole has recently fused with the plasma membrane (which would be above the plane of this page) and released the water from the cell.

FEATURE INVESTIGATION

Agre Discovered That Osmosis Occurs More Quickly in Cells with Transport Proteins That Allow the Facilitated Diffusion of Water

In living cells, the flow of water may occur by passive diffusion through the phospholipid bilayer. However, in the 1980s, researchers also discovered that certain cell types allow water to move across the plasma membrane at a much faster rate than would be predicted by passive diffusion. For example, water moves very quickly across the membrane of red blood cells, which causes them to shrink and swell in response to changes in extracellular

solute concentrations. Likewise, bladder and kidney cells, which play a key role in regulating water balance in the bodies of vertebrates, allow the rapid movement of water across their membranes. Based on these observations, researchers speculated that certain cell types might have proteins in their plasma membranes that permit the rapid movement of water.

One approach that is used to characterize a new protein is to first identify a protein based on its relative abundance in a particular cell type, and then attempt to determine the protein's function. This rationale was applied to the discovery of proteins that allow the rapid movement of water across membranes.

Peter Agre and his colleagues first identified a protein that was abundant in red blood cells and kidney cells, but not found in many other cell types. Though they initially did not know the function of the protein, its physical structure was similar to other proteins that were already known to function as transport proteins. They named this protein CHIP28, which stands for <u>ch</u>annel-forming <u>i</u>ntegral membrane <u>p</u>rotein with a molecular mass of <u>28</u>,000 Da. During the course of their studies, they also identified and isolated the gene that encodes CHIP28.

In 1992, Agre and his colleagues conducted experiments to determine if CHIP28 functions in the transport of water across membranes (**Figure 5.15**). Because they already had isolated the gene that encodes CHIP28, they could make many copies of this gene in a test tube (*in vitro*) using gene cloning techniques

Figure 5.15   The discovery of water channels.

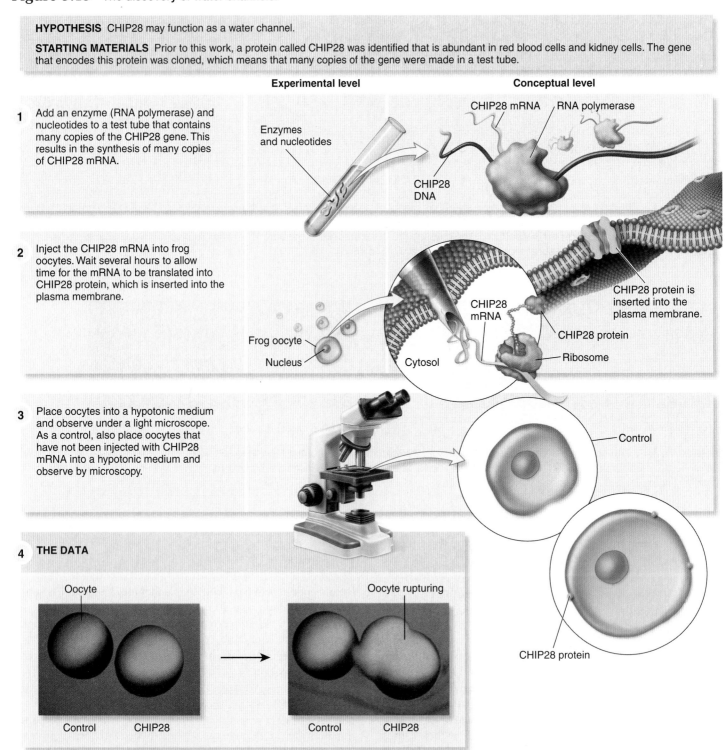

HYPOTHESIS   CHIP28 may function as a water channel.

STARTING MATERIALS   Prior to this work, a protein called CHIP28 was identified that is abundant in red blood cells and kidney cells. The gene that encodes this protein was cloned, which means that many copies of the gene were made in a test tube.

Experimental level   Conceptual level

1   Add an enzyme (RNA polymerase) and nucleotides to a test tube that contains many copies of the CHIP28 gene. This results in the synthesis of many copies of CHIP28 mRNA.

Enzymes and nucleotides

CHIP28 mRNA   RNA polymerase

CHIP28 DNA

2   Inject the CHIP28 mRNA into frog oocytes. Wait several hours to allow time for the mRNA to be translated into CHIP28 protein, which is inserted into the plasma membrane.

Frog oocyte
Nucleus
Cytosol
CHIP28 mRNA
CHIP28 protein is inserted into the plasma membrane.
CHIP28 protein
Ribosome

3   Place oocytes into a hypotonic medium and observe under a light microscope. As a control, also place oocytes that have not been injected with CHIP28 mRNA into a hypotonic medium and observe by microscopy.

Control

CHIP28 protein

4   **THE DATA**

Oocyte

Oocyte rupturing

Control   CHIP28

Control   CHIP28

(see Chapter 20). Starting with many copies of the gene *in vitro*, they added an enzyme to transcribe the gene into mRNA that encodes the CHIP28 protein. This mRNA was then injected into frog oocytes, chosen because frog oocytes are large, easy to inject, and lack pre-existing proteins in their plasma membranes that allow the rapid movement of water. After injection, the mRNA was expected to be translated into CHIP28 proteins that should be inserted into the plasma membrane of the oocytes. After allowing sufficient time for this to occur, the oocytes were placed in a hypotonic medium. As a control, oocytes that had not been injected with CHIP28 mRNA were also exposed to a hypotonic medium.

As you can see in the data, a striking difference was observed between oocytes that expressed CHIP28 versus the control. Within minutes, oocytes that contained the CHIP28 protein were seen to swell due to the rapid uptake of water. Three to 5 minutes after being placed in a hypotonic medium, they actually burst! By comparison, the control oocytes did not swell as rapidly, and they did not rupture even after 1 hour. Taken together, these results are consistent with the hypothesis that CHIP28 functions as a transport protein that allows the facilitated diffusion of water across the membrane. Many subsequent studies confirmed this observation. Later, CHIP28 was renamed **aquaporin** to indicate its newly identified function of allowing water to diffuse through a pore in the membrane (**Figure 5.16**). More recently, the three-dimensional structure of aquaporin was determined (see inset to Figure 5.16). Agre was awarded the Nobel Prize in 2003 for this work.

Aquaporin is an example of a transport protein called a channel. Next, we will discuss the characteristics of channels and other types of transport proteins.

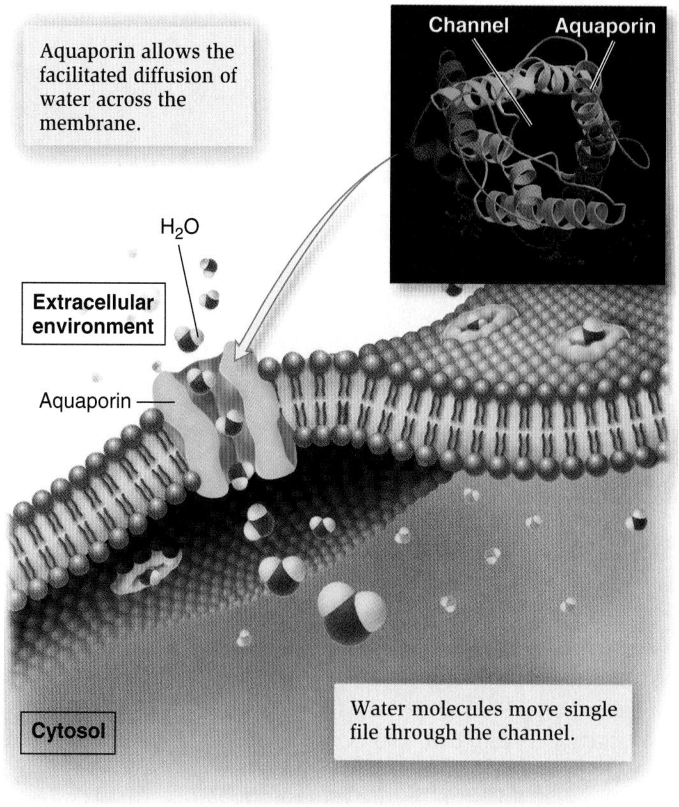

Figure 5.16 Function and structure of aquaporin. Aquaporin is found in the membrane of certain cell types and allows the rapid diffusion of water across the membrane. The inset shows the structure of aquaporin, which was determined by X-ray crystallography.

Transport Proteins Cause Biological Membranes to Be Selectively Permeable

Because the phospholipid bilayer is a physical barrier to the passive diffusion of ions and most hydrophilic molecules, cells are able to separate their internal contents from their external environment. However, this barrier also poses a severe problem because cells must take up nutrients from the environment and export waste products. To overcome this dilemma, species have evolved a multitude of transport proteins—transmembrane proteins that provide a passageway for the movement of ions and hydrophilic molecules across membranes. Transport proteins enable biological membranes to be selectively permeable. We can categorize transport proteins into two classes, channels and transporters, based on the manner in which they move solutes across the membrane.

Channels **Channels** are transmembrane proteins that form an open passageway for the facilitated diffusion of ions or molecules across the membrane (**Figure 5.17**). In other words, solutes move directly through a channel to get to the other side. Aquaporin, discussed in the Feature Investigation, is a channel that allows the movement of water across the membrane. When a

channel is open, the transmembrane movement of solutes can be extremely rapid, up to 100 million ions or molecules per second!

Most channels are **gated**, which means they can open to allow the diffusion of solutes and close to prohibit diffusion. The phenomenon of gating allows cells to regulate the movement of solutes. Researchers have discovered a variety of gating mechanisms (**Figure 15.18**). Gating sometimes involves the direct binding of a molecule to the channel protein itself. **Ligand-gated channels** are controlled by the noncovalent binding of small molecules—called ligands—such as hormones or neurotransmitters. These ligands are often important in the transmission of signals between nerve and muscle cells or between two nerve cells. Alternatively, intracellular proteins may bind noncovalently to channels and control their ability to open and close. For example, certain types of calcium channels that are found in nerve cells are controlled by regulatory proteins that bind to the channel and cause it to open. Another gating mechanism involves the covalent binding of a small molecule, such as a phosphate group, to the channel protein. Regulatory proteins involved in cell-signaling pathways may covalently attach phosphate to proteins as a way to regulate their function. In some cases, the targets of these regulatory proteins are channels.

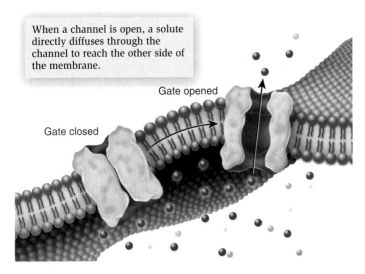

When a channel is open, a solute directly diffuses through the channel to reach the other side of the membrane.

Gate opened

Gate closed

Figure 5.17 Mechanism of transport by a channel protein.

As an example, chloride channels in the human lung are opened by phosphorylation.

Channel gating can also occur by mechanisms that do not involve the direct binding of a molecule to the channel protein. For example, some channels are **voltage-gated**, meaning that the channel opens and closes in response to changes in the amount of electric charge across the membrane. Sodium and potassium channels in nerve cells are voltage-gated. Another interesting gating mechanism involves **mechanosensitive channels**, which are sensitive to changes in membrane tension. For example, our ability to hear depends, in part, on the functioning of mechanosensitive channels in the cells of the inner ear that are sensitive to different frequencies of sound. The opening of these ion channels in response to sound transmits signals to the brain that a particular frequency has been detected.

Transporters **Transporters**, also known as **carriers**, bind their solutes in a hydrophilic pocket and undergo a conformational change that switches the exposure of the pocket to the other side of the membrane (**Figure 5.19**). Transporters tend to be much slower than channels. Their rate of transport is typically 100 to 1,000 ions or molecules per second. Transporters provide the principal pathway for the uptake of organic molecules, such as sugars, amino acids, and nucleotides. In animals, they also allow cells to take up certain hormones and neurotransmitters. In addition, many transporters play a key role in export. Waste-products of cellular metabolism must be released from cells before they reach toxic levels. For example, a transporter removes lactic acid, a by-product of muscle cells during exercise. Excessive lactic acid buildup is partly responsible for the burning sensation you feel during a strenuous workout. Other transporters, which are involved with ion transport, play an important role in cellular processes such as regulating internal pH and controlling cell volume.

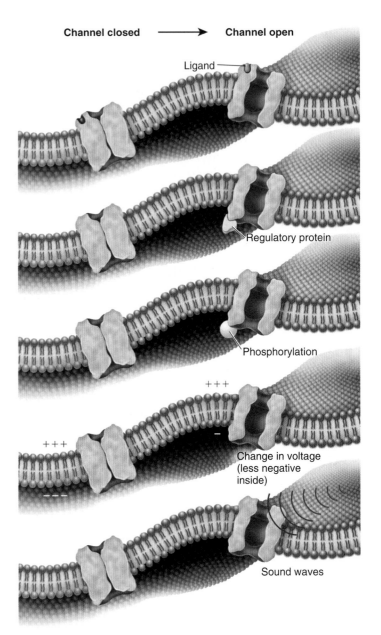

Channel closed ⟶ Channel open

Ligand

Regulatory protein

Phosphorylation

+++   +++
−   − − −

Change in voltage (less negative inside)

Sound waves

Figure 5.18 Different ways that channels are gated.

Transporters are subdivided according to the number of solutes they bind and the direction of transport (**Figure 5.20**). **Uniporters** bind a single molecule or ion and transport it across the membrane. **Symporters** or **cotransporters** bind two or more ions or molecules and transport them in the same direction. **Antiporters** bind two or more ions or molecules and transport them in opposite directions.

A **pump** is a transporter that directly couples its conformational changes to an energy source, such as ATP hydrolysis (**Figure 5.21**). The conformational changes of pumps are energetically driven. A common category of pumps found in all living cells are **ATP-driven pumps**, which have a binding site for ATP.

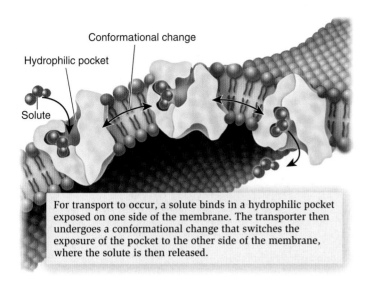

For transport to occur, a solute binds in a hydrophilic pocket exposed on one side of the membrane. The transporter then undergoes a conformational change that switches the exposure of the pocket to the other side of the membrane, where the solute is then released.

Figure 5.19 Mechanism of transport by a transporter, also called a carrier.

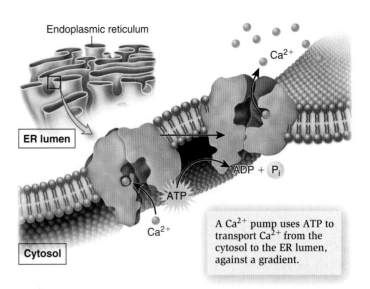

A Ca^{2+} pump uses ATP to transport Ca^{2+} from the cytosol to the ER lumen, against a gradient.

Figure 5.21 Transporters that function as pumps.

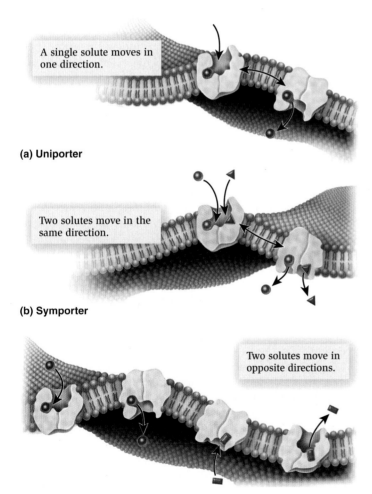

A single solute moves in one direction.

(a) Uniporter

Two solutes move in the same direction.

(b) Symporter

Two solutes move in opposite directions.

(c) Antiporter

Figure 5.20 Types of transporters based on the direction of transport. **(a)** Uniporter. **(b)** Symporter. **(c)** Antiporter.

The hydrolysis of ATP provides energy that controls the sequence of conformational changes. The energy obtained from ATP hydrolysis can be used to pump solutes against a gradient. Pumps can be uniporters, symporters, or antiporters. As discussed next, pumps use energy to achieve active transport.

Active Transport Is the Movement of Substances Against a Gradient

Active transport is the movement of a solute across a membrane against its gradient—that is, from a region of low concentration to higher concentration. Active transport is energetically unfavorable and requires the input of energy. **Primary active transport** involves the functioning of pumps that directly use energy to transport a solute against a gradient. **Figure 5.22** shows a pump that uses ATP to transport H$^+$ against a gradient. Such a pump can establish a large H$^+$ electrochemical gradient across a membrane.

Secondary active transport involves the utilization of a pre-existing gradient to drive the active transport of a solute (Figure 5.22). For example, an H$^+$/sucrose symporter can utilize an H$^+$ electrochemical gradient, established by an ion pump, to move sucrose against its concentration gradient. In this regard, only sucrose is actively transported. Hydrogen ions move down (with) their electrochemical gradient. H$^+$/solute symporters are more common in bacteria, fungi, algae, and plant cells, because H$^+$ pumps are found in their plasma membranes. In animal cells, a pump that exports Na$^+$ maintains the Na$^+$ gradient across the plasma membrane. Na$^+$/solute symporters are prevalent in animal cells.

Symport enables cells to actively import nutrients against a gradient. Symport proteins use the energy stored in the electrochemical gradient of Na$^+$ or H$^+$ to power the uphill movement of organic solutes such as sugars, amino acids, and other needed

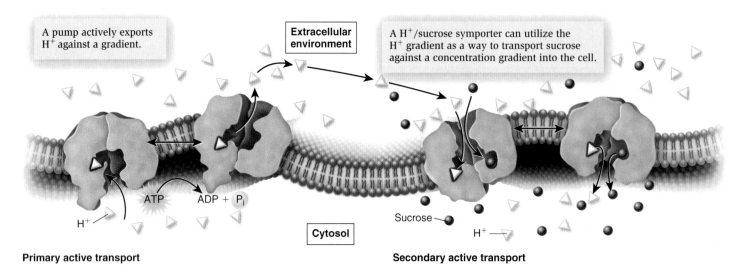

Figure 5.22 **Types of active transport.** During primary active transport, a pump directly uses energy, in this case from ATP, and generates a gradient. The pump shown here uses ATP to establish an H⁺ electrochemical gradient. Secondary active transport via symport involves the utilization of this gradient to drive the active transport of a solute, such as sucrose.

solutes. Therefore, with symporters in their plasma membrane, cells can scavenge nutrients from the extracellular environment and accumulate them to high levels within the cytoplasm.

ATP-Driven Ion Pumps Generate Ion Electrochemical Gradients

The concept of active transport was discovered in the 1940s based on the study of ion movements using radioisotopes of Na^+ and K^+. After analyzing the movement of these ions across the plasma membrane of muscle cells, nerve cells, and red blood cells, researchers determined that the export of sodium ions (Na^+) is coupled to the import of potassium ions (K^+) (**Figure 5.23a**). In the late 1950s, Danish biochemist Jens Skou proposed that a single transporter is responsible for this phenomenon. By studying the membranes of nerve cells from crabs, he was the first person to describe an ATP-driven ion pump, which was later named the Na^+/K^+-ATPase. This pump can actively transport Na^+ and K^+ against their gradients by using the energy from ATP hydrolysis.

Interestingly, Skou initially had trouble characterizing this pump. He focused his work on the large nerve cells found in the shore crab (*Carcinus maenas*). In membranes from these cells, he was able to identify a transporter that could hydrolyze ATP, but the rate of hydrolysis was too low to account for the known levels of ATP hydrolysis associated with Na^+ and K^+ pumping. When he added Na^+ to his membranes, the ATP hydrolysis rate was not greatly affected. Then he tried adding K^+, but the ATP hydrolysis rate still did not increase. This was a frustrating period for Skou. Eventually, he did the critical experiment in which he added both Na^+ and K^+ to his membranes. With both ions present, ATP hydrolysis soared dramatically. This observation led to the identification and purification of the Na^+/K^+-ATPase. Jens Skou was awarded the Nobel Prize in 1997, over 40 years after his original work.

Let's take a closer look at the Na^+/K^+-ATPase that Skou discovered. Every time one ATP is hydrolyzed, the Na^+/K^+-ATPase functions as an antiporter that pumps three Na^+ into the extracellular environment and two K^+ into the cytosol. Because one cycle of pumping results in the net export of one positive charge, the Na^+/K^+-ATPase also produces an electrical gradient across the membrane. For this reason, it is considered an **electrogenic pump**, meaning that it generates an electrical gradient. The plasma membrane of a typical animal cell contains thousands of Na^+/K^+-ATPase pumps.

By studying the interactions of Na^+, K^+, and ATP with the Na^+/K^+-ATPase, researchers have pieced together a molecular roadmap of the steps that direct the pumping of ions across the membrane. These steps are termed the **reaction mechanism** (**Figure 5.23b**). A central precept of the reaction mechanism is that the Na^+/K^+-ATPase can alternate between two conformations, designated E1 and E2. In E1, the ion-binding sites are accessible from the cytosol—sodium ions bind tightly to this conformation while potassium ions have a low affinity. In E2, the ion-binding sites are accessible from the extracellular environment—sodium ions have a low affinity and potassium ions bind tightly.

To examine the reaction mechanism, let's begin with the E1 conformation. Three sodium ions bind to the Na^+/K^+-ATPase from the cytosol (Figure 5.23b). When this occurs, ATP is hydrolyzed to ADP and phosphate. Temporarily, the phosphate is covalently bound to the pump, an event called phosphorylation. The pump then switches to the E2 conformation. The sodium ions are released into the extracellular environment because they have a lower affinity for the E2 conformation, and then two potassium ions bind from the outside. The binding of K^+ causes the release of phosphate, which in turn causes a switch to E1. Because the E1 conformation has a low affinity for K^+, the potassium ions are released into the cytosol. The Na^+/K^+-ATPase is now ready for another round of pumping.

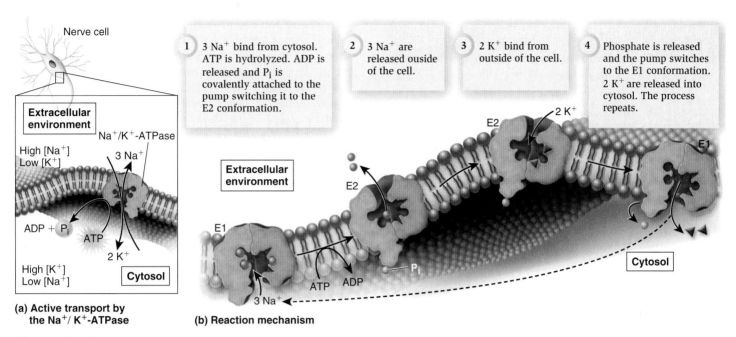

**(a) Active transport by
the Na⁺/ K⁺-ATPase**

(b) Reaction mechanism

Figure 5.23   Structure and function of the Na⁺/K⁺-ATPase.   **(a)** Active transport by the Na⁺/K⁺-ATPase. Each time this protein hydrolyzes one ATP molecule, it pumps out three Na⁺ and pumps in two K⁺. **(b)** Reaction mechanism. The figure illustrates the protein conformational changes between E1 and E2. As this occurs, ATP is hydrolyzed to ADP and phosphate. During the reaction mechanism, phosphate is covalently attached to the protein but is released after potassium ions bind.

Biological inquiry: If a cell had ATP and sodium ions, but potassium ions were missing, how far through the reaction mechanism could the Na⁺/K⁺-ATPase proceed?

The Na⁺/K⁺-ATPase is a key cellular enzyme in animal cells because it functions as an ion pump that maintains Na⁺ and K⁺ gradients across the plasma membrane. Many other types of ion pumps are also found in the plasma membrane and in organellar membranes. Ion pumps play the primary role in the formation and maintenance of ion gradients that drive many important cellular processes (**Table 5.4**). Biologists have come to understand that the transport of ions against their gradients is a never-ending activity of all living cells. ATP is commonly the source of energy to drive ion pumps, and cells typically use a substantial portion of their cellular ATP to keep them working. For example, nerve cells use up to 70% of their ATP just to operate ion pumps!

Macromolecules and Large Particles Are Transported via Endocytosis and Exocytosis

We have seen that most small substances are transported via membrane proteins such as pumps, transporters, and channels, which provide a passageway for the movement of substances across the membrane. Eukaryotic cells have two other mechanisms, exocytosis and endocytosis, to transport larger molecules such as proteins and polysaccharides, and even very large particles. Both mechanisms involve the packaging of the transported substance, sometimes called the cargo, into a membrane vesicle or vacuole. **Table 5.5** describes important examples of exocytosis and endocytosis.

Table 5.4	Important Functions of Ion Electrochemical Gradients
Function	**Description**
Transport of ions and molecules	Symporters and antiporters use H⁺ and Na⁺ gradients to take up nutrients and export waste products.
Production of energy intermediates	In the mitochondrion and chloroplast, H⁺ gradients are used to synthesize ATP.
Regulation of cystolic pH	Transporters sense pH changes and regulate the internal pH.
Osmotic regulation	Animal cells control their internal volume by regulating ion gradients between the cytosol and extracellular fluid.
Nerve signaling	Na⁺ and K⁺ gradients are involved in conducting action potentials, the signals transmitted by nerve cells.
Muscle contraction	Ca²⁺ gradients regulate the ability of muscle fibers to contract.
Bacterial swimming	H⁺ gradients drive the rotation of bacterial flagella.

Exocytosis Exocytosis is a process in which material inside the cell, which is packaged into vesicles, is excreted into the extracellular environment (**Figure 5.24**). These vesicles are usually derived from the Golgi apparatus. As the vesicles form, a specific cargo is loaded into their interior. For example, in animal cells, large polysaccharides are made within the lumen of the Golgi and packaged within vesicles that bud from the Golgi.

Table 5.5	Examples of Exocytosis and Endocytosis
Exocytosis	**Description**
Hormones	Certain hormones, such as insulin, are composed of polypeptides. To exert its effect, insulin is secreted via exocytosis into the bloodstream from B cells of the pancreas.
Digestive enzymes	Digestive enzymes that function in the lumen of the small intestine are secreted via exocytosis from cells of the pancreas.
Extracellular matrix	Most of the components of the extracellular matrix that surrounds animal cells are secreted via exocytosis.
Endocytosis	**Description**
Uptake of vital nutrients	Many important nutrients are very insoluble in the bloodstream. Therefore, they are bound to proteins in the blood and then taken into cells via endocytosis. Examples include the uptake of lipids (bound to low-density lipoprotein) and iron (bound to transferrin protein).
Root nodules	Nitrogen-fixing root nodules found in certain species of plants such as legumes are formed by the endocytosis of bacteria. After endocytosis, the bacterial cells are contained within a membrane-enclosed compartment in the nitrogen-fixing tissue of functional nodules.
Immune system	Cells of the immune system, known as macrophages, engulf and destroy bacteria via endocytosis.

The budding process involves the formation of a protein coat around the emerging vesicle. The assembly of coat proteins on the surface of the membrane causes the bud to form. Eventually, the bud separates from the membrane to form a vesicle. After the vesicle is released, the coat is shed. Finally, the vesicle fuses with the plasma membrane and releases its contents into the extracellular medium.

The process of exocytosis illustrates the dynamic and fluid nature of membranes. They readily bud and fuse with other membranes. The same is true for endocytosis, which is described next.

Endocytosis   During **endocytosis**, the plasma membrane invaginates, or folds inward, to form a vesicle that brings substances into the cell (**Figure 5.25**). A common form of endocytosis is **receptor-mediated endocytosis**, in which a receptor is specific for a given cargo. When a receptor binds to that cargo, this stimulates the binding of coat proteins to the membrane, which initiates the formation of a vesicle. Many receptors aggregate together as a protein coat forms around the vesicle. Once inside the cell, the vesicle sheds its coat. In most cases, the vesicle fuses with an internal membrane organelle, such as a lysosome, and the receptor releases its cargo. Depending on the cargo, the lysosome may release it directly into the cytosol or digest it into simpler building blocks before releasing it.

Other specialized forms of endocytosis occur in certain types of cells. **Pinocytosis** (meaning "cell drinking") involves the formation of membrane vesicles from the plasma membrane as a way for cells to internalize the extracellular fluid. This allows cells to sample the extracellular solutes. Pinocytosis is particularly important in cells that are actively involved in nutrient absorption, such as cells that line the intestine in animals.

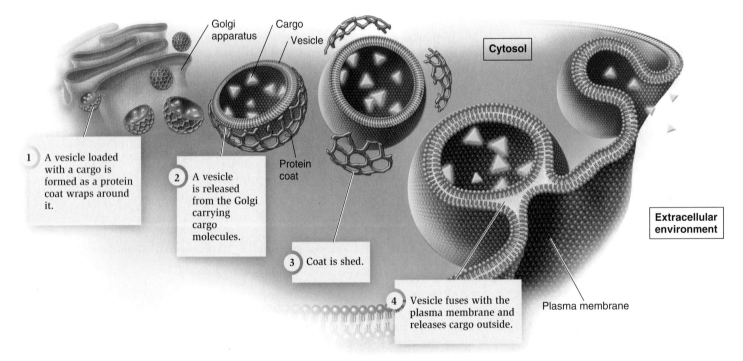

Figure 5.24   Exocytosis.   Membrane vesicles bud from an organelle inside the cell, such as the Golgi apparatus, and are loaded with a specific cargo. The budding process involves the formation of a protein coat around the emerging vesicle, which is later shed. When the vesicle fuses with the plasma membrane, it releases its contents into the extracellular environment.

Phagocytosis ("cell eating") is an extreme form of endocytosis. It involves the formation of an enormous membrane vesicle called a phagosome, or phagocytic vacuole, that engulfs a large particle such as a bacterium. Only certain kinds of cells can carry out phagocytosis. For example, macrophages, which are cells of the immune system in mammals, kill bacteria via phagocytosis. Once inside the cell, the phagosome fuses with lysosomes and the digestive enzymes within the lysosomes destroy the bacterium.

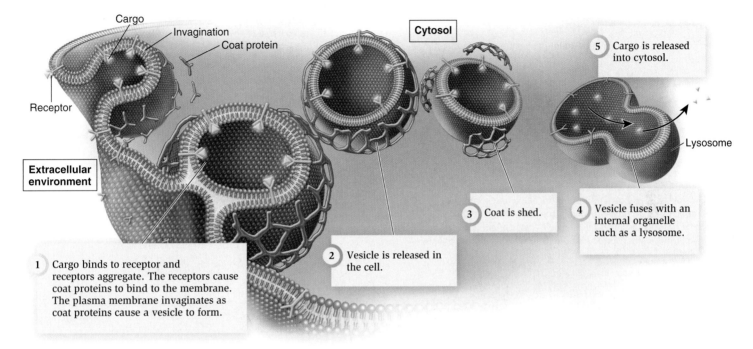

Figure 5.25 **Receptor-mediated endocytosis.** A cargo binds to a receptor, which stimulates the aggregation of many receptors and the formation of a vesicle with a protein coat. Once inside the cell, the vesicle sheds its coat. In most cases, the vesicle fuses with an internal membrane organelle and releases its cargo into the cytosol.

CHAPTER SUMMARY

5.1 Membrane Structure

- Cellular membranes are dynamic structures that separate a cell from its surroundings yet provide an interface to carry out vital cellular activities. One of their crucial functions is membrane transport. (Table 5.1)
- The accepted model of the plasma membrane is the fluid-mosaic model, and its basic framework is the phospholipid bilayer. Cellular membranes also contain proteins, and most membranes have attached carbohydrates. (Figure 5.1, Table 5.2)
- Proteins can bind to membranes in three different ways: as transmembrane proteins, lipid-anchored proteins, or peripheral membrane proteins. Transmembrane proteins and lipid-anchored proteins are classified as integral membrane proteins. Researchers are working to identify new membrane proteins and their functions because these proteins are so important biologically and medically. (Figure 5.2, Table 5.3)
- Bilayer semifluidity is essential for normal cell function, growth, and division. The chemical properties of phospholipids, such as tail length, the presence of double bonds, and the presence of cholesterol, have a profound effect on the fluidity of the phospholipid bilayer. (Figures 5.3, 5.4, 5.5, 5.6)
- Glycosylation, which produces glycolipids or glycoproteins, has a variety of cellular functions. Carbohydrate can serve as a recognition marker or a protective cell coat. (Figure 5.7)

- Electron microscopy is a valuable tool for studying membrane structure and function. Freeze fracture electron microscopy (FFEM) can be used to analyze the interiors of phospholipid bilayers. (Figure 5.8)

5.2 Membrane Transport

- Living cells maintain a constant internal environment that is separated from their external environment. This involves establishing transmembrane gradients across the plasma membrane and organellar membranes. (Figure 5.9, Table 5.4)
- Diffusion occurs when a solute moves from a region of high concentration to a region of lower concentration. Passive diffusion occurs through a membrane without the aid of a transport protein. (Figure 5.10)
- Passive transport refers to the diffusion of a solute across a membrane in a process that does not require an input of energy. Passive transport can occur via passive diffusion or facilitated diffusion. (Figure 5.11)
- In the process of osmosis, water diffuses through a membrane from a solution that is hypotonic (lower solute concentration) into a solution that is hypertonic (higher solute concentration). Solutions with identical solute concentrations are isotonic. The tendency of water to move into any cell creates an osmotic (turgor) pressure. (Figures 5.12, 5.13, 5.14)
- Transport proteins enable biological membranes to be selectively permeable. The two classes of transport proteins are channels and transporters. Channels form an open passageway for the direct

diffusion of solutes across the membrane; one example is aquaporin, which allows the movement of water. Most channels are gated, which allows cells to regulate the movement of solutes. Transporters (carriers), which tend to be slower than channels, bind their solutes in a hydrophilic pocket and undergo a conformational change that switches the exposure of the pocket to the other side of the membrane. A pump is a transporter that directly couples its conformational changes to an energy source. All living cells contain ATP-driven pumps. (Figures 5.15, 5.16, 5.17, 5.18, 5.19, 5.20, 5.21)

- Active transport is the movement of a solute across a membrane against its gradient. Primary active transport involves pumps that directly use energy and generate a solute gradient. Secondary active transport involves the utilization of a pre-existing gradient. (Figure 5.22)

- The Na^+/K^+-ATPase is an electrogenic ATP-driven pump. The reaction mechanism refers to the steps that direct the pumping of ions across the membrane. (Figure 5.23)

- Eukaryotic cells have two other mechanisms, exocytosis and endocytosis, to transport large molecules and particles. Exocytosis is a process in which material inside the cell is packaged into vesicles and excreted into the extracellular environment. During endocytosis, the plasma membrane folds inward to form a vesicle that brings substances into the cell. Forms of endocytosis include pinocytosis, phagocytosis, and receptor-mediated endocytosis. (Figures 5.24, 5.25, Table 5.5)

TEST YOURSELF

1. Which of the following statements best describes the chemical composition of biomembranes?
   a. Biomembranes are bilayers of proteins with associated lipids and carbohydrates.
   b. Biomembranes are composed of two layers, one layer of phospholipids and one layer of proteins.
   c. Biomembranes are bilayers of phospholipids with associated proteins and carbohydrates.
   d. Biomembranes are composed of equal numbers of phospholipids, proteins, and carbohydrates.
   e. Biomembranes are composed of lipids with proteins attached to the outer surface.

2. _____ is a lipid that helps stabilize membranes of animal cells by regulating fluidity as temperature changes.
   a. Cholesterol   d. ATP
   b. Prostaglandin   e. Acetone
   c. Glycerol

3. The presence of double bonds in the fatty acyl tail will
   a. decrease fluidity because of the attraction between the unsaturated tails.
   b. increase fluidity due to the difficulty of the kinked acyl tail to interact.
   c. decrease fluidity by increasing the space between the phospholipids.
   d. increase fluidity by allowing more room for cholesterol to move into the membrane.
   e. decrease fluidity by decreasing the amount of proteins in the membrane.

4. Carbohydrates of the plasma membrane
   a. are associated with a protein or lipid.
   b. are located on the outer surface of the membrane.
   c. can function as cell markers for recognition by other cells.
   d. all of the above.
   e. a and c only.

5. Which of the following can easily diffuse through a lipid bilayer?
   a. sodium ions   d. oxygen
   b. amino acids   e. DNA
   c. glucose

6. The tendency for Na^+ to move into the cell is due to
   a. the higher numbers of Na^+ outside the cell resulting in a chemical concentration gradient.
   b. the net negative charge inside the cell attracting the positively charged Na^+.
   c. the attractive force of K^+ inside the cell pulling Na^+ into the cell.
   d. all of the above.
   e. a and b only.

7. The hydrostatic pressure required to stop osmosis is
   a. an electrochemical gradient.   d. osmotic pressure.
   b. filtration.   e. partial pressure.
   c. tonicity.

8. The selectively permeable characteristic of plasma membranes is mainly due to the presence of
   a. phospholipids.
   b. transport proteins.
   c. glycolipids on the outer surface of the membrane.
   d. concentration gradients across the membrane.
   e. cholesterol.

9. During _____ , materials are moved across the plasma membrane against their concentration gradient.
   a. facilitated diffusion   d. filtration
   b. osmosis   e. simple diffusion
   c. active transport

10. Large particles or large volumes of fluid can be brought into the cell by
    a. facilitated diffusion.   d. exocytosis.
    b. active transport.   e. all of the above.
    c. endocytosis.

CONCEPTUAL QUESTIONS

1. Explain the fluid-mosaic model of membrane structure.
2. What are three types of membrane proteins?
3. What is the difference between passive diffusion and passive transport?

EXPERIMENTAL QUESTIONS

1. What observations led to the experiment of Figure 5.15 to identify proteins that may increase water movement into the cell?
2. How did Agre and associates choose a candidate protein that may function as a water channel in plasma membranes? What was the hypothesis tested by the researchers? Briefly explain how they were able to test their hypothesis.
3. What were the results of the experiment of Figure 5.15? Do they support the proposed hypothesis?

COLLABORATIVE QUESTIONS

1. Discuss the concept of solute concentrations in cells.
2. Discuss the two categories of transport proteins found in plasma membranes.

www.brookerbiology.com

This website includes answers to the Biological Inquiry questions found in the figure legends and all end-of-chapter questions.

6

SYSTEMS BIOLOGY OF CELL ORGANIZATION

CHAPTER OUTLINE

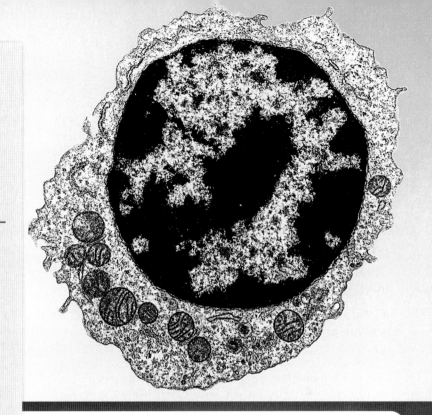

Electron micrograph of a lymphocyte, a type of white blood cell. This cell has a large nucleus and several mitochondria (colored blue). A cell can be viewed as a system of four interacting parts: the nucleus, endomembrane system, cytosol, and semiautonomous organelles.

The first few chapters of this textbook laid the foundation for understanding cell structure and function. We learned that life depends on organic molecules, which form the building blocks for macromolecules such as proteins, nucleic acids, and carbohydrates. In addition, we considered cell organization at a higher level. Cells contain complex structures such as membranes, chromosomes, ribosomes, and a cytoskeleton. Eukaryotic cells have organelles that provide specialized compartments to carry out various cellular functions.

Thus far, we have surveyed the structures and functions of cells with an emphasis on describing the various parts of cells. We have taken a reductionist approach, which involves reducing a complex system to simpler components to understand how the system works. In cell biology, reductionists study the parts of a cell as individual units. In this chapter, however, we will view the cell from a broader perspective. In **systems biology**, researchers study living organisms in terms of their underlying network structure—groups of structural and functional connections—rather than their individual molecular components. A "system" can be anything from a metabolic pathway to a cell, an organ, or even an entire organism. In this chapter, we focus on the cell as a system. Our goal is to understand how the organization of a cell arises by complex interactions between its various components and compartments. In the first section, we will examine the general principles of cell organization. In the remaining two sections we focus on dynamic interactions among the different compartments of eukaryotic cells.

6.1 Principles of Cell Organization

Now that we are familiar with the general properties of cells and membranes, we can ask, How are the various parts of a cell formed and maintained? We usually think of a cell as having form and structure, and at any given instant, it does. However, a cell is also profoundly dynamic, which we can better appreciate when we look at its organization from the perspective of systems biology. Let's consider a football analogy. A living cell is less like a football field—with goalposts, lines, and turf—and more like the players who follow rules and have various formations and movements. Like the players in a football game, the components of a cell are dynamic entities. Like a successful team, these components work together as a system to maintain cell organization and carry out vital functions.

We begin this section by considering the phenomena that underlie the existence of cells. These include information, namely, a genome, functional molecules, and pre-existing organization. We will then examine how the genome allows cells to synthesize proteins at the correct time and in the correct cell type. Likewise, the genome provides proteins with sorting signals that are recognized by a sorting system, which directs them to the proper cellular location. This system, which is critical for cell organization, will be described in later sections.

Another factor that underlies cell organization is the ability of certain proteins to interact with each other to form larger complexes, sometimes called molecular machines. We will examine how molecular machines assemble from their individual components, and how they carry out complex functions and provide cell organization. Finally, the organization of living cells is a dynamic process that involves the turnover of cellular molecules and macromolecules. We will also explore how macromolecules such as proteins are broken down to their building blocks so that a cell can continually replenish its macromolecules.

Information, Functional Molecules, and Organization Must Already Exist for Cells to Maintain Their Structure

As discussed in Chapter 22, the first primitive cells arose from nonliving materials between 3.5 and 4.0 billion years ago. According to the cell doctrine, *all modern cells come from pre-existing cells by division.* Modern cells, which are much more complex than the first primitive cells, can grow, adapt, and modify their organization, but they do not arise spontaneously from nonliving materials. At least three key factors are responsible for this principle. First, all cells must possess a genome, which provides the information to make RNA and proteins. The genomes of modern species are the products of 3.5–4.0 billion years of evolution and contain the information to make the thousands of proteins necessary to maintain cell structure and function.

Even so, if a researcher were able to synthesize the genome of a living organism and put it in a test tube full of water, nothing would happen. Living cells require a second ingredient— pre-existing molecules such as enzymes and organic molecules— to make things happen. For instance, RNA polymerase, a protein that functions as an enzyme, is needed to make new RNA molecules, using nucleotides (organic molecules) as building blocks and DNA as a template. As another example, RNA molecules and proteins are needed to construct a ribosome, which is a critical component for synthesizing polypeptides. Cell vitality requires a genome to provide information and also active molecules such as RNA, proteins, and small molecules to access that information.

So let's suppose that a researcher could somehow synthesize the genome of a species and produce all of its RNA molecules and proteins. That would be an amazing feat! If the genome, RNAs, and proteins were combined in a test tube with other small molecules that are needed for energy and as building blocks, do you think a cell would arise? The answer is no. Some enzymatic activity would probably occur, but a living cell would not result. In addition to a genome and functional molecules, cells require a third key factor: pre-existing organization. For example, cells rely on a plasma membrane, which contains multiple transport proteins that allow the selective uptake and excretion of ions and molecules. In addition, organelles compartmentalize cells, and most organelles must be made from pre-existing organelles.

Thus, the formation of cells relies on a genome, functional molecules, and organization, all of which come from pre-existing cells. In the rest of this chapter, we will examine the interplay that occurs among these three phenomena to maintain cellular organization and promote the formation of cells.

Cell Organization Relies on Genetic Information, Which Produces a Proteome

The genome of every organism contains the information necessary to produce a system of RNA and protein molecules that provides the foundation for cell structure, function, and organization. An important paradigm in biology is that "structure determines function." The information in most genes is used to make mRNA molecules that encode the amino acid sequences of proteins. The amino acid sequence of proteins, together with chemical principles, governs their three-dimensional structure. The three-dimensional structure of proteins, in turn, determines their function.

Although the genome contains the information to make proteins with specific structures and functions, the study of individual proteins does not allow us to completely understand how the parts of cells are made, and how they maintain cellular organization. To appreciate the dynamic form and function of living cells, we need to take a broader, more integrative look at their molecular components.

1. *The proteome—the entire collection of proteins that a cell makes—is largely responsible for the structures and functions of living cells* (**Figure 6.1a**). Some proteins play a role in cell shape and organization. Other proteins and a few RNA molecules function as enzymes to synthesize or break down other cellular components. For example, as discussed later in this chapter, phospholipids are made by enzymes in the cell. The synthesis of most components that form the foundation for cell structure relies on enzymes. Some exceptions are water and inorganic ions, which are taken up from the environment. Likewise, transport proteins are important in the uptake and export of ions and molecules across cell membranes. Finally, the activities of cells are controlled by many proteins that are generally known as regulatory proteins. As described next, some of these proteins regulate genes in the cell nucleus, while others regulate the functions of other proteins.

2. *Gene and protein regulation cause the proteome to be dynamic.* In multicellular organisms, the regulation of genes causes the amounts of proteins to vary in different cell types. This allows a multicellular organism to have cells with specialized structures and functions (**Figure 6.1b**). Nerve and muscle cells have a different organization because their proteomes are different. In addition, the regulation of genes and proteins allows a cell to respond in a dynamic way to changes in the environment (**Figure 6.1c**). For example, when a cell is exposed to a higher temperature, it will produce proteins that help it cope with the increased heat.

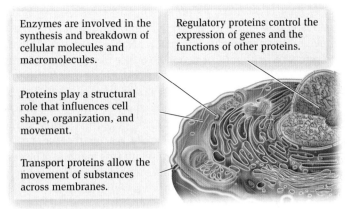

Enzymes are involved in the synthesis and breakdown of cellular molecules and macromolecules.

Regulatory proteins control the expression of genes and the functions of other proteins.

Proteins play a structural role that influences cell shape, organization, and movement.

Transport proteins allow the movement of substances across membranes.

(a) The proteome is a diverse collection of proteins that carry out cell functions and promote cell organization.

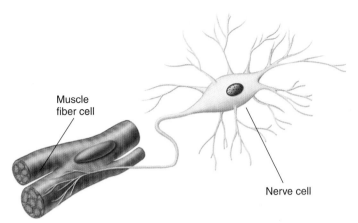

Muscle fiber cell

Nerve cell

(b) Differences in cell morphology among specialized cells can be attributed to differences in the proteome.

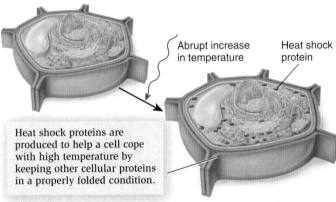

Abrupt increase in temperature

Heat shock protein

Heat shock proteins are produced to help a cell cope with high temperature by keeping other cellular proteins in a properly folded condition.

(c) Cells adapt to environmental changes by altering the composition of their proteomes.

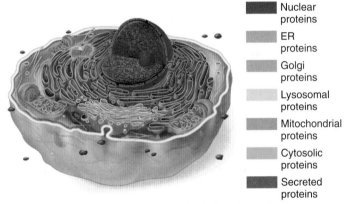

Nuclear proteins

ER proteins

Golgi proteins

Lysosomal proteins

Mitochondrial proteins

Cytosolic proteins

Secreted proteins

(d) Proteins have sorting signals within their amino acid sequences that direct them to the correct cellular compartment.

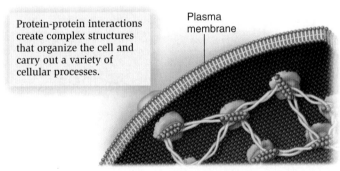

Protein-protein interactions create complex structures that organize the cell and carry out a variety of cellular processes.

Plasma membrane

(e) Proteins may have surfaces that cause them to interlock via protein-protein interactions to form larger cellular structures.

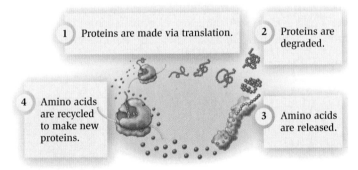

1 Proteins are made via translation.

2 Proteins are degraded.

4 Amino acids are recycled to make new proteins.

3 Amino acids are released.

(f) Cellular macromolecules are made and later broken down to recycle their building blocks.

Figure 6.1   Genomes and proteomes and their relationship to cell structure, function, and organization.

3. *Proteins have **sorting signals**—short amino acid sequences in their structure—that direct them to their correct location* (**Figure 6.1d**). For example, one sorting signal directs certain proteins to the mitochondria while a different sorting signal sends other proteins to the endoplasmic reticulum. The last two sections of this chapter will explore the molecular mechanisms that facilitate protein sorting, a key event that maintains cell organization.

4. *Because their structures may bind to each other and interlock, proteins often undergo **protein-protein interactions**.* These interactions are very specific and can build larger structures that provide organization to the cell (**Figure 6.1e**). An example is the cytoskeleton that forms filaments in the cell. In addition, protein-protein interactions can produce molecular machines that carry out complex cellular functions.

5. *Because most molecules and macromolecules in cells are short-lived, cells must continually synthesize new components and break down unwanted components.* Proteins, for example, are made during the process of translation and typically exist for just several minutes or a few hours (**Figure 6.1f**). As discussed later, cells have different mechanisms to degrade proteins to individual amino acids so that the amino acids can be recycled— that is, used to make new proteins.

Interactions Among Proteins and RNA Molecules Make Complex Molecular Machines

A machine is an object that has moving parts and does useful work. If the size of the machine is measured in nanometers, it is appropriately called a **molecular machine**. Even a single protein could be considered a molecular machine if it undergoes conformational changes as part of its function. The association of proteins with each other and also with RNA molecules may form larger molecular machines. These machines provide structure and organization to cells and enable them to carry out complicated processes.

Large molecular machines are formed by an assembly process. In some cases, interactions between the protein components of a machine may occur spontaneously, without requiring an input of energy. Sometimes additional proteins are needed for the machine to form but are not retained in its final structure. Some machines may require an input of energy, such as from ATP hydrolysis, to promote the assembly process.

Figure 6.2 describes the assembly of ATP synthase, a machine that makes ATP. Because all living organisms use ATP for energy, ATP synthase is found in both prokaryotes and eukaryotes. ATP synthase is composed of eight different protein subunits called *a*, *b*, *c*, alpha (α), beta (β), gamma (γ), delta (δ),

and epsilon (ϵ). The *a*, *b*, and *c* subunits are transmembrane proteins, found either in the bacterial plasma membrane or the mitochondrial and thylakoid membranes of eukaryotes. Nine to twelve of the *c* subunits assemble together to form a ring in the membrane, and one *a* subunit and two *b* subunits bind to this ring. The α, β, γ, δ, and ϵ subunits associate with each other to form a complex of three α subunits, three β subunits, and one subunit each of γ, δ, and ϵ. This complex then binds to the membrane components to complete the assembly process.

Why does ATP synthase assemble in this manner? The reason is **molecular recognition**—surfaces on the various protein subunits recognize each other in a very specific way, causing them to bind to each other and promote the assembly process. Said another way, the amino acid sequences of these proteins produce surfaces that fold in a way that causes the proteins to interlock. Thus, the amino acid sequences of proteins, which are stored in the genome, contain the information for protein-protein interactions.

Molecular machines carry out complex cellular functions. The ribosome (**Figure 6.3a**), a molecular machine composed of

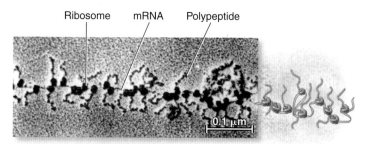

(a) **Ribosomes in the act of making polypeptides**

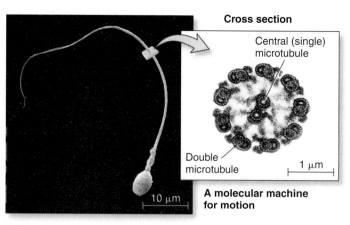

(b) **The flagella of sperm contain a molecular machine for locomotion**

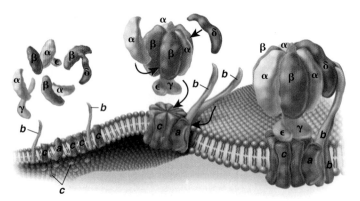

Figure 6.2   Assembly of a molecular machine, the ATP synthase found in bacteria, mitochondria, and chloroplasts. Nine to twelve of the *c* subunits form a ring in the membrane, and one *a* subunit and two *b* subunits bind to the ring. The α, β, γ, δ, and ϵ subunits form a complex of three α subunits, three β subunits, and one subunit each of γ, δ, and ε. This complex binds to the membrane components.

Biological inquiry: Explain why the ATP synthase assembles the way it does.

Figure 6.3   Other examples of molecular machines. **(a)** The ribosome, which plays a role in protein synthesis, is composed of many types of proteins and several large RNA molecules. In the electron micrograph shown here, many ribosomes are gliding along an mRNA molecule, synthesizing polypeptides as they go. **(b)** The flagellum of a sperm contains a molecular machine composed of microtubules and accessory proteins. The cross section shows the 9 + 2 arrangement of microtubules in which nine double microtubules form a ring with two central microtubules that are single microtublules.

many types of proteins and several large RNA molecules, functions as a molecular arena for the synthesis of new polypeptides. The flagellum (**Figure 6.3b**) is a molecular machine composed of microtubules, motor proteins, and many other proteins that enables eukaryotic cells, such as sperm cells, to move.

Molecular machines are also vital in promoting cell organization. Perhaps the most important example is the cytoskeleton, which we consider next.

The Cytoskeleton Is a Molecular Machine That Organizes the Cell and Directs Cellular Movements

Recall from Chapter 4 that the cytoskeleton plays a key role in cell organization and many of the dynamic processes that maintain it. For example, in many cell types, actin filaments form a band just inside the plasma membrane that provides mechanical strength and plays a role in cell shape. Protein-protein interactions occur between actin and many other cellular proteins. Actin filaments are sometimes linked to proteins that are embedded in the plasma membrane, an important factor in the shape of many cells such as the biconcave-disk appearance of human red blood cells (**Figure 6.4**).

The cytoskeleton also organizes and directs intracellular and cellular movements. For example, various types of intracellular cargo, including chromosomes and even organelles such as mitochondria and chloroplasts, are transported within the cell by moving along microtubules and actin filaments. For instance, chloroplasts are sometimes moved to the side of a plant cell that receives more light. **Figure 6.5** illustrates how a **vesicle**—a small, membrane-enclosed sac—moves along microtubules in a nerve cell. In this example, accessory proteins connect a motor protein to the vesicle. The motor protein uses the energy from ATP hydrolysis to "walk" along a microtubule.

Molecules Are Broken Down and Their Building Blocks Are Recycled

Thus far, we have considered how the interactions of cellular components provide organization and complex functions to living cells. The maintenance of cell organization is a dynamic process. Except for DNA, which is stably maintained and inherited from cell to cell, other large molecules such as RNA, proteins, lipids, and polysaccharides have finite lifetimes. Biologists often speak of the **half-life** of molecules, which is the time it takes for 50% of the molecules to be broken down and recycled. For example, a population of mRNA molecules in prokaryotes has an average half-life of about 5 minutes, while mRNAs in eukaryotes tend to exist for longer periods of time, on the order of 30 minutes to 24 hours or even several days.

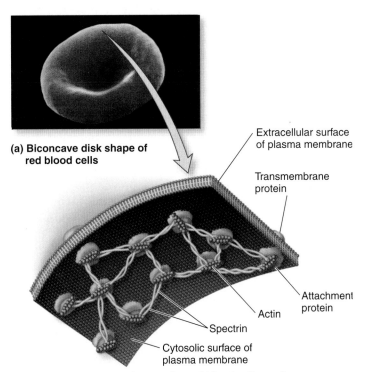

(a) Biconcave disk shape of red blood cells

(b) Cytoskeletal connections to the red blood cell membrane

Figure 6.4 Role of the cytoskeleton in promoting cell shape.   Many different proteins are involved in forming the shape of a cell. **(a)** A micrograph of a red blood cell, which looks like a biconcave disk. **(b)** To create this shape, proteins within the red blood cell membrane are anchored to an intricate group of cytoskeletal proteins including actin and spectrin.

Biological inquiry: Describe the types of protein-protein interactions that produce the biconcave-disk shape of red blood cells.

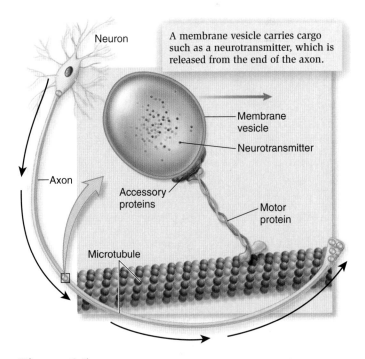

Figure 6.5 Movement of a membrane vesicle along a microtubule.   In this example, a motor protein walks along a microtubule in the axon of a nerve cell. The vesicle carries a neurotransmitter, which is released at the end of the axon. Accessory proteins link the motor protein to the vesicle and also control the activity of the motor protein.

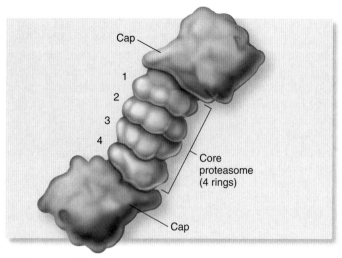

(a) Structure of the eukaryotic proteasome

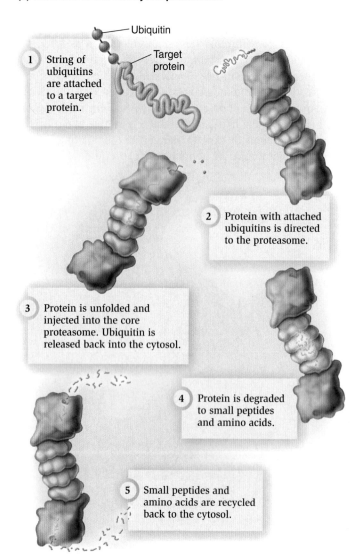

(b) Steps of protein degradation in eukaryotic cells

Figure 6.6   Protein degradation via the proteasome.

The breakdown of large, cellular molecules and the recycling of their building blocks occur by a variety of mechanisms. As discussed in Chapter 4, lysosomes can degrade materials in the cytosol by a process called autophagy (refer back to Figure 4.20). The components of a mitochondrion, for example, can be degraded in this manner, and building blocks are returned to the cytosol, where they can be used to make new macromolecules. Lysosomes also degrade proteins that are imported into the cell via endocytosis. In addition, cytosolic enzymes break down RNA, polysaccharides, and lipids into smaller building blocks. For example, ribonucleases are enzymes that degrade mRNA molecules.

To survive and respond to environmental changes, cells must continually degrade proteins that are faulty or nonfunctional and synthesize new ones. To be degraded, proteins are recognized by **proteases**—enzymes that cleave the bonds between adjacent amino acids. Although lysosomes in eukaryotic cells are involved in protein breakdown via autophagy and endocytosis, the primary pathway for protein degradation in archaea and eukaryotic cells is via a molecular machine called a **proteasome**. The core of the proteasome is formed from four stacked rings, each composed of seven protein subunits (**Figure 6.6a**). The proteasomes of eukaryotic cells also contain cap structures at each end that control the entry of proteins into the proteasome.

In eukaryotic cells, unwanted proteins are directed to a proteasome by the covalent attachment of a small protein called **ubiquitin**. **Figure 6.6b** describes the steps of protein degradation via eukaryotic proteasomes. First, a string of ubiquitin proteins are attached to the target protein. This event directs the protein to a proteasome cap, which has binding sites for ubiquitin. The cap also has enzymes that unfold the protein and inject it into the internal cavity of the proteasome core. The ubiquitin proteins are removed during entry and return to the cytosol. Inside the proteasome, proteases degrade the protein into small peptides and amino acids. The process is completed when the peptides and amino acids are recycled back into the cytosol. The amino acids can be used to make new proteins.

Ubiquitin-targeting has two advantages. First, the enzymes that attach ubiquitin to its target recognize improperly folded proteins, allowing cells to identify and degrade nonfunctional components. Second, changes in cellular conditions may warrant the rapid breakdown of particular proteins. For example, cell division requires a series of stages called the cell cycle, which depends on the degradation of specific proteins. Ubiquitin targeting directs these proteins to the proteasome for degradation.

Eukaryotic Cells Are a System of Four Interacting Parts That Work Together

We can view a eukaryotic cell as a system of four interacting parts: the interior of the nucleus, the cytosol, the endomembrane system, and the semiautonomous organelles (**Figure 6.7**). These four regions play a role in their own structure and organization, as well as the structure and organization of the entire cell.

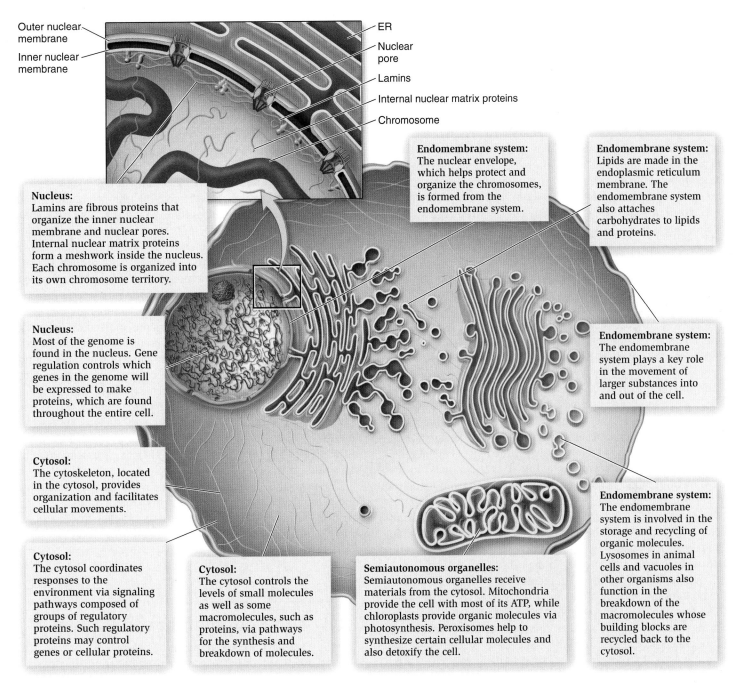

Outer nuclear membrane

Inner nuclear membrane

ER

Nuclear pore

Lamins

Internal nuclear matrix proteins

Chromosome

Endomembrane system: The nuclear envelope, which helps protect and organize the chromosomes, is formed from the endomembrane system.

Endomembrane system: Lipids are made in the endoplasmic reticulum membrane. The endomembrane system also attaches carbohydrates to lipids and proteins.

Nucleus: Lamins are fibrous proteins that organize the inner nuclear membrane and nuclear pores. Internal nuclear matrix proteins form a meshwork inside the nucleus. Each chromosome is organized into its own chromosome territory.

Nucleus: Most of the genome is found in the nucleus. Gene regulation controls which genes in the genome will be expressed to make proteins, which are found throughout the entire cell.

Endomembrane system: The endomembrane system plays a key role in the movement of larger substances into and out of the cell.

Cytosol: The cytoskeleton, located in the cytosol, provides organization and facilitates cellular movements.

Cytosol: The cytosol coordinates responses to the environment via signaling pathways composed of groups of regulatory proteins. Such regulatory proteins may control genes or cellular proteins.

Cytosol: The cytosol controls the levels of small molecules as well as some macromolecules, such as proteins, via pathways for the synthesis and breakdown of molecules.

Semiautonomous organelles: Semiautonomous organelles receive materials from the cytosol. Mitochondria provide the cell with most of its ATP, while chloroplasts provide organic molecules via photosynthesis. Peroxisomes help to synthesize certain cellular molecules and also detoxify the cell.

Endomembrane system: The endomembrane system is involved in the storage and recycling of organic molecules. Lysosomes in animal cells and vacuoles in other organisms also function in the breakdown of the macromolecules whose building blocks are recycled back to the cytosol.

Figure 6.7   **The four interacting parts of eukaryotic cells.**   These include the nucleus, cytosol, endomembrane system, and semiautonomous organelles.

Nucleus The nucleus houses the genome. Earlier in this chapter, we learned how the genome plays a key role in producing the proteome. The collection of proteins that a cell makes is largely responsible for the structure and function of the entire cell. Gene regulation, which occurs in the cell nucleus, is very important in creating specific cell types and enabling cells to respond to environmental changes. Chapters 12 and 13 will examine the topics of gene expression and regulation in greater detail.

The nucleus itself is organized by a collection of filamentous proteins called the nuclear matrix (see inset to Figure 6.7). These proteins form extensive protein-protein interactions that perform two roles. First, proteins known as lamins lie along the nuclear envelope and help to organize the inner nuclear membrane and nuclear pores. Second, internal nuclear matrix proteins form a meshwork inside the nucleus. Each chromosome is organized into its own chromosome territory (refer back to Figure 4.17).

Cytosol The cytosol is the region that is outside of the organelles and inside the plasma membrane. It is an important coordination center for cell function and organization. Along with the plasma membrane, the cytosol coordinates responses to the environment. Factors in the environment may stimulate signaling pathways in the cytosol that affect the functions of cellular proteins and change the expression of genes in the cell nucleus.

The cytosol also has a large impact on cell structure because it is the compartment where many small molecules are metabolized in the cell. The region receives molecules that are taken up from the environment. In addition, many pathways for the synthesis and breakdown of cellular molecules are found in the cytosol, and pathways in organelles are often regulated by events there.

A particularly important component of cell organization is the cytoskeleton, which is found in the cytosol. The formation and function of the cytoskeleton is caused by an amazing series of protein-protein interactions. As discussed earlier, the cytoskeleton provides organization to the cell and facilitates cellular movements. In most cells, the cytoskeleton is a dynamic structure, enabling its composition to respond to environmental and developmental changes.

Endomembrane System The endomembrane system can be viewed as a smaller system within the confines of a cell, which is a larger system. The endomembrane system includes the nuclear envelope, endoplasmic reticulum (ER), Golgi apparatus, lysosomes, vacuoles, secretory vesicles, and plasma membrane. This system forms a **secretory pathway** that is crucial in the movement of larger substances, such as proteins and carbohydrates out of the cell. The export of proteins and carbohydrates plays a key role in the organization of materials that surround cells. The structure of this extracellular matrix is discussed in Chapter 10. This pathway can also run in reverse, the **endocytic pathway**, to take substances into the cell.

A key feature of the endomembrane system is that the membranes are very dynamic and their structures change over time. In some cases, the change can be dramatic. For example, during cell division, the nuclear envelope breaks up into membrane vesicles, thereby allowing the release of chromosomes into the cytosol so they can be sorted to daughter cells. Later, vesicles coalesce to re-form a nuclear envelope in each daughter cell. The ability of the nuclear envelope to break up into vesicles and later re-form a nuclear envelope is a vital feature of cell division in eukaryotic cells.

The endomembrane system also contributes to the overall structure and organization of eukaryotic cells in other ways. Most of a cell's lipids are made in the endoplasmic reticulum membrane and distributed to other parts of the cell. In addition, the endomembrane system attaches carbohydrates to lipids and proteins. This process plays a role in protein sorting, and also helps to organize the materials that are found outside of cells.

Finally, another important function of the endomembrane system that serves the needs of the entire cell is the storage and recycling of organic molecules. Vacuoles often play a role in the storage of organic molecules such as proteins, carbohydrates, and fats. When needed, lysosomes in animal cells and vacuoles in the cells of other organisms also assist in breaking down these macromolecules. The building blocks are then recycled back to the cytosol and used to construct new macromolecules.

Semiautonomous Organelles The semiautonomous organelles include the mitochondria, chloroplasts, and peroxisomes. Regarding organization, these organelles tend to be rather independent. They exist in the cytosol much like a bacterium would grow in a laboratory medium. While a bacterium would take up essential nutrients from the growth medium, the semiautonomous organelles take up molecules from the cytosol. The organelles use these molecules to carry out their functions and maintain their organization. Like bacteria, the semiautonomous organelles divide by binary fission to produce more of themselves.

Although the semiautonomous organelles rely on the rest of the cell for many of their key components, they also give back to the cell in ways that are vital to maintaining cell organization. Mitochondria take up organic molecules from the cytosol and give back ATP, which is used throughout the cell to drive processes that are energetically unfavorable. This energy is crucial for cell organization. The chloroplasts capture light energy and synthesize organic molecules. These organic molecules also store energy and can be broken down when energy is needed. In addition, organic molecules, such as sugars and amino acids, are used as building blocks to synthesize many different types of cellular molecules, such as carbohydrate polymers and proteins.

Later in this chapter, we will focus on how mitochondria and chloroplasts are made and how they maintain their distinct organization. The functions of these organelles involve many interesting pathways that are described in greater detail in Chapters 7 and 8, respectively.

6.2 The Endomembrane System

Thus far, we have examined some of the general features that account for the maintenance of cell organization. In this section, we will take a closer look at the organization of the endomembrane system. As mentioned earlier, this system is a collection of membranes and cell compartments in eukaryotic cells that includes the nuclear envelope, endoplasmic reticulum (ER), Golgi apparatus, lysosomes, vacuoles, secretory vesicles, and plasma membrane (**Figure 6.8**). The intracellular organelles of the endomembrane system reside in the cytosol. The system is impressively dynamic. Much of its activity is related to the transport of membrane vesicles between the various compartments. Transport of vesicles occurs in both directions. For example, membrane vesicles bud from the ER and fuse with the Golgi, and vesicles from the Golgi can return to the ER. As we learned in Chapter 5, exocytosis involves the fusion of intracellular vesicles with the plasma membrane, while endocytosis

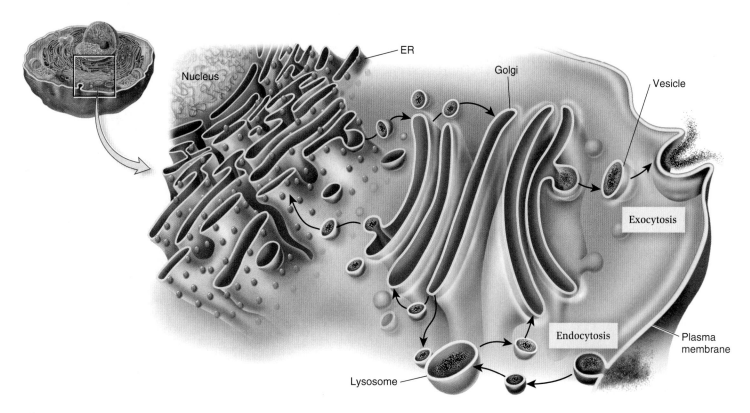

Figure 6.8 **The dynamic nature of the endomembrane system.**   Vesicle transport occurs in both directions, allowing materials to be shared among the various membranes and compartments of the endomembrane system.

involves the inward folding of the plasma membrane to form intracellular vesicles.

The endomembrane system is critical for lipid synthesis, protein synthesis and sorting, and the attachment of carbohydrates to lipids and proteins. Its dynamic nature serves to distribute these materials throughout the cell, modify them for use inside the cell, or process them for secretion to be used outside the cell. The past few decades have seen exciting advances in our understanding of how these events occur at the molecular level. In this section, we will examine the roles of the endomembrane system in cell structure, function, and organization.

Lipid Synthesis Occurs at the ER Membrane

In eukaryotic cells, the cytosol and endomembrane system work together to synthesize most lipids. This process occurs at the cytosolic leaflet of the ER membrane. **Figure 6.9** shows a simplified pathway for the synthesis of phospholipids, the main components of cell and organelle membranes. The building blocks for a phospholipid are two fatty acids each with an acyl tail, one glycerol molecule, one phosphate, and a polar group. These building blocks are made via enzymes in the cytosol or they are taken into cells from the diet. To begin the process of phospholipid synthesis, the fatty acids are activated by attachment to an organic molecule called coenzyme A (CoA). This acti-

vation promotes the bonding of the two fatty acids to a glycerol-phosphate molecule, and the resulting molecule is inserted into the cytosolic leaflet of the ER membrane. The phosphate is removed from glycerol, and then a polar molecule that is linked to phosphate is attached to glycerol. In this example, the polar head group contains choline, but many other types are possible. Phospholipids are initially made in the cytosolic leaflet, but flippases in the ER membrane transfer some to the other leaflet.

The lipids that are made in the ER membrane can be transferred to other membranes in the cell by a variety of mechanisms. Phospholipids in the ER can diffuse laterally to the nuclear envelope (**Figure 6.10a**). In addition, lipids can be transported through the cytosol via vesicles to the Golgi, lysosomes, vacuoles, and plasma membrane (**Figure 6.10b**). A third mode of lipid movement involves **lipid exchange proteins**, which extract a lipid from one membrane, diffuse through the cell, and insert the lipid into another membrane (**Figure 6.10c**). Such transfer can occur between any two membranes, even between the endomembrane system and semiautonomous organelles. For example, lipid exchange proteins can transfer lipids between the ER and mitochondria. In addition, chloroplasts and mitochondria can synthesize certain types of lipids that can be transferred from these organelles to other cellular membranes via lipid exchange proteins.

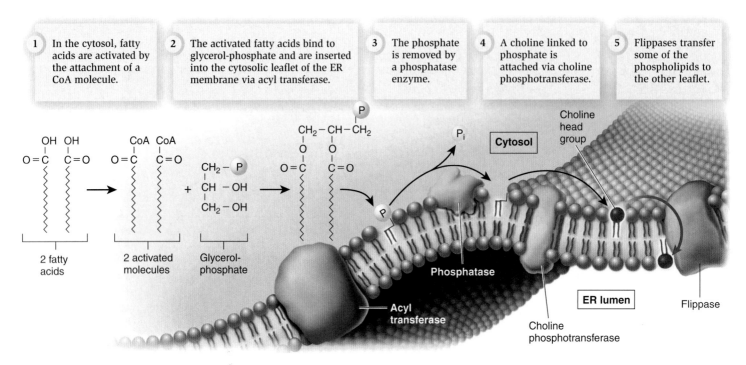

Figure 6.9   A simplified pathway for the synthesis of membrane phospholipids at the ER membrane.

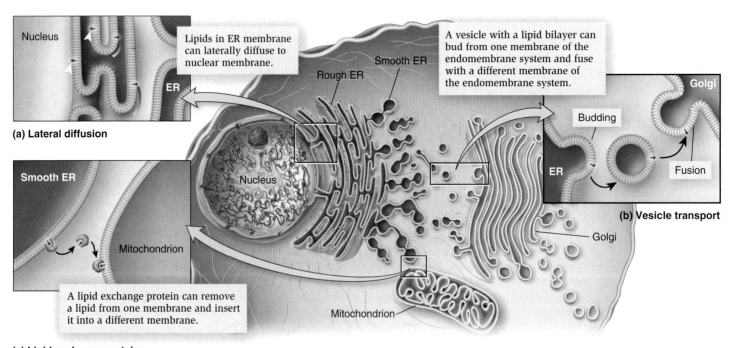

Figure 6.10   **Mechanisms of lipid transfer throughout a eukaryotic cell.**   As shown in the insets, lipids can be distributed throughout the cell in various ways. **(a)** Lateral diffusion occurs between the ER and nuclear envelope. **(b)** Vesicle transport occurs among the membranes of the endomembrane system. **(c)** Lipid exchange proteins can transfer lipids between any two membranes, such as between the ER and a mitochondrion.

FEATURE INVESTIGATION

Palade Demonstrated That Secreted Proteins Move Sequentially Through Organelles of the Endomembrane System

Eukaryotic cells make thousands of different proteins. In most cases, a protein functions in only one compartment within a cell, or it functions only after it is secreted from the cell. Therefore, proteins must be sorted to the correct locations. One of the first indications that proteins are sorted intracellularly came from studies by George Palade and his collaborators in the 1960s.

Palade's team conducted **pulse-chase experiments**, in which the researchers administered a pulse of radioactive amino acids to cells so that they made radioactive proteins. A few minutes later, the cells were given a large amount of non-radioactive amino acids. This is called a "chase" because it chases away the ability of the cells to make any more radioactive proteins. In this way, radioactive proteins were produced only briefly. Because they were labeled with radioactivity, the fate of these proteins could be monitored over time. The goal of a pulse-chase experiment is to determine where the radioactive proteins are produced and the pathways they take as they travel through a cell.

Palade chose to study the cells of the pancreas. This organ secretes enzymes and protein hormones that play a role in digestion. Therefore, these cells were chosen because their primary activity is protein secretion. To study the pathway for protein secretion, Palade and colleagues injected a radioactive version of the amino acid leucine into the bloodstream of guinea pigs, followed 3 minutes later by an injection of non-radioactive leucine (**Figure 6.11**). At various times after the second injection, samples of pancreatic cells were removed from the animals. The cells were then prepared for transmission electron microscopy (see Chapter 4). The sample was stained with a heavy metal that became bound to membranes and showed the locations of the cell organelles. In addition, the sample was coated with a radiation-sensitive emulsion. When radiation was emitted from radioactive proteins, it interacted with the emulsion in a way that caused the precipitation of silver atoms, which became tightly bound to the sample. In this way, the precipitated silver atoms marked the location of the radiolabeled proteins. Unprecipitated silver chloride in the emulsion was later washed away. Because silver atoms are electron dense, they produce dark spots in a transmission electron micrograph. Therefore, dark spots revealed the locations of radioactive proteins.

Figure 6.11   Palade's use of the pulse-chase method to study protein secretion.

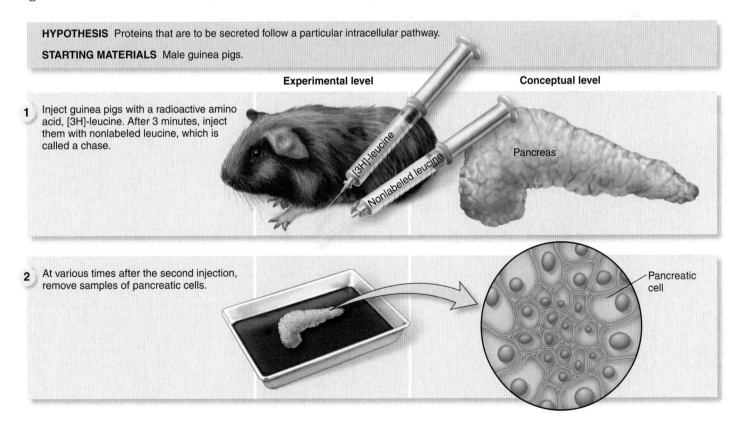

HYPOTHESIS Proteins that are to be secreted follow a particular intracellular pathway.

STARTING MATERIALS Male guinea pigs.

Experimental level   Conceptual level

1 Inject guinea pigs with a radioactive amino acid, [3H]-leucine. After 3 minutes, inject them with nonlabeled leucine, which is called a chase.

[3H]-leucine
Nonlabeled leucine
Pancreas

2 At various times after the second injection, remove samples of pancreatic cells.

Pancreatic cell

3 Stain the sample with osmium tetroxide, which is a heavy metal that binds to membranes.

Osmium tetroxide

Sample from pancreas

4 Cut thin sections of the samples, and place a thin layer of radiation-sensitive emulsion over the sample. Allow time for radioactive emission from radiolabeled proteins to precipitate silver atoms in the emulsion.

Thin section

Add photoemulsion

5 Observe the sample under a transmisson electron microscope.

See Chapter 4 for a description of TEM.

6 THE DATA

Nucleus

ER

Golgi

Secretory vesicles

Time after chase

5 min

Rough ER

Nucleus

Labeled proteins

5 minutes after chase

15 min

>30 min

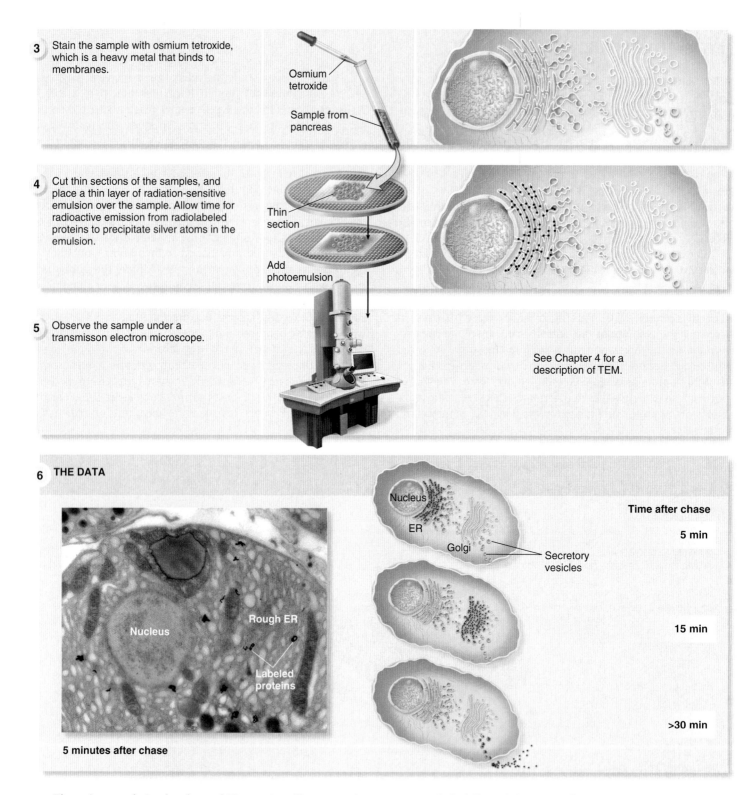

The micrograph in the data of Figure 6.11 illustrates the results that were observed 5 minutes after the completion of the pulse-chase injections. Very dark objects, namely radioactive proteins, were observed in the rough ER. As shown schematically to the right of the actual data, later time points indicated that the radioactive proteins moved from the ER to the Golgi, and then to secretory vesicles near the plasma membrane. In this way, Palade followed the intracellular pathway of protein movement. His experiments provided the first evidence that secreted proteins were synthesized into the rough ER and moved through a series of cellular compartments before they were secreted. These findings caused researchers to wonder how proteins are targeted to particular organelles and how they move from one compartment to another. These topics are described next.

Protein Localization Involves Sorting Signals and Vesicle Transport

Since Palade's pioneering studies, scientists have learned a great deal about the localization of proteins. The process of evolution has produced a proteome in every organism in which each type of protein functions in a particular cellular compartment or performs its role after being secreted from the cell. For example, acid hydrolases function in the lysosome to degrade macromolecules. In eukaryotes, most proteins contain short stretches of amino acid sequences that direct them to their correct cellular location. These sequences are called **sorting signals** or **traffic signals**. Each sorting signal is recognized by specific cellular components that facilitate the proper routing of that protein. **Table 6.1** describes the sorting signals found in proteins that are destined for the nucleus, endomembrane system, or secretion. We will consider the signals involved in semiautonomous organelles later in this chapter.

Most eukaryotic proteins begin their synthesis on ribosomes in the cytosol. The cytosol provides amino acids, which are used as building blocks to make these proteins. The synthesis of a protein, a process called translation, is completed in the cytosol for those proteins destined for the cytosol, nucleus, mitochondria, chloroplasts, or peroxisomes. Cytosolic proteins lack any sorting signal, so they stay there. By comparison, the uptake of proteins into the nucleus, mitochondria, chloroplasts, and peroxisomes occurs after the protein is completely made (that is, completely translated). This is called **post-translational sorting** because sorting does not happen until translation is finished. We will examine the uptake of proteins into the mitochondrion later in the chapter. By comparison, the synthesis of other eukaryotic proteins begins in the cytosol and then halts temporarily until the ribosome has become bound to the ER membrane. After this occurs, translation resumes and the polypeptide is synthesized into the ER lumen or ER membrane. Proteins that are destined for the ER, Golgi, lysosome, vacuole, plasma membrane, or secretion are first directed to the ER. This is **cotranslational sorting** because the first step in the sorting process begins while translation is occurring.

The concept of sorting signals in proteins was first proposed by Günter Blobel in the 1970s. Blobel and colleagues discovered a sorting signal in proteins that sends them to the ER membrane, which is the first step in cotranslational sorting (**Figure 6.12**). To be directed to the rough ER membrane, a polypeptide must contain a sorting signal called an **ER signal sequence**, which is usually located near the amino terminus. As the ribosome is making the polypeptide in the cytosol, the ER signal sequence emerges from the ribosome and is recognized by a protein/RNA complex called a **signal recognition particle (SRP)**. The SRP has two functions. First, it recognizes the ER signal sequence and pauses translation. Second, SRP binds to a receptor in the ER membrane, which docks the ribosome over a channel. At this stage, SRP is released and translation resumes. The growing polypeptide is threaded through the channel to cross the ER membrane. In most cases, the ER signal sequence is removed by signal peptidase. If the protein is not a membrane protein, it will be released into the lumen of the ER. In 1999, Blobel won the Nobel Prize for his discovery of sorting signals in proteins. It is worth noting that the process shown in Figure 6.12 illustrates another important role of protein-protein interactions—a series of interactions causes the steps of a process to occur in a specific order.

Some proteins are meant to function in the ER. Such proteins contain ER retention signals in addition to the ER signal sequence. Alternatively, other proteins that are destined for the Golgi, lysosomes, vacuoles, plasma membrane, or secretion must be sorted to these other locations. Such proteins leave the ER and are transported to their correct location. This transport process occurs via membrane vesicles that are formed from one compartment and then move through the cytosol and fuse with another compartment. Vesicles from the ER may go to the Golgi, and then vesicles from the Golgi may go to the lysosomes, vacuoles, or plasma membrane. Sorting signals within their amino acid sequences are responsible for directing them to their correct location.

Table 6.1	Sorting Signals of Proteins That Are Destined for the Nucleus, Endomembrane System, or Secretion
Type of signal	**Description**
Nuclear-localization signal	Can be located almost anywhere in the polypeptide sequence. The signal sequence is four to eight amino acids in length and contains several positively charged residues and usually one or more prolines.
ER signal	A sequence of about 6 to 12 amino acids near the amino terminus that is composed of mostly nonpolar amino acids.
ER retention signal	A sequence of four amino acids, lysine-aspartic acid-glutamic acid-leucine, located at the carboxyl terminus of the protein.
Golgi retention signal	A sequence of 20 hydrophobic amino acids that form a transmembrane segment flanked by positively charged residues.
Lysosome-sorting signal	A grouping of amino acids in the tertiary structure of of a polypeptide. Positively charged residues within this grouping are thought to play an important role. This grouping causes lysosomal proteins to be covalently modified to contain a mannose-6-phosphate residue (a carbohydrate), which directs the protein to the lysosome.

Destination of a cellular protein	Type of signal the protein contains within its amino acid sequence
Nucleus	Nuclear-localization signal.
ER	ER signal and an ER retention signal.
Golgi	ER signal and a Golgi retention signal.
Lysosome	ER signal and a lysosomal sorting signal.
Plasma membrane	ER signal and a hydrophobic transmembrane domain that anchors it in the membrane.
Secretion	ER signal. No additional signal required.

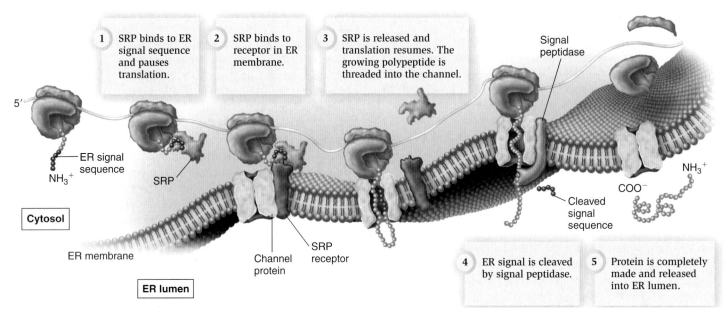

Figure 6.12   First step in cotranslational protein localization: cotranslational sorting.

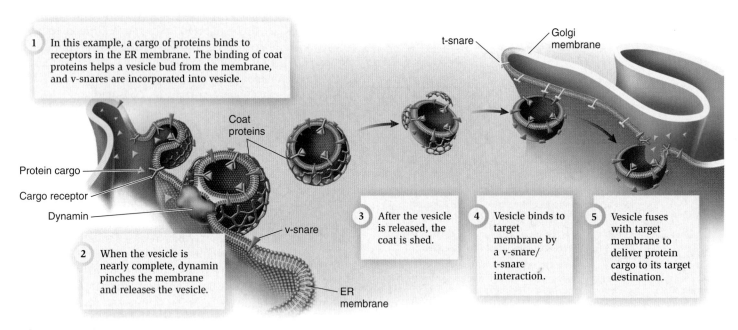

Figure 6.13   Second step in cotranslational protein localization: vesicle transport from the endoplasmic reticulum.

Figure 6.13 describes vesicle transport from the ER to the Golgi. A cargo, such as soluble protein molecules, is loaded into a developing vesicle by binding to cargo receptors in the ER membrane. Vesicle formation is facilitated by **coat proteins**, which help a vesicle to bud from a given membrane. As a vesicle forms, other proteins called **v-snares** are incorporated into the vesicle membrane, hence the name v-snare. Many types of v-snares are known to exist; the particular v-snare that is found in a vesicle membrane depends on the type of cargo that it carries. Finally, a protein called dynamin pinches the membrane and releases the vesicle. After a vesicle is released from one compartment such as the ER, the coat is shed. The vesicle then travels through the cytosol. But how does the vesicle know where to go? The answer is that the v-snares in the vesicle membrane are recognized by **t-snares** in a target membrane. After the v-snare recognizes a t-snare, the vesicle fuses with the membrane containing the t-snare. The recognition between v-snares and t-snares ensures that a vesicle carrying a specific cargo moves to the correct target membrane in the cell. Like the sorting of proteins to the ER membrane, the formation and sorting of vesicles also involves a series of protein-protein interactions that cause the steps to occur in a defined manner.

Most Transmembrane Proteins Are First Inserted into the ER Membrane

Our previous discussion of protein targeting involved a soluble protein (that is, a nonmembrane protein) that had an ER signal sequence. After the signal was removed, the protein was released into the ER lumen. With the exception of proteins destined for semiautonomous organelles, most membrane proteins are recognized by SRPs and synthesized into the ER membrane. From there, they may be transported via vesicles to other membranes of the endomembrane system.

As discussed in Chapter 5, if a sequence within a polypeptide contains a stretch of 20 amino acids that are mostly hydrophobic, this region will become a transmembrane segment. In the example shown in **Figure 6.14**, the polypeptide contains one such sequence. After the ER signal sequence is cleaved or removed, this will create a membrane protein with a single transmembrane segment. Other polypeptides may contain two or more transmembrane segments. Each time a polypeptide sequence contains a stretch of 20 hydrophobic amino acids, an additional transmembrane segment is synthesized into the membrane. For some membrane proteins, the ER signal sequence may not be removed. When it remains, it will usually function as a transmembrane segment.

Glycosylation of Proteins Occurs in the ER and Golgi Apparatus

Glycosylation is the attachment of carbohydrate to a protein, producing a glycoprotein. Carbohydrates may also be attached to lipids by glycosylation, but here we will focus on the glycosylation of proteins. In proteins, glycosylation may aid in protein folding, and it may protect a protein from extracellular factors that could harm its structure. In addition, glycosylation may play a role in protein sorting. For example, proteins destined for the lysosome have attached carbohydrate that serves as a sorting signal (see Table 6.1).

Two forms of protein glycosylation are known to occur in eukaryotes: N-linked and O-linked. N-linked glycosylation, which also occurs in archaea, involves the attachment of a carbohydrate to the amino acid asparagine in a polypeptide chain. It is called N-linked because the carbohydrate attaches to a nitrogen atom of the asparagine side chain. For this to occur, a group of 14 sugar molecules are built onto a lipid called dolichol. This carbohydrate tree is then transferred to an asparagine as a polypeptide is synthesized into the ER lumen (**Figure 6.15**). The carbohydrate tree is attached only to asparagines occurring in the sequence asparagine-X-serine or asparagine-X-threonine, where X could be any amino acid except proline. An enzyme in the ER, oligosaccharide transferase, recognizes this sequence and transfers the carbohydrate tree from dolichol to the asparagine.

Following this initial glycosylation step, the carbohydrate tree is further modified as other enzymes in the ER attach additional sugars or remove sugars. After a glycosylated protein is transferred to the Golgi by vesicle transport, enzymes in the Golgi usually modify the carbohydrate tree as well. N-linked glycosylation commonly occurs on membrane proteins

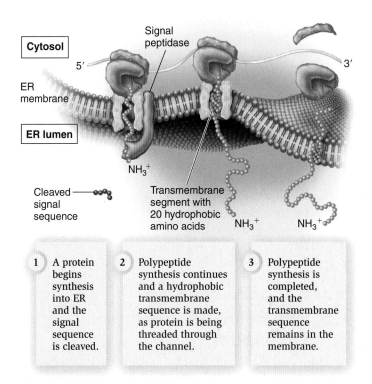

Figure 6.14   Insertion of membrane proteins into the ER membrane.

Biological inquiry: What structural feature of a protein causes a region to form a transmembrane segment?

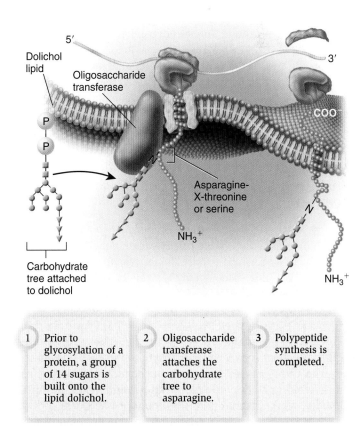

Figure 6.15   N-linked glycosylation in the endoplasmic reticulum.

that are transported to the cell surface. In some cell surface proteins, N-linked glycosylation plays a role in cell-to-cell recognition, a crucial phenomenon in the migration of cells during embryonic development in animals.

The second form of glycosylation, O-linked glycosylation, occurs only in the Golgi apparatus. This form involves the addition of a string of sugars to the oxygen atom of serine or threonine side chains in polypeptides. In animals, O-linked glycosylation is important for the production of proteoglycans, which are highly glycosylated proteins that are secreted from cells and help to organize the extracellular matrix that surrounds cells. Proteoglycans are also a component of mucus, a slimy material that coats many cell surfaces and is secreted into fluids such as saliva. High concentrations of carbohydrates give mucus its slimy texture.

6.3 The Semiautonomous Organelles

The other types of organelles found in the cytosol are the semi-autonomous organelles—mitochondria, chloroplasts, and peroxisomes—so named because they divide by fission to produce more of themselves. In Chapter 4, we examined their general structures and functions. Although they are compartments within the cytosol, the mitochondria, chloroplasts, and peroxisomes are somewhat like independent systems. For example, mitochondria and chloroplasts have their own genetic material, synthesize some proteins, and divide independently of when the cell divides. However, they are not entirely autonomous because they rely on the rest of the cell for raw materials and even import most of their proteins from the cytosol. As we will examine in this section, the seemingly mysterious behavior of these organelles can be traced to their evolutionary origin about 2 billion years ago.

Mitochondria and Chloroplasts Contain Their Own Genetic Material and Divide by Binary Fission

To appreciate the structure and organization of mitochondria and chloroplasts, we need to briefly examine their genetic properties. In 1951, Y. Chiba exposed plant cells to Feulgen, a DNA-specific dye, and discovered that the chloroplasts became stained. Based on this observation, he was the first to suggest that chloroplasts contain their own DNA. Researchers in the 1970s and 1980s isolated DNA from both chloroplasts and mitochondria. These studies revealed that the DNA of these organelles resembled smaller versions of bacterial chromosomes.

The chromosomes found in mitochondria and chloroplasts are referred to as the **mitochondrial genome** and **chloroplast genome**, while the chromosomes found in the nucleus of the cell constitute the **nuclear genome**. The genomes of most mito-

chondria and chloroplasts are composed of a single circular, double-stranded chromosome. Compared to the nuclear genome, they are very small. For example, the amount of DNA in the human nuclear genome (about 3 billion base pairs) is about 200,000 times greater than in the mitochondrial genome. In terms of genes, the human genome has approximately 20,000 to 25,000 different genes while the human mitochondrial genome has only several dozen. Chloroplast genomes tend to be larger than mitochondrial genomes, and they have a correspondingly greater number of genes. Depending on the particular species of plant or algae, a chloroplast genome is about 10 times larger than the mitochondrial genome of human cells.

Just as the genomes of mitochondria and chloroplasts resemble bacterial genomes, the production of new mitochondria and chloroplasts bears a striking resemblance to the division of bacterial cells. Like their bacterial counterparts, mitochondria and chloroplasts increase in number via **binary fission**, or splitting in two. **Figure 6.16** illustrates the process for mitochondria. The mitochondrial genome in the nucleoid is duplicated and the organelle divides into two separate organelles. Mitochondrial and chloroplast division are needed to maintain a full

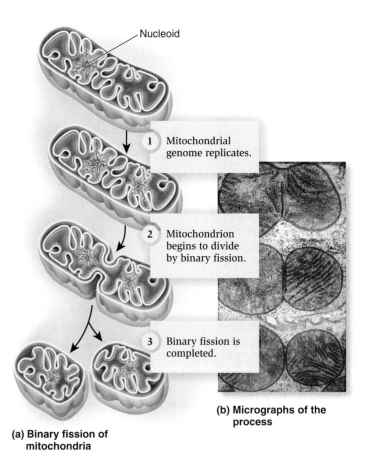

Nucleoid

1 Mitochondrial genome replicates.

2 Mitochondrion begins to divide by binary fission.

3 Binary fission is completed.

(a) Binary fission of mitochondria

(b) Micrographs of the process

Figure 6.16   Division of mitochondria by binary fission. **(a)** The mitochondrial genome is duplicated and the organelle divides into two separate organelles. **(b)** Micrographs of the process.

complement of these organelles when cell growth occurs following cell division. In addition, environmental conditions may influence the sizes and numbers of these organelles. For example, when plants are exposed to more sunlight, the number of chloroplasts in leaf cells increases.

GENOMES & PROTEOMES

Mitochondria and Chloroplasts Are Derived from Ancient Symbiotic Relationships

The observation that mitochondria and chloroplasts contain their own genetic material may seem puzzling. Perhaps you might think that it would be simpler for a eukaryotic cell to have all of its genetic material in the nucleus. The distinct genomes of mitochondria and chloroplasts can be traced to their evolutionary origin, which involved an ancient symbiotic association.

A symbiotic relationship occurs when two different species live in direct contact with each other. **Endosymbiosis** describes a symbiotic relationship in which the smaller species—the symbiont—actually lives inside (*endo-*, inside) the larger species. In 1883, Andreas Schimper proposed that chloroplasts were descended from an endosymbiotic relationship between cyanobacteria (a bacterium capable of photosynthesis) and eukaryotic cells. In 1922, Ivan Wallin also hypothesized an endosymbiotic origin for mitochondria.

In spite of these interesting ideas, the question of endosymbiosis was largely ignored until the discovery that mitochondria and chloroplasts contain their own genetic material. In 1970, the issue of endosymbiosis as the origin of mitochondria and chloroplasts was revived by Lynn Margulis in her book *Origin of Eukaryotic Cells*. During the 1970s and 1980s, the advent of molecular genetic techniques allowed researchers to analyze genes from mitochondria, chloroplasts, bacteria, and eukaryotic nuclear genomes. Researchers discovered that genes in mitochondria and chloroplasts are very similar to bacterial genes. Likewise, mitochondria and chloroplasts are strikingly similar in size and shape to certain bacterial species. These observations provided strong support for the **endosymbiosis theory**, which proposes that mitochondria and chloroplasts originated from bacteria that took up residence within a primordial eukaryotic cell (**Figure 6.17**). Over the next 2 billion years, the characteristics of the intracellular bacterial cell gradually changed to those of a mitochondrion or chloroplast. We will return to this topic in Chapter 22.

Symbiosis occurs because the relationship is beneficial to one or both species. According to the endosymbiosis theory, this relationship provided eukaryotic cells with useful cellular characteristics. Chloroplasts, which were derived from cyanobacteria, have the ability to carry out photosynthesis. This benefits plant cells by giving them the ability to use the energy from sunlight. It is less clear how the relationship would have been beneficial to a cyanobacterium. By comparison, mitochondria are

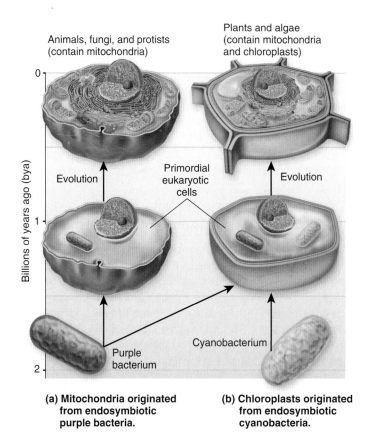

(a) Mitochondria originated from endosymbiotic purple bacteria.

(b) Chloroplasts originated from endosymbiotic cyanobacteria.

Figure 6.17   **The endosymbiosis theory.**   **(a)** According to this concept, modern mitochondria were derived from purple bacteria, also called α-proteobacteria. Over the course of evolution, their characteristics changed into those found in mitochondria today. **(b)** A similar phenomenon occurred for chloroplasts, which were derived from cyanobacteria, a bacterium that is capable of photosynthesis.

Biological inquiry: Discuss the similarities and differences between modern bacteria and mitochondria.

thought to have been derived from a different type of bacteria known as purple bacteria or α-proteobacteria. In this case, the endosymbiotic relationship enabled eukaryotic cells to synthesize greater amounts of ATP.

During the evolution of eukaryotic species, genes that were originally found in the genome of the primordial cyanobacteria and purple bacteria have been transferred from the organelles to the nucleus. This has occurred many times throughout evolution, so that modern mitochondria and chloroplasts have lost most of the genes that still exist in present-day purple bacteria and cyanobacteria. Some biologists have proposed that peroxisomes may also have arisen by an endosymbiotic relationship but have lost all of their genetic material. Alternatively, others suggest that peroxisomes may have their origins in the endomembrane system. The evolutionary origin of peroxisomes remains unclear.

Some researchers speculate that the movement of genes into the nucleus makes it easier for the cell to control the structure, function, and division of mitochondria and chloroplasts. In modern cells, hundreds of different proteins that make up these organelles are encoded by genes that have been transferred to the nucleus. These proteins are made in the cytosol, and then taken up into mitochondria or chloroplasts. We will discuss this topic next.

Most Proteins Are Sorted to Mitochondria, Chloroplasts, and Peroxisomes Post-Translationally

The organization of semiautonomous organelles is largely dependent on the uptake of proteins from the cytosol. Most proteins in mitochondria and chloroplasts, and all proteins in peroxisomes, are synthesized in the cytosol and taken up into their respective organelles. For example, most proteins involved in ATP synthesis are made in the cytosol and taken up into mitochondria after they have been completely synthesized. For this to occur, a protein must have the appropriate targeting sequence

as part of its amino acid sequence. **Table 6.2** summarizes the targeting sequences that direct proteins to mitochondria, chloroplasts, and peroxisomes.

As one example of post-translational sorting, let's consider how a protein is directed to the mitochondrial matrix. As described in **Figure 6.18**, this process involves a series of intricate protein-protein interactions. A protein that is destined for the mitochondrial matrix is first made in the cytosol, where proteins called chaperones keep it in an unfolded state. A receptor protein in the outer mitochondrial membrane recognizes the matrix targeting sequence. The protein is released from the chaperone as it is transferred to a channel in the outer mitochondrial membrane. Because it is in an unfolded state, the mitochon-drial protein can be threaded through this channel, and then through another channel in the inner mitochondrial membrane. These channels lie close to each other at contact sites between the outer and inner membranes. As the protein emerges in the matrix, other chaperone proteins that were already in the matrix continue to keep it unfolded. Eventually, the matrix targeting sequence is cleaved and the entire protein is threaded into the matrix. At this stage, the chaperone proteins are released and the protein can adopt its three-dimensional structure.

Table 6.2	Targeting Sequences of Proteins That Are Destined for Semiautonomous Organelles*
Destination	**Mitochondria**
Matrix	Contains a matrix targeting sequence that is usually a short sequence at the amino terminus of a protein with several positively charged residues (that is, lysine and arginine). This sequence folds into an α-helix in which the positive charges are on one face of the helix.
Outer-membrane	Has a matrix targeting sequence followed by a stop transfer sequence that prevents passage through the outer membrane channel.
Intermembrane space	Contains a matrix targeting sequence followed by a cleavage site that causes the release of the protein into the intermembrane space.
Inner-membrane	Contains a matrix targeting sequence and one or more transmembrane regions.
	Chloroplasts
Stroma	Contains a stroma targeting sequence that is an uncharged α-helix with polar amino acids along one side.
Outer-membrane	Not well understood, but may have a stroma targeting sequence and a stop transfer sequence.
Intermembrane space	Not well understood, but may have a stroma targeting sequence and a cleavage site that causes the release of the protein into the intermembrane space.
Inner-membrane	Contains a stroma targeting sequence and one or more transmembrane regions.
Thylakoid membrane	Also has a stroma targeting sequence followed by a thylakoid targeting sequence that is a stretch of hydrophobic amino acids.
	Peroxisomes
Peroxisome membrane and lumen	Most peroxisomal proteins contain a specific sequence of three amino acids, serine-lysine-leucine, that is located near the carboxyl terminus of the protein. A few peroxisomal proteins have a 26 amino acid sorting sequence at the amino terminus.

*These are the most common types of targeting sequences, also called sorting signals. Variations are known to occur in the amino acid sequences that function as the sorting signals.

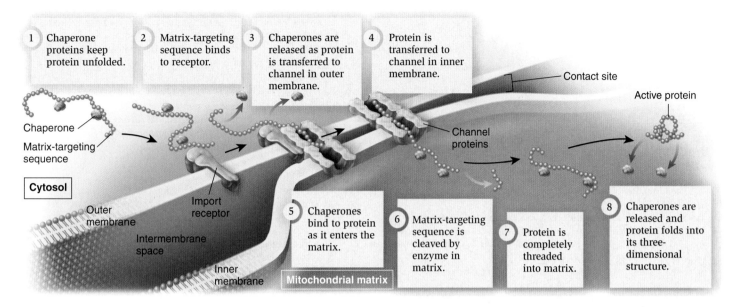

Figure 6.18 Post-translational sorting of a protein to the mitochondrial matrix.

Biological inquiry: What do you think would happen if chaperone proteins did not bind to a mitochondrial matrix protein before it was imported into the mitochondrion?

CHAPTER SUMMARY

6.1 Principles of Cell Organization

- In systems biology, researchers study living organisms in terms of their underlying network structure—groups of structural and functional connections—rather than their individual molecular components.

- The maintenance of cell structure relies on the genome, functional molecules, and pre-existing organization. Other factors include the ability of certain proteins to interact with each other to form molecular machines, and the dynamic turnover of cellular molecules and macromolecules.

- Modern cells can grow, adapt, and modify their organization, but they do not arise spontaneously from nonliving materials.

- Cell organization depends on genetic information in the cell nucleus, which produces a proteome. (Figure 6.1)

- Interactions among proteins and RNA molecules form molecular machines that carry out complex cellular functions. (Figures 6.2, 6.3)

- The cytoskeleton is a molecular machine that provides cell organization and directs cellular movements. (Figures 6.4, 6.5)

- The maintenance of cell organization is a dynamic process that involves breaking down molecules and recycling their building blocks. (Figure 6.6)

- In eukaryotic cells, four regions work together to produce dynamic organization. The nucleus houses the genome, which plays a key role in producing the proteome. The cytosol is an important coordination center for cell metabolism and organization. The organelles of the endomembrane system perform several important functions in eukaryotic cells. The semiautonomous organelles (mitochondria, chloroplasts, and peroxisomes) perform a variety of crucial functions. (Figure 6.7)

6.2 The Endomembrane System

- In eukaryotic cells, the cytosol and endomembrane system work together to synthesize most lipids. The endomembrane system includes the nuclear envelope, endoplasmic reticulum, Golgi apparatus, lysosomes, vacuoles, and plasma membrane. (Figures 6.8, 6.9, 6.10)

- Palade's pulse-chase experiments demonstrated that secreted proteins move sequentially through the organelles of the endomembrane system. (Figure 6.11)

- Protein localization involves sorting signals and vesicle transport. (Table 6.1, Figures 6.12, 6.13)

- Most transmembrane proteins are first inserted into the ER membrane and then transported via vesicles to other membranes of the endomembrane system. (Figure 6.14)

- Glycosylation of proteins occurs in the ER and Golgi apparatus. Glycosylation may help proteins fold properly, protect them from extracellular factors, and assist in protein sorting. (Figure 6.15)

6.3 The Semiautonomous Organelles

- Mitochondria and chloroplasts contain their own genetic material and divide by binary fission. (Figure 6.16)

- According to the endosymbiosis theory, mitochondria and chloroplasts have evolved from bacteria that took up residence in early eukaryotic cells. (Figure 6.17)

- Most proteins are sorted to mitochondria, chloroplasts, and peroxisomes post-translationally. (Table 6.2, Figure 6.18)

TEST YOURSELF

1. The main structural elements of cells that produce cellular organization are
   a. proteins.
   b. organelles.
   c. membranes.
   d. all of the above.
   e. a and c only.

2. Which of the following statements best supports the requirements to make new cells?
   a. The formation of new cells relies solely on the presence of the genome.
   b. New cell formation requires the correct genetic information and the building blocks necessary to produce the cellular components.
   c. New cell production requires the genome, functional molecules, and pre-existing organization.
   d. The formation of new cells requires the appropriate genetic information and functional molecules for cellular activity only.
   e. All of the above.

3. Large molecular complexes that perform different cellular activities that involve changes in molecular conformation are called molecular
   a. clocks.
   b. motors.
   c. machines.
   d. proteins.
   e. proteomes.

4. Protein conformation is important to protein function. The assembly of many complex proteins relies on _____ , where surfaces of subunits recognize each other and bind together.
   a. protein sorting
   b. traffic signaling
   c. post-transcriptional changes
   d. molecular recognition
   e. proteasome activity

5. In the nucleus, proteins help maintain organization by
   a. forming a meshwork in the nucleus that organizes each chromosome into its own chromosome territory.
   b. organizing the outer nuclear membrane.
   c. organizing the inner nuclear membrane.
   d. all of the above.
   e. a and c only.

6. The cytoskeleton is an important feature of the cytosol that provides organization by
   a. determining cell shape.
   b. determining the structure of the endomembrane system.
   c. transporting proteins to the endoplasmic reticulum for protein sorting.
   d. recycling membrane-bounded proteins.
   e. all of the above

7. Proteins that function to move lipids from one membrane to another are called
   a. lipases.
   b. membrane-bounded lipoproteins.
   c. proteases.
   d. lipid exchange proteins.
   e. phospholipids.

8. Protein sorting in the cell is possible due to
   a. sorting signals in the amino acid sequences of proteins that determine protein destinations in the cell.
   b. chaperone proteins that function to direct all proteins to the proper location inside or outside the cell.
   c. formation of protein sorting vesicles that carry proteins from the Golgi to lysosomes.
   d. DNA sequences that remain part of the proteins that determine cellular destination.
   e. all of the above.

9. Proteins that remain in the cytosol as opposed to passing through the endomembrane system are sorted
   a. prior to translation by pretranslational sorting.
   b. during translation by cotranslational sorting.
   c. after translation by post-translational sorting.
   d. both b and c.
   e. none of the above.

10. Vesicles move to the appropriate membrane in the cell by the recognition of _____ , proteins in the target membrane that act as binding sites for the vesicle.
    a. v-snares
    b. traffic signals
    c. coat proteins
    d. chaperones
    e. t-snares

CONCEPTUAL QUESTIONS

1. List the components of the endomembrane system and briefly describe the functions of each.

2. Briefly explain how sorting signals function in protein localization.

3. Define glycosylation.

EXPERIMENTAL QUESTIONS

1. Explain the procedure of a pulse-chase experiment as described in Figure 6.11. What was the purpose of the approach?

2. Why were pancreatic cells used for the investigation of Figure 6.11?

3. What were the results of the experiment of Figure 6.11? What did the researchers conclude?

COLLABORATIVE QUESTIONS

1. What roles do the genome and proteome play in the organization of cells?

2. Discuss the theory of how the mitochondria and chloroplast were initially formed.

www.brookerbiology.com
This website includes answers to the Biological Inquiry questions found in the figure legends and all end-of-chapter questions.

7

ENZYMES, METABOLISM, AND CELLULAR RESPIRATION

CHAPTER OUTLINE

Metabolism of food. The food we eat contains a variety of organic molecules that we use for energy.

As discussed in Chapter 2, a **chemical reaction** is a process in which one or more substances are changed into other substances. Such reactions can result in molecules attaching to each other to form larger molecules, molecules breaking apart to form two or more smaller molecules, rearrangements of atoms within molecules, or the transfer of electrons from one atom to another. Every living cell continuously performs thousands of such chemical reactions to sustain life. The term **metabolism** is used to describe the sum total of all chemical reactions that occur within an organism. The term also refers to a specific set of chemical reactions occurring at the cellular level. For example, biologists may speak of sugar metabolism or fat metabolism. Most metabolism involves the breakdown or synthesis of organic molecules. In Chapter 6, we learned that cells maintain their structure by using organic molecules. Such molecules provide the building blocks to construct cells, and the chemical bonds within organic molecules store energy that can be used to drive cellular processes. A key emphasis of this chapter is how, through chemical reactions, cells utilize energy that is stored within the chemical bonds of organic molecules such as the sugar glucose.

When we eat food, we are using much of that food for energy. People often speak of "burning calories." While it is true that metabolism does generate some heat, the chemical reactions that take place in the cells of living organisms are uniquely different from those that occur, say, in a fire. When wood is burned, the reaction produces enormous amounts of heat in a short period of time; the reaction lacks control. In contrast, the metabolism that occurs in living cells is extremely controlled. The food molecules from which we harvest energy give up that energy in a very restrained manner rather than all at once, as in a fire. An underlying theme in metabolism involves the remarkable control that cells possess when coordinating chemical reactions that utilize energy.

In this chapter, we will begin with a general discussion of chemical reactions. We will examine what factors control the direction of a chemical reaction and what determines its rate, paying particular attention to the role of enzymes, a type of biological catalyst. We then consider metabolism at the cellular level. First, we will examine some of the general features of chemical reactions that are vital for the energy needs of living cells. We will also explore the variety of ways in which metabolic processes are regulated and survey a group of chemical reactions that involves the breakdown of carbohydrates, namely, the sugar glucose. As you will learn, cells carry out an intricate series of reactions so that glucose can be "burned" in a very controlled fashion. Finally, the last section explores the synthesis of natural products that play specialized roles in many species.

7.1 Energy, Chemical Reactions, and Enzymes

Two general factors govern the fate of a given chemical reaction in a living cell—its direction and rate. To illustrate this point, let's consider a generalized chemical reaction such as

$$aA + bB \rightleftharpoons cC + dD$$

where A and B are the reactants, C and D are the products, and a, b, c, and d are the number of moles of reactants and products. This reaction is reversible, which means that A + B could be converted to C + D, or C + D could be converted to A + B. The direction of the reaction, whether C + D are made (the forward direction) or A + B are made (the reverse direction), depends on energy and on the concentrations of A, B, C, and D.

In this section, we will begin by examining the interplay of energy and the concentration of reactants as they govern the direction of a chemical reaction. You will learn that cells use energy intermediate molecules, such as ATP, to drive chemical reactions in a desired direction. Many types of chemical reactions, particularly those that involve organic molecules, proceed at a very slow rate unless facilitated by a biological catalyst. In the second part of this section, we will examine how catalysts called enzymes are critical cellular components that speed up the rates of chemical reactions in living organisms.

Energy Exists in Many Forms

To understand why a chemical reaction occurs, we first need to consider **energy**, which we will define as the ability to promote change. Physicists often consider energy in two forms: kinetic energy and potential energy (**Figure 7.1**). **Kinetic energy** is energy associated with movement, such as the movement of a baseball bat from one location to another. By comparison, **potential energy** is the energy that a substance possesses due to its structure or location. The energy contained within covalent bonds in molecules is a type of potential energy called **chemical energy**. The breakage of those bonds is one way that living cells can harness this energy to perform cellular functions. **Table 7.1** summarizes chemical and other forms of energy that are important in biological systems.

An important issue in biology is the ability of energy to be converted from one form to another. The study of energy interconversions is called **thermodynamics**. Physicists have determined that two laws govern energy interconversions:

1. **The first law of thermodynamics**—The first law states that energy cannot be created or destroyed; it is also called the *law of conservation of energy*. However, energy can be transferred from one place to another and can be

(a) Kinetic energy **(b) Potential energy**

Covalent bonds in glucose store energy.

Figure 7.1 **Examples of energy.** (a) Kinetic energy, such as swinging a bat, is energy associated with motion. (b) Potential energy is stored energy. Chemical bonds in molecules such as glucose store large amounts of chemical energy.

transformed from one type to another (as when, for example, chemical energy is transformed into heat).

2. **The second law of thermodynamics**—The second law states that the transfer of energy or the transformation of energy from one form to another increases the **entropy**, or degree of disorder of a system (**Figure 7.2**). When energy is converted from one form to another, the increase in entropy causes some energy to become unusable by living organisms.

Next, we will see how these two laws place limits on the ways that living cells can use energy for their own needs.

The Change in Free Energy Determines the Direction of a Chemical Reaction or Any Other Cellular Process

From the perspective of living organisms, energy is a critical component that is necessary for life to exist. Energy powers many cellular processes including chemical reactions, cellular

Table 7.1	Types of Energy That Are Important in Biology	
Energy type	**Description**	**Biological example**
Light	Light is a form of electromagnetic radiation that is visible to the eye. The energy of light is packaged in photons.	During photosynthesis, light energy is captured by pigments in chloroplasts (Chapter 8). Ultimately, this energy is used to reduce carbon, thus producing organic molecules.
Heat	Heat is the transfer of kinetic energy from one object to another, or from an energy source to an object. In biology, heat is often viewed as energy that can be transferred due to a difference in temperature between two objects or locations.	Many organisms, such as humans, maintain their bodies at a constant temperature. This is achieved by chemical reactions that generate heat.
Mechanical	Mechanical energy is the energy that is possessed by an object due to its motion or its position relative to other objects.	In animals, mechanical energy is associated with movements due to muscle contraction such as walking.
Chemical	Chemical energy is energy stored in the chemical bonds of molecules. When the bonds are broken and rearranged, this can release large amounts of energy.	The covalent bonds in organic molecules, such as glucose and ATP, store large amounts of energy. When these bonds are broken, the chemical energy released can be used to drive cellular processes.
Electrical/Ion gradient	The movement of charge or the separation of charge can provide energy. Also, a difference in ion concentration across a membrane constitutes an electrochemical gradient gradient, which is a source of potential energy.	High-energy electrons can release energy (that is, drop down to lower energy levels). The energy that is released can be used to drive cellular processes such as the pumping of H^+ across membranes (as discussed later in this chapter).

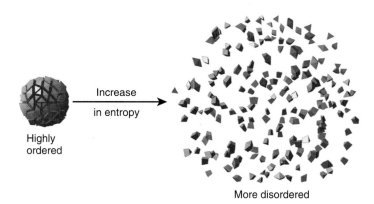

Figure 7.2 Entropy. Entropy is a measure of the disorder of a system. An increase in entropy means an increase in disorder.

Biological inquiry: Which do you think has more entropy, a NaCl crystal at the bottom of a beaker of water or the same beaker of water after the Na⁺ and Cl⁻ in the crystal have dissolved in the water?

movements such as those occurring in muscle contraction, and the maintenance of cell organization. To understand how living organisms use energy, we need to distinguish between the energy that can be used to do work (usable energy) and the energy that cannot do work (unusable energy).

$$Total\ energy\ =\ Usable\ energy\ +\ Unusable\ energy$$

Why is some energy unusable? The main culprit is entropy. As stated by the second law of thermodynamics, energy transformations involve an increase in entropy, a measure of the disorder that cannot be harnessed to do work. For living organisms, the total energy is termed **enthalpy (H)** and the usable energy—the amount of available energy that can be used to do work—is called the **free energy (G)**. The letter G is in recognition of J. Willard Gibbs, who proposed the concept of free energy in 1878. The unusable energy is the system's entropy (S). Gibbs proposed that these three factors are related to each other in the following way:

$$H\ =\ G\ +\ TS$$

where T is the absolute temperature in Kelvin (K). Because our focus is on free energy, we can rearrange this equation as

$$G\ =\ H\ -\ TS$$

A critical issue in biology is whether a process will or will not occur spontaneously. For example, will glucose be broken down into carbon dioxide and water? Another way of framing this question is to ask, Is the breakdown of glucose a spontaneous reaction? A spontaneous reaction or process is one that will occur without an additional input of energy. However, a spontaneous reaction does not necessarily proceed quickly. In some cases, the rate of a spontaneous reaction can be quite slow.

The key way to evaluate if a reaction is spontaneous is to determine the free energy change that occurs as a result of the chemical reaction.

$$\Delta G\ =\ \Delta H\ -\ T\Delta S$$

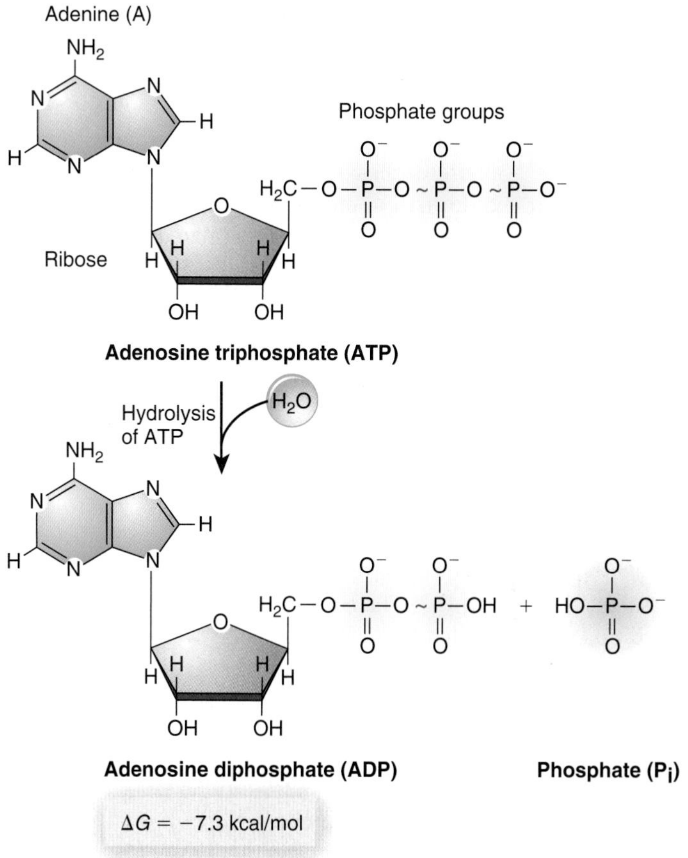

$$\Delta G = -7.3\ kcal/mol$$

Figure 7.3 The hydrolysis of ATP to ADP and P$_i$. As shown in this figure, ATP has a net charge of −4, while ADP and P$_i$ are shown with net charges of −2 each. When these compounds are shown in chemical reactions with other molecules, the net charges will also be shown. Otherwise, these compounds will simply be designated ATP, ADP, and P$_i$. It should also be noted that at neutral pH, ADP^{2-} will dissociate to ADP^{3-} and H$^+$. Likewise, P$_i^{2-}$ also dissociates to P$_i^{3-}$ + H$^+$ at neutral pH.

where the Δ sign indicates a change, such as before and after a chemical reaction. If the reaction has a negative free energy change ($\Delta G < 0$), this means that free energy is released. Such a reaction is said to be **exergonic.** Exergonic reactions are spontaneous. Alternatively, if a reaction has a positive free energy change ($\Delta G > 0$), requiring the addition of free energy from the environment, it is termed **endergonic.** An endergonic reaction is not a spontaneous reaction.

If ΔG for a chemical reaction is negative, the reaction favors the formation of products, while a reaction with a positive ΔG favors the formation of reactants. Chemists have determined free energy changes for a variety of chemical reactions. **Adenosine triphosphate (ATP)** is a molecule that is a common energy source for all cells. Let's look at the breakdown of ATP to adenosine diphosphate (ADP) and inorganic phosphate (P$_i$). Because water is used to remove a phosphate group, chemists refer to this as the hydrolysis of ATP (**Figure 7.3**). In the reaction of converting 1 mole of ATP to 1 mole of ADP and P$_i$, ΔG equals −7.3 kcal/mole. Because this is a negative value, the reaction strongly favors the formation of products. As discussed later in this chapter, the energy that is liberated by the hydrolysis of ATP is used to drive a variety of cellular processes.

Even when a chemical reaction is associated with a negative free energy change, not all of the reactants are converted to products. The reaction reaches a state of **chemical equilibrium** in which the rate of formation of products equals the rate of formation of reactants. According to the generalized equation:

$$aA + bB \rightleftharpoons cC + dD$$

An equilibrium occurs, such that:

$$K_{eq} = \frac{[C]^c[D]^d}{[A]^a[B]^b}$$

where K_{eq} is the equilibrium constant.

Biologists make two simplifying assumptions when determining values for equilibrium constants. First, the concentration of water does not change during the reaction and the pH remains constant at pH 7. The equilibrium constant under these conditions is designated K_{eq}'. If water is one of the reactants, as in a hydrolysis reaction, it is not included in the chemical equilibrium equation. As an example, let's consider the chemical equilibrium for the hydrolysis of ATP.

$$ATP^{4-} + H_2O \rightleftharpoons ADP^{2-} + P_i^{2-}$$

$$K_{eq}' = \frac{[ADP][P_i]}{[ATP]}$$

Experimentally, the value for K_{eq}' for this reaction has been determined and found to be approximately 1,650,000 M. Such a large value indicates that the equilibrium greatly favors the formation of products—ADP and P_i.

Cells Use ATP to Drive Endergonic Reactions

An important issue that faces living organisms is that many vital processes require the addition of free energy, that is, they are endergonic and will not occur spontaneously. Fortunately, organisms have a strategy to overcome this problem. If an endergonic reaction is coupled to an exergonic reaction, the endergonic reaction will proceed spontaneously if the net free energy change for both processes combined is negative. For example, consider the following reactions:

Glucose + phosphate^{2-} → Glucose-phosphate^{2-} + H_2O
$\Delta G = +3.3$ kcal/mole

$ATP^{4-} + H_2O$ → $ATP^{2-} + P_i^{2-}$ $\Delta G = -7.3$ kcal/mole

Coupled reaction:

Glucose + ATP^{4-} → Glucose-phosphate^{2-} + ADP^{2-}
$\Delta G = -4.0$ kcal/mole

The first reaction, in which phosphate is covalently attached to glucose, is endergonic, while the second, the hydrolysis of ATP, is exergonic. By itself, the first reaction would not be spontaneous. If the two reactions are coupled, however, the net free

energy change for both reactions combined is exergonic. In the coupled reaction, a phosphate is directly transferred from ATP to glucose; this coupled reaction proceeds spontaneously because the net free energy change is negative. As discussed later, the transfer of phosphate from ATP to glucose is a first step in the breakdown of glucose to smaller molecules. Exergonic reactions, such as the breakdown of ATP, are commonly coupled to cellular processes that would otherwise be endergonic.

Enzymes Increase the Rates of Chemical Reactions

Thus far we have examined aspects of energy and considered how the laws of physics are related to the direction of chemical reactions. If a chemical reaction has a negative free energy change, the reaction will be spontaneous; it will tend to proceed in the direction of reactants to products. While thermodynamics governs the direction of an energy transformation, it does not control the rate of a chemical reaction. For example, the breakdown of the molecules in gasoline to smaller molecules is a highly exergonic reaction. Even so, we could place gasoline and oxygen in a container and nothing much would happen (provided it wasn't near a flame). If we came back several days later, we would expect to see the gasoline still sitting there. Perhaps if we came back in a few million years, the gasoline would have been broken down. On a timescale of months or a few years, however, the chemical reaction would proceed very slowly.

For most chemical reactions in cells to proceed at a rapid pace, a catalyst is needed. A **catalyst** is an agent that speeds up the rate of a chemical reaction without being consumed during the reaction. In living cells, the most common catalysts are **enzymes**, protein molecules that accelerate chemical reactions. The term was coined in 1876 by a German physiologist, Wilhelm Kühne, who discovered the enzyme trypsin in pancreatic juice. Interestingly, a few biological catalysts are RNA molecules called **ribozymes**. For example, RNA molecules within ribosomes catalyze the formation of bonds that link amino acids to each other.

Why are catalysts necessary to speed up a chemical reaction? When a covalent bond is broken or formed, this process initially involves the straining or contortion of one or more bonds in the starting molecule(s) and it may involve the positioning of two molecules so that they interact with each other properly. Let's consider the reaction in which ATP is used to attach a phosphate to glucose.

Glucose + ATP^{4-} → Glucose-phosphate^{2-} + ADP^{2-}

For a reaction to occur between glucose and ATP, they must collide in the correct orientation and possess enough energy so that chemical bonds can be changed. As glucose and ATP approach each other, their electron clouds cause repulsion. To overcome this repulsion, an initial input of energy, called the **activation energy**, is required (**Figure 7.4**). Activation energy allows the molecules to get close enough to cause a rearrangement of bonds. With the input of activation energy, glucose and ATP can achieve a **transition state** in which the original bonds have stretched to their limit. Once the reactants have reached

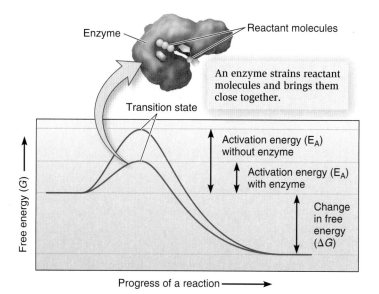

Figure 7.4 Activation energy of a chemical reaction. This figure depicts an exergonic reaction. The activation energy is needed for molecules to achieve a transition state. One way that enzymes lower the activation energy is by straining the reactants so that less energy is required to attain the transition state. A second way is by binding two reactants so they are close to each other and in a favorable orientation.

Biological inquiry: How does lowering the activation energy affect the rate of a chemical reaction?

the transition state, the chemical reaction can readily proceed to the formation of products.

The activation energy required to achieve the transition state is a barrier to the formation of products. This barrier is the reason why the rate of many chemical reactions is very slow. There are two common ways to overcome this barrier and thereby accelerate a chemical reaction. First, the reactants could be exposed to a large amount of heat. For example, as we noted previously, if gasoline is sitting at room temperature, nothing much happens. However, if the gasoline is exposed to a flame or spark, it breaks down rapidly, perhaps at an explosive rate! Alternatively, a second strategy is to lower the activation energy barrier. Enzymes lower the activation energy to a point where a small amount of available heat can push the reactants to a transition state.

How do enzymes work to lower the activation energy barrier of chemical reactions? Enzymes are large proteins that bind relatively small reactants (Figure 7.4). When bound to an enzyme, the bonds in the reactants can be strained (that is, stretched), thereby making it easier for them to achieve the transition state. This is one way that enzymes lower the activation energy. In addition, when a chemical reaction involves two or more reactants, the enzyme provides a site where the reactants are positioned very close to each other and in an orientation that facilitates the formation of new covalent bonds. This also lowers the necessary activation energy for a chemical reaction.

Straining the reactants and bringing them close together are two common ways that enzymes lower the activation energy barrier. In addition, enzymes may facilitate a chemical reaction by

changing the local environment of the reactants. For example, amino acids in an enzyme may have charges that affect the chemistry of the reactants. In some cases, enzymes lower the activation energy by directly participating in the chemical reaction. For example, certain enzymes that hydrolyze ATP form a covalent bond between phosphate and an amino acid in the enzyme. However, this is a very temporary condition. The covalent bond between phosphate and the amino acid is quickly broken, releasing phosphate and returning the amino acid back to its original condition. An important example of such an enzyme is Na^+/K^+-ATPase, described in Chapter 5 (refer back to Figure 5.23).

Enzymes Recognize Their Substrates with High Specificity and Undergo Conformational Changes

Thus far, we have considered how enzymes lower the activation energy of a chemical reaction and thereby increase its rate. Let's consider some other features of enzymes that enable them to serve as effective catalysts in chemical reactions. The **active site** is the location in an enzyme where the chemical reaction takes place. The **substrates** for an enzyme are the reactant molecules and/or ions that bind to an enzyme at the active site and participate in the chemical reaction. For example, hexokinase is an enzyme whose substrates are glucose and ATP (**Figure 7.5**). The binding between an enzyme and substrate produces an **enzyme-substrate complex**.

A key feature of nearly all enzymes is that they bind their substrates with a **high affinity** or high degree of specificity. For example, because hexokinase binds glucose very well, we say it has a high affinity for glucose. By comparison, hexokinase has a low affinity for other sugars, such as fructose and galactose, which have similar structures to glucose. In 1894, the German scientist Emil Fischer proposed that the recognition of a substrate by an enzyme resembles the interaction between a lock and key: only the right-sized key (the substrate) will fit into the keyhole (active site) of the lock (the enzyme). Further research revealed that the interaction between an enzyme and its substrates also involves movements or conformational changes in the enzyme itself. As shown in Figure 7.5, these conformational changes cause the substrates to bind more tightly to the enzyme, a phenomenon called **induced fit**. Only after this conformational change takes place does the enzyme catalyze the conversion of reactants to products.

Some enzymes require additional nonprotein molecules or ions to carry out their functions. **Prosthetic groups** are small molecules that are permanently attached to the surface of an enzyme and aid in catalysis. **Cofactors** are usually inorganic ions, such as Fe^{3+} or Zn^{2+}, that temporarily bind to the surface of an enzyme and promote a chemical reaction. Finally, some enzymes use **coenzymes**, organic molecules that participate in the chemical reaction but are left unchanged after the reaction is completed.

The ability of enzymes to increase the rate of a chemical reaction is also affected by the surrounding conditions. In particular, the temperature and pH play an important role in the proper functioning of enzymes. Most enzymes function maximally in a narrow range of temperature and pH. For example, many human

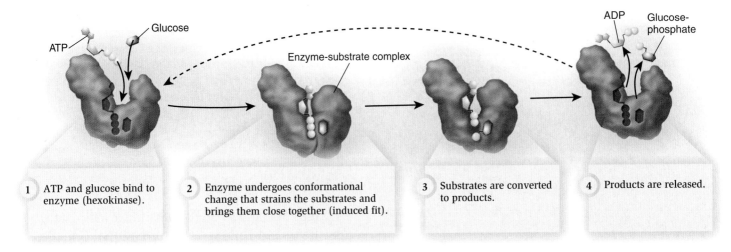

1. ATP and glucose bind to enzyme (hexokinase).

2. Enzyme undergoes conformational change that strains the substrates and brings them close together (induced fit).

3. Substrates are converted to products.

4. Products are released.

Figure 7.5 **The steps of an enzyme-catalyzed reaction.** The example shown here involves the enzyme hexokinase, which binds glucose and ATP. The products are glucose-phosphate and ADP, which are released from the enzyme.

enzymes work best at 37°C (98.6°F), which is the body's normal temperature. If the temperature was several degrees above or below this value, the function of many cytosolic enzymes would be greatly inhibited. Similarly, enzyme function is sensitive to pH. Many cytosolic enzymes function optimally at pH 7.2, the pH normally found in the cytosol of humans cells. If the pH was significantly above or below this value, enzyme function would be decreased.

7.2 Overview of Metabolism

In the previous section, we examined the underlying factors that govern individual chemical reactions. In living cells, chemical reactions are often coordinated with each other and occur in sequences called **metabolic pathways**, each step of which is catalyzed by a specific enzyme (**Figure 7.6**). These pathways are categorized according to whether the reactions lead to the breakdown or synthesis of substances. **Catabolic reactions** result in the breakdown of molecules into smaller molecules. Such reactions are often exergonic. By comparison, **anabolic reactions** promote the synthesis of larger molecules from smaller precursor molecules. This process usually is endergonic and, in living cells, must be coupled to an exergonic reaction. In this section, we will survey the general features of catabolic and anabolic reactions, and explore the ways in which these metabolic pathways are controlled.

Catabolic Reactions Recycle Organic Building Blocks and Produce Energy Intermediates Such as ATP and NADH

Catabolic reactions involve the breakdown of macromolecules or smaller organic molecules. One reason for the breakdown of these molecules is to recycle the building blocks needed to construct new macromolecules. For example, proteins are composed of a linear sequence of amino acids. When a protein is improp-

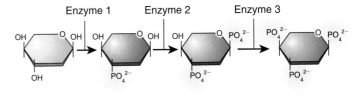

Enzyme 1   Enzyme 2   Enzyme 3

Initial substrate   Intermediate 1   Intermediate 2   Final product

Figure 7.6 **A metabolic pathway.** In a metabolic pathway, a series of different enzymes catalyze the changes in the structure of a molecule, beginning with a starting substrate and ending with a final product.

erly folded or is no longer needed by a cell, the peptide bonds between amino acids in such a protein are broken by enzymes called proteases. This generates amino acids that can be used in the construction of new proteins.

Proteases
Protein →→→→→→→→→→ Many individual amino acids

Similarly, the breakdown of RNA by enzymes called nucleases produces nucleotides that can be used in the synthesis of new RNA molecules.

Nucleases
RNA →→→→→→→→→→ Many individual nucleotides

The breakdown of macromolecules, such as unneeded proteins and RNA molecules, allows a cell to recycle the building blocks that comprise those macromolecules and use them to make new macromolecules.

A second reason for the breakdown of macromolecules and smaller organic molecules is to obtain energy that can be used to drive endergonic processes in the cell. Covalent bonds store a large amount of energy. However, when cells break covalent bonds in organic molecules such as carbohydrates and proteins, they do not directly use the energy that is released in this process.

Instead, the released energy is stored in **energy intermediates**, molecules such as ATP and NADH, that are directly used to drive endergonic reactions in cells.

As an example, let's consider the breakdown of glucose into two molecules of pyruvate. As we'll discuss later in this chapter, the breakdown of glucose to pyruvate involves a catabolic pathway called glycolysis. Some of the energy that is released during the breakage of covalent bonds in glucose is harnessed to synthesize ATP. However, this does not occur in a single step. Rather, glycolysis involves a series of steps in which covalent bonds are broken and rearranged. This process creates molecules that can readily donate a phosphate group to ADP, thereby creating ATP. For example, phosphoenolpyruvate has a phosphate group attached to pyruvate. Due to the arrangement of bonds in phosphoenolpyruvate, this phosphate bond is easily broken. Therefore, the phosphate can be readily transferred to ADP

$$\text{Phosphoenolpyruvate} + \text{ADP} \rightarrow \text{Pyruvate} + \text{ATP}$$
$$\Delta G = -7.5 \text{ kcal/mole}$$

This is an exergonic reaction and therefore favors the formation of products. In this step of glycolysis, the breakdown of an organic molecule, namely, phosphoenolpyruvate, results in the synthesis of an energy intermediate molecule, ATP, which can then be used by a cell to drive endergonic reactions. This way of synthesizing ATP, termed **substrate-level phosphorylation**, occurs when an enzyme directly transfers a phosphate from one molecule to a different molecule. In this case, a phosphate is transferred from phosphoenolpyruvate to ADP. Another way to make ATP is via **chemiosmosis**. In this process, energy stored in an ion electrochemical gradient is used to make ATP from ADP and P_i. We will consider this mechanism later in the chapter.

An important event that may occur during the breakdown of small organic molecules is **oxidation**, a process that involves the removal of electrons. This event is called oxidation because oxygen is frequently involved in chemical reactions that remove electrons from other molecules. By comparison, **reduction** is the addition of electrons to an atom or molecule. Reduction is so named because the addition of a negatively charged electron reduces the net charge of a molecule.

Electrons do not exist freely in solution. When an atom or molecule is oxidized, the electron that is removed must be transferred to another atom or molecule, which becomes reduced. This type of reaction is termed a **redox reaction**, which is short for a reduction-oxidation reaction. As a generalized equation, an electron may be transferred from molecule A to molecule B as follows:

$$Ae^- + B \rightarrow A + Be^-$$

As shown in the right side of this reaction, A has been oxidized (that is, had an electron removed) and B has been reduced (that is, had an electron added). In general, a substance that has been oxidized has less energy, while a substance that has been reduced has more energy.

During the oxidation of organic molecules such as glucose, the electrons are used to create energy intermediates such as

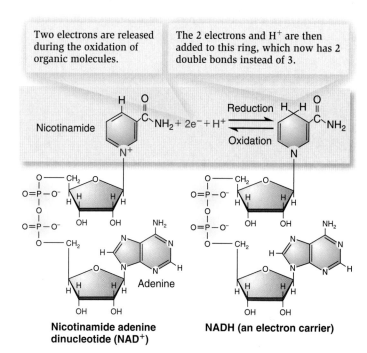

Two electrons are released during the oxidation of organic molecules.

The 2 electrons and H$^+$ are then added to this ring, which now has 2 double bonds instead of 3.

Nicotinamide adenine dinucleotide (NAD$^+$)

NADH (an electron carrier)

Figure 7.7   **The reduction of NAD$^+$ to create NADH.** NAD$^+$ is composed of two nucleotides, one with an adenine base and one with a nicotinamide base. The oxidation of organic molecules releases electrons that can bind to NAD$^+$ (and along with a hydrogen ion) result in the formation of NADH. The two electrons and H$^+$ are incorporated into the nicotinamide ring. Note: the actual net charges of NAD$^+$ and NADH are minus one and minus two, respectively. They are designated NAD$^+$ and NADH to emphasize the net charge of the nicotinamide ring, which is involved in oxidation-reduction reactions.

NADH (**Figure 7.7**). In this process, an organic molecule has been oxidized and **NAD$^+$ (nicotinamide adenine dinucleotide)** has been reduced to NADH. Cells use NADH in two common ways. First, as we will see, the oxidation of NADH is a highly exergonic reaction that can be used to make ATP. Second, NADH can donate electrons to other organic molecules and thereby energize them. Such energized molecules can more readily form covalent bonds. Therefore, as described next, NADH is often needed in anabolic reactions that involve the synthesis of larger molecules through the formation of covalent bonds between smaller molecules.

Anabolic Reactions Require an Input of Energy to Make Larger Molecules

Anabolic reactions are also called **biosynthetic reactions**, because they are necessary to make larger molecules and macromolecules. We will examine the synthesis of macromolecules in several chapters of this textbook. For example, RNA and protein biosynthesis are described in Chapter 12. Cells also need to synthesize small organic molecules, such as amino acids and fats, if they are not readily available from food sources. Such molecules are made by the formation of covalent linkages between precursor molecules. For example, glutamate (an amino acid) is made by the covalent linkage between α-ketoglutarate (a product of sugar metabolism) and ammonium.

$$\text{α-ketoglutarate} \quad \text{Ammonium} \quad \text{Glutamate}$$

COO⁻ written as:

$$
\begin{array}{l}
\text{COO}^- \\
|\\
\text{CH}_2\\
|\\
\text{CH}_2\\
|\\
\text{C=O}\\
|\\
\text{COO}^-
\end{array}
+ NH_4^+ + NADH \longrightarrow
\begin{array}{l}
\text{COO}^-\\
|\\
\text{CH}_2\\
|\\
\text{CH}_2\\
|\\
\text{H}_3\text{N}^+\text{—C—COO}^-\\
|\\
\text{H}
\end{array}
+ NAD^+ + H_2O
$$

α-ketoglutarate   Ammonium   Glutamate

Another amino acid, glutamine, is made from glutamate and ammonium.

$$
\begin{array}{l}
\text{COO}^-\\
|\\
\text{CH}_2\\
|\\
\text{CH}_2\\
|\\
\text{H}_3\text{N}^+\text{—C—COO}^-\\
|\\
\text{H}
\end{array}
+ NH_4^+ + ATP^{4-} + H_2O \longrightarrow
\begin{array}{l}
\text{O=C—NH}_2\\
|\\
\text{CH}_2\\
|\\
\text{CH}_2\\
|\\
\text{H}_3\text{N}^+\text{—C—COO}^-\\
|\\
\text{H}
\end{array}
+ ADP^{2-} + P_i^{2-}
$$

Glutamate   Ammonium   Glutamine

In both reactions, an energy intermediate molecule such as NADH or ATP is needed to drive the reaction forward.

Table 7.2	Examples of Proteins That Use ATP for Energy
Type	**Description**
Metabolic enzymes	Many enzymes use ATP to catalyze endergonic reactions. For example, hexokinase uses ATP to attach phosphate to glucose.
Transporters	Ion pumps, such as the Na⁺/K⁺-ATPase, use ATP to pump ions against a gradient (see Chapter 5).
Motor proteins	Motor proteins such as myosin use ATP to facilitate cellular movement, as in muscle contraction (see Chapter 46).
Chaperones	Chaperones are proteins that use ATP to aid in the folding and unfolding of cellular proteins (see Chapter 6).
DNA-modifying enzymes	Many proteins such as helicases and topoisomerases use ATP to modify the conformation of DNA (see Chapter 11).
Aminoacyl-tRNA synthetases	These enzymes use ATP to attach amino acids to tRNAs (see Chapter 12).
Protein kinases	Protein kinases are regulatory proteins that use ATP to attach a phosphate to proteins, thereby affecting the function of the phosphorylated protein (see Chapter 9).

GENOMES & PROTEOMES

Many Proteins Use ATP as a Source of Energy

Over the past several decades, researchers have studied the functions of many types of proteins and discovered numerous examples in which a protein uses ATP to drive a cellular process (**Table 7.2**). In humans, a typical cell uses millions of ATP molecules per second. At the same time, the breakdown of food molecules releases energy that allows us to make more ATP from ADP and P_i. The turnover of ATP occurs at a remarkable pace. An average person hydrolyzes about 100 pounds of ATP per day, yet we do not have 100 pounds of ATP in our bodies. For this to happen, each ATP undergoes about 10,000 cycles of hydrolysis and resynthesis (from ADP and P_i) during an ordinary day (**Figure 7.8**).

By studying the structures of many proteins that use ATP, biochemists have discovered that particular amino acid sequences within proteins function as ATP-binding sites. This information has allowed researchers to predict whether a newly discovered protein uses ATP or not. When an entire genome sequence of a species is experimentally determined, the genes that encode proteins can be analyzed to find out if the encoded proteins have ATP-binding sites in their amino acid sequences. Using this approach, researchers have been able to analyze proteomes—all of the proteins that a given cell can make—and estimate the percentage of proteins that are able to bind ATP. (Most of these proteins are expected to use ATP as a source of energy, though some of them may simply bind ATP without hydrolyzing it to ADP and P_i.) This approach has been applied to the proteomes of bacteria, archaea, and eukaryotes. On average, over 20% of all proteins bind ATP. However, this number

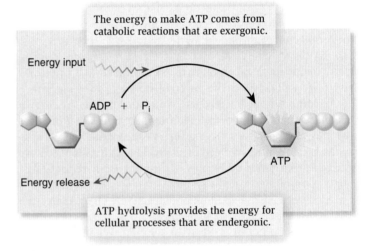

Figure 7.8   The ATP cycle. Living cells continuously recycle ATP. The breakdown of food molecules is used to make ATP from ADP and P_i. The hydrolysis of ATP to ADP and P_i is used to drive many different endergonic reactions and processes that occur in cells.

Biological inquiry: If a large amount of ADP was broken down in the cell, how would this affect the ATP cycle?

is likely to be an underestimate of the total percentage of ATP-utilizing proteins because we may not have identified all of the types of ATP-binding sites in proteins. In humans, who have an estimated genome size of 20,000 to 25,000 different genes, a minimum of 4,000 to 5,000 of those genes encode proteins that use ATP. From these numbers, we can see the enormous importance of ATP as a source of energy for living cells.

Metabolic Pathways Are Regulated in Three General Ways

Before we end our general discussion of metabolism, let's consider the various ways in which chemical reactions are regulated in living cells. The regulation of catabolic pathways is important, so that a cell breaks down organic molecules when energy is needed but conserves them when an adequate supply of energy intermediates is available. The control of anabolic pathways is essential so that a cell does not waste energy making too much of the products of such pathways. The regulation of catabolic and anabolic pathways occurs at the genetic, cellular, and biochemical levels.

Gene Regulation Because enzymes in every metabolic pathway are encoded by genes, one way that cells control chemical reactions is via gene regulation. For example, if a bacterial cell is not exposed to a particular sugar in its environment, it will turn off the genes that encode the enzymes that are needed to break down that sugar. Alternatively, if the sugar becomes available, the genes are switched on. Chapter 13 examines the steps of gene regulation in detail.

Cellular Regulation Metabolism is also coordinated at the cellular level. Cells integrate signals from their environment and adjust their chemical reactions to adapt to those signals. As discussed in Chapter 9, cell-signaling pathways often lead to the activation of protein kinases that covalently attach a phosphate group to target proteins. For example, when people are frightened, they secrete a hormone called epinephrine into their bloodstream. This hormone binds to the surface of muscle cells and stimulates an intracellular pathway that leads to the phosphorylation of several intracellular proteins, including enzymes involved in carbohydrate metabolism. These activated enzymes promote the breakdown of carbohydrates, an event that supplies the frightened individual with more energy. Epinephrine is sometimes called the "fight-or-flight" hormone because the added energy prepares an individual to either stay and fight or run away. After a person is no longer frightened, hormone levels drop and other enzymes called phosphatases remove the phosphate groups from enzymes, thereby restoring the original level of carbohydrate metabolism.

Biochemical Regulation A third and very prominent way that metabolic pathways are controlled is at the biochemical level. In this case, the binding of a molecule to an enzyme directly regulates its function. Biochemical regulation is typically categorized according to the site where the regulatory molecule binds. Let's consider two types of regulation that involve regulatory molecules that inhibit enzyme function.

Competitive inhibitors are molecules that bind to the active site of an enzyme and inhibit the ability of the substrate to bind. In other words, such inhibitors "compete" with the substrate for the ability to bind to the enzyme. Competitive inhibitors usually have a structure that mimics the structure of the enzyme's substrate. Competitive inhibition can be overcome by increasing the concentration of the substrate and decreasing the concentration of the inhibitor.

Noncompetitive inhibitors bind to an enzyme at a location that is outside the active site and inhibit the enzyme's function. An example is a form of regulation called **feedback inhibition**, in which the product of a metabolic pathway inhibits an enzyme that acts early in the pathway, thus preventing the overaccumulation of the product (**Figure 7.9**). Many metabolic pathways use feedback inhibition as a form of biochemical regulation. In such cases, the inhibited enzyme has two binding sites. One site is the active site, where the reactants are converted to products. In addition, enzymes that are controlled by feedback inhibition also have an **allosteric site**, where a molecule can bind noncovalently and affect the function of the active site. The binding of a molecule to an allosteric site causes a conformational change in the enzyme that inhibits its catalytic function. Allosteric sites are often found in the enzymes that catalyze the early steps in a metabolic pathway. Such allosteric sites typically bind molecules that are the products of the metabolic pathway. When the products bind to these sites, they inhibit the function of these enzymes and thereby prevent the formation of too much product.

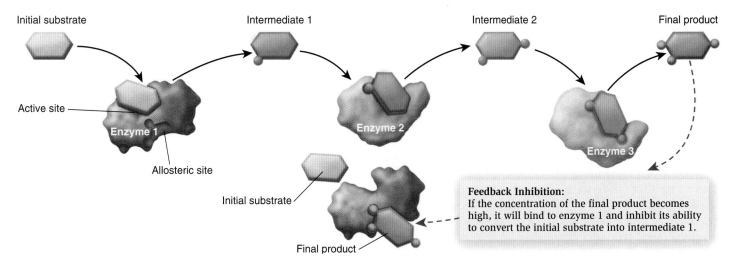

Figure 7.9 **Feedback inhibition.** In this process, the product of a metabolic pathway inhibits an enzyme that functions in the pathway, thereby preventing the overaccumulation of the product.

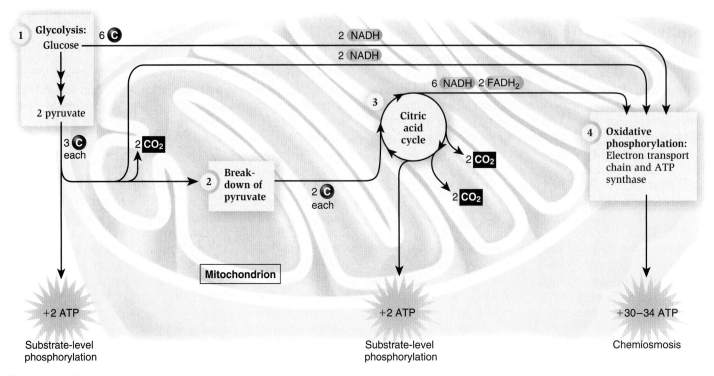

Figure 7.10 **An overview of glucose metabolism.** Glycolysis occurs in the cytosol and results in the breakdown of glucose into two pyruvates, producing two ATP and two NADH molecules. The two pyruvates enter the mitochondrion, where they are broken down into two acetyl groups (each attached to CoA) and two CO_2 molecules. Two molecules of NADH are made in the process. The two acetyl groups then enter the citric acid cycle, where they are broken down to four CO_2 molecules. Two ATP, six NADH, and two $FADH_2$ are synthesized. The NADH and $FADH_2$ molecules that are made during these various steps are then used during oxidative phosphorylation to synthesize more ATP molecules. The maximum yield of ATP is 34 to 38 molecules for every glucose that is completely broken down.

Cellular and biochemical regulation are important and rapid ways to control chemical reactions in a cell. But when considering a metabolic pathway composed of several enzymes, which enzyme in a pathway should be controlled? In many cases, a metabolic pathway has a **rate-limiting step**, which is the slowest step in a pathway. If the rate-limiting step is inhibited or occurs at a faster rate, such changes will have the greatest impact on the formation of the product of the metabolic pathway. Rather than affecting all of the enzymes in a metabolic pathway, cellular and biochemical regulation are often directed at the enzyme that catalyzes the rate-limiting step. This is an efficient and rapid way to control the amount of product of a pathway.

7.3 Cellular Respiration

Cellular respiration is a process by which living cells obtain energy from organic molecules. A primary aim of cellular respiration is to make the energy intermediates ATP and NADH. When oxygen (O_2) is used, this process is termed **aerobic respiration**. During aerobic respiration, O_2 is consumed and CO_2 is released. When we breathe, we inhale the oxygen that is needed for aerobic respiration and exhale the CO_2 that is a by-product of the process. For this reason, the term respiration has a second meaning, which is the act of breathing.

Different types of organic molecules, such as carbohydrates, proteins, and fats, can be used as energy sources to drive aerobic respiration.

$$\text{Organic molecules} + O_2 \rightarrow CO_2 + H_2O + \text{Energy}$$

In this section, we will largely focus on the use of glucose as an energy source for cellular respiration.

$$\underset{\text{Glucose}}{C_6H_{12}O_6} + 6\,O_2 \rightarrow 6\,CO_2 + 6\,H_2O + \text{Energy intermediates} + \text{Heat}$$

We will examine the metabolic pathways in which glucose is broken down into carbon dioxide and water, thereby releasing a large amount of energy that is used to make many ATP molecules. In so doing, we will focus on four pathways: (1) glycolysis, (2) the breakdown of pyruvate, (3) the citric acid cycle, and (4) oxidative phosphorylation. We will conclude our discussion of cellular respiration with a consideration of the metabolism of other organic molecules, such as proteins and fats, and an examination of anaerobic respiration, a second form of respiration in which cells can oxidize fuel and generate ATP without using oxygen.

Several Metabolic Pathways Are Involved in the Breakdown of Glucose to CO_2

Before we examine the details of cellular respiration, let's take a look at the entire process. We will focus on the breakdown of glucose in a eukaryotic cell in the presence of oxygen. The covalent bonds within glucose contain a large amount of chemical bond energy. When glucose is broken down, ultimately to CO_2 and water, the energy within those bonds is released and used to make three types of energy intermediates: ATP, NADH, and $FADH_2$. The following is an overview of the stages that occur during the breakdown of glucose (**Figure 7.10**):

1. **Glycolysis:** In glycolysis, glucose (6 C, meaning a compound with six carbon atoms) is broken down in the cytosol to two pyruvate molecules (3 C each), producing a net gain of two ATP molecules, via substrate-level phosphorylation, and two NADH molecules.

2. **Breakdown of pyruvate to an acetyl group:** The two pyruvate molecules enter the mitochondrion, where each one is broken down to an acetyl group (2 C) and one CO_2 molecule. For each pyruvate broken down, one NADH molecule is made.

3. **Citric acid cycle:** Each acetyl group (2 C) is broken down to two CO_2 molecules. One ATP, three NADH, and one $FADH_2$ are made in this process. Because there are two acetyl groups, the total yield is four CO_2, two ATP via substrate-level phosphorylation, six NADH, and two $FADH_2$.

4. **Oxidative phosphorylation:** The NADH and $FADH_2$ made in the three previous stages contain high-energy electrons that can be readily transferred in a redox reaction to other molecules. Once removed, these high-energy electrons release some energy and that energy is harnessed to make approximately 30 to 34 ATP molecules via chemiosmosis. As discussed later, oxidative phosphorylation consists of two com- ponents, the electron transport chain and the ATP synthase.

Now, let's examine in detail the chemical changes that take place in each of these four stages.

Stage 1: Glycolysis Is a Metabolic Pathway That Breaks Down Glucose to Pyruvate

Glycolysis (from the Greek *glykos*, sweet, and *lysis*, splitting) involves the breakdown of glucose, a simple sugar. This process can occur in the presence or absence of oxygen, that is, under aerobic or anaerobic conditions. Our understanding of glycolysis has a rich history. In 1897, Hans Buchner and Eduard Buchner made an accidental discovery. They were interested in manufacturing cell-free extracts of yeast for possible clinical use. This cell-free extract contained only the internal contents of yeast cells, not the intact cells themselves. To preserve these extracts, they added sucrose, a commonly used preservative in 19th-century chemistry. To their great surprise, they discovered that the cell-free extract converted the sucrose to ethanol. The significance of this finding was extraordinary. The Buchners showed for the first time that metabolism could take place outside of living cells. This observation is considered by many as the birth of **biochemistry**, the study of the chemistry of living organisms.

The Buchners' findings paved the way for the in-depth investigation of the breakdown of glucose. During the 1930s, the efforts of several German biochemists, including Gustav Embden, Otto Meyerhof, and Jacob Parnas, determined that the process involved 10 steps, each one catalyzed by a different enzyme. The elucidation of these steps was a major achievement in the field of biochemistry. Researchers have since discovered that glycolysis is the common pathway for glucose breakdown in bacteria, archaea, and eukaryotes. Remarkably, the steps of glycolysis are virtually identical in nearly all living species, suggesting that glycolysis arose very early in the evolution of life on our planet.

The 10 steps of glycolysis can be grouped into three phases (**Figure 7.11**). The first phase (steps 1–3) involves an energy

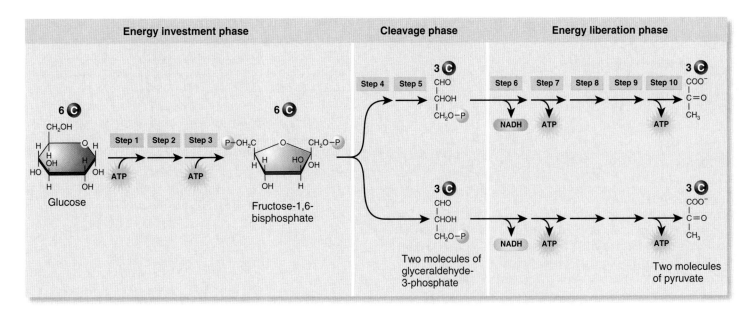

Figure 7.11   Overview of glycolysis.

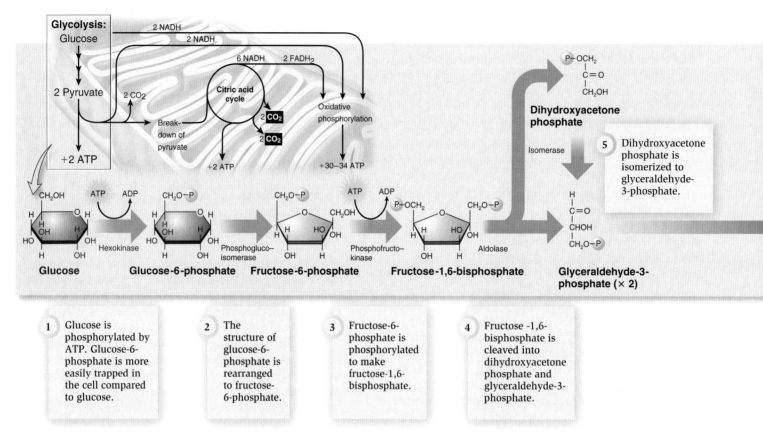

1 Glucose is phosphorylated by ATP. Glucose-6-phosphate is more easily trapped in the cell compared to glucose.

2 The structure of glucose-6-phosphate is rearranged to fructose-6-phosphate.

3 Fructose-6-phosphate is phosphorylated to make fructose-1,6-bisphosphate.

4 Fructose -1,6-bisphosphate is cleaved into dihydroxyacetone phosphate and glyceraldehyde-3-phosphate.

Figure 7.12 An inside look at the steps of glycolysis.

investment. Two ATP molecules are hydrolyzed to create fructose-1,6-bisphosphate. The cleavage phase (steps 4–5) breaks a six-carbon molecule into two molecules of glyceraldehyde-3-phosphate. The third phase (steps 6–10) liberates energy. The two glyceraldehyde-3-phosphate molecules are broken down to two pyruvate molecules. This produces two molecules of NADH and four molecules of ATP. Because two molecules of ATP are used in the energy investment phase, the net yield of ATP is two molecules. **Figure 7.12** describes the details of the 10 reactions of glycolysis. The net reaction of glycolysis is:

$$C_6H_{12}O_6 \ + \ 2 \ NAD^+ \ + \ 2 \ ADP^{2-} \ + \ 2 \ P_i^{2-} \ \rightarrow$$
Glucose

$$2 \ CH_3(C{=}O)COO^- \ + \ 2 \ H^+ \ + \ 2 \ NADH \ + \ 2 \ ATP^{4-} \ + \ 2 \ H_2O$$
Pyruvate

When a cell has a sufficient amount of ATP, feedback inhibition occurs in glycolysis. At high concentration, ATP binds to an allosteric site in phosphofructokinase, which catalyzes the third step in glycolysis and is thought to be the rate-limiting step. When ATP binds to this allosteric site, a conformational change occurs that renders the enzyme functionally inactive. This prevents the further breakdown of glucose and thereby inhibits the overproduction of ATP.

Stage 2: Pyruvate Enters the Mitochondrion and Is Broken Down to an Acetyl Group and CO_2

In eukaryotes, pyruvate is made in the cytosol and then transported into the mitochondrion. Once in the mitochondrial matrix, pyruvate molecules are broken down by an enzyme complex called pyruvate dehydrogenase (**Figure 7.13**). A molecule of CO_2 is removed from each pyruvate and the remaining acetyl group is attached to an organic molecule called coenzyme A (CoA) to create acetyl CoA. During this process, two high-energy electrons are removed from pyruvate and transferred to NAD^+ and together with H^+ create a molecule of NADH. For each pyruvate, the net reaction is:

$$\overset{O \quad O}{\underset{Pyruvate}{^-O-\overset{\|}{C}-\overset{\|}{C}-CH_3}} \ + \ \underset{CoA}{CoA\text{-}SH} \ + \ NAD^+ \ \rightarrow$$

$$\underset{Aceytl \ CoA}{CoA-S-\overset{\overset{O}{\|}}{C}-CH_3} + \ CO_2 \ + \ NADH$$

The acetyl group is attached to CoA via a covalent bond to a sulfur atom. The hydrolysis of this bond releases a large amount of

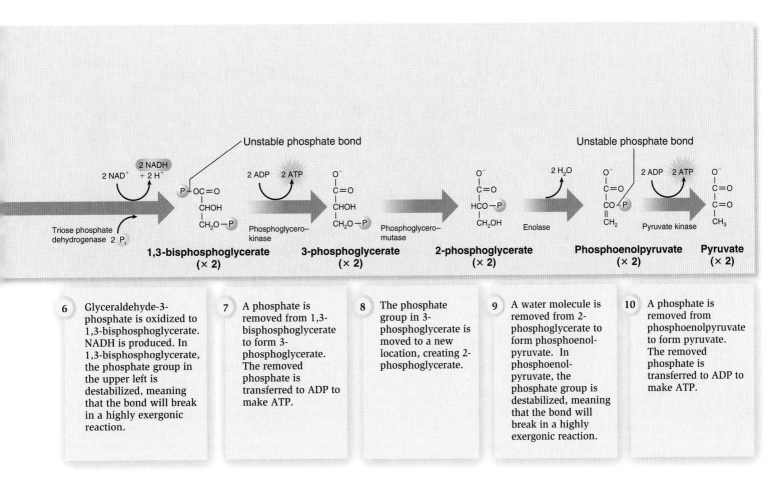

6. Glyceraldehyde-3-phosphate is oxidized to 1,3-bisphosphoglycerate. NADH is produced. In 1,3-bisphosphoglycerate, the phosphate group in the upper left is destabilized, meaning that the bond will break in a highly exergonic reaction.

7. A phosphate is removed from 1,3-bisphosphoglycerate to form 3-phosphoglycerate. The removed phosphate is transferred to ADP to make ATP.

8. The phosphate group in 3-phosphoglycerate is moved to a new location, creating 2-phosphoglycerate.

9. A water molecule is removed from 2-phosphoglycerate to form phosphoenol-pyruvate. In phosphoenol-pyruvate, the phosphate group is destabilized, meaning that the bond will break in a highly exergonic reaction.

10. A phosphate is removed from phosphoenolpyruvate to form pyruvate. The removed phosphate is transferred to ADP to make ATP.

free energy, making it possible for the acetyl group to be transferred to other organic molecules. As described next, the acetyl group attached to CoA enters the citric acid cycle.

Stage 3: During the Citric Acid Cycle, an Acetyl Group Is Oxidized to Two CO_2 Molecules

The third stage of sugar metabolism introduces a new concept, that of the **metabolic cycle**. During a metabolic cycle, particular molecules enter the cycle while others leave; the process is cyclical because it involves a series of organic molecules that are regenerated with each turn of the cycle. The idea of a metabolic cycle was first proposed in the early 1930s by German biochemist Hans Krebs. While studying carbohydrate metabolism, he analyzed cell extracts from pigeon muscle and determined that citric acid and other organic molecules participated in a cycle that resulted in the breakdown of carbohydrates to carbon dioxide. This cycle is called the **citric acid cycle** or the Krebs cycle, in honor of Krebs, who was awarded the Nobel Prize in 1953.

An overview of the citric acid cycle is shown in **Figure 7.14**. At the beginning of the cycle, the acetyl group is removed from acetyl CoA and attached to oxaloacetate (4 C) to form citrate (6 C), also called citric acid. In a series of several steps, two CO_2 molecules are released. As this occurs, three molecules of NADH,

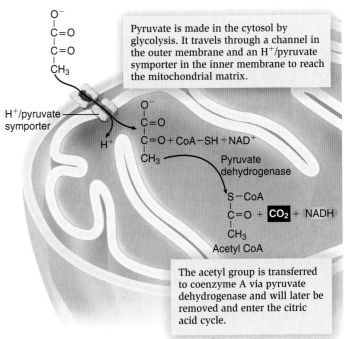

Pyruvate is made in the cytosol by glycolysis. It travels through a channel in the outer membrane and an H^+/pyruvate symporter in the inner membrane to reach the mitochondrial matrix.

The acetyl group is transferred to coenzyme A via pyruvate dehydrogenase and will later be removed and enter the citric acid cycle.

Figure 7.13 **Breakdown of pyruvate and the attachment of an acetyl group to CoA.** Pyruvate enters the mitochondrion by traveling through a channel in the outer membrane and then through an H^+/pyruvate symporter in the inner membrane.

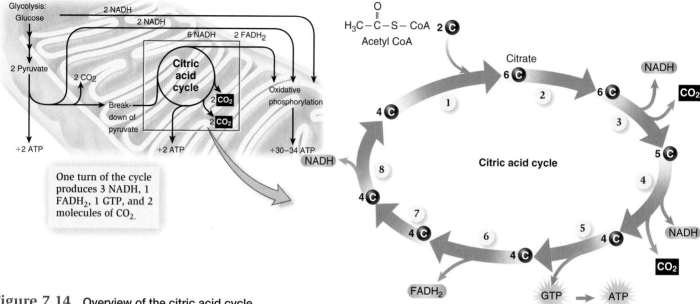

Figure 7.14 Overview of the citric acid cycle.

one molecule of $FADH_2$, and one molecule of GTP are made. The GTP is used to make ATP. After eight steps, oxaloacetate is regenerated so that the cycle can begin again, provided acetyl CoA is available. **Figure 7.15** shows a more detailed view of the citric acid cycle. For each acetyl group attached to CoA, the net reaction of the citric acid cycle is:

$$\text{Acetyl-CoA} + 3\,H_2O + 3\,NAD^+ + FAD + GDP^{2-} + P_i^{2-} \rightarrow$$
$$\text{CoA-SH} + 2\,CO_2 + 3\,NADH + FADH_2 + GTP^{4-}$$

Competitive inhibition is one way that the citric acid cycle is regulated. Oxaloacetate is a competitive inhibitor of succinate dehydrogenase (Figure 7.15). Therefore, when oxaloacetate levels become too high, this inhibits succinate dehydrogenase and slows down the citric acid cycle.

Stage 4: During Oxidative Phosphorylation, NADH and FADH2 Are Used to Make More ATP

Up to this point, the oxidation of glucose has yielded 6 molecules of CO_2, 4 molecules of ATP, 10 molecules of NADH, and 2 molecules of $FADH_2$. Let's now consider how high-energy electrons are removed from NADH and $FADH_2$ to make more ATP. This process is called **oxidative phosphorylation** because NADH and $FADH_2$ are oxidized due to the removal of electrons, and ATP is made by the phosphorylation of ADP (**Figure 7.16**). Oxidative phosphorylation usually occurs under aerobic conditions, which means that it typically requires oxygen. As described next, the oxidative process involves the electron transport chain, while the phosphorylation occurs via the ATP synthase.

Electron Transport Chain The **electron transport chain** consists of a group of protein complexes and small organic molecules embedded in the inner mitochondrial membrane. These components are referred to as an electron transport chain because the components can accept and donate electrons to each

other in a linear manner (Figure 7.16). Most of the members of the chain are protein complexes (designated I to IV) that have prosthetic groups. For example, cytochrome oxidase contains two prosthetic groups, each with an iron atom. The iron in each prosthetic group can readily accept and release an electron. One of the members of the electron transport chain, ubiquinone (Q), is not a protein. Rather, ubiquinone is a small organic molecule that can accept and release an electron and can diffuse through the lipid bilayer.

The red line in Figure 7.16 shows the path of electrons as they flow along the electron transport chain. This path is a series of redox reactions in which electrons are transferred to components with increasingly higher electronegativity. At the beginning of the chain, a pair of high-energy electrons from NADH are transferred one at a time to NADH dehydrogenase (complex I), and then to ubiquinone (Q), cytochrome b-c_1 (complex III), cytochrome c, cytochrome oxidase (complex IV), and finally O_2. At the end of the chain, 2 electrons, 2 H^+, and 1/2 O_2 combine to form a molecule of water. Similarly, $FADH_2$ transfers electrons to succinate reductase (complex II), then to ubiquinone, and the rest of the chain.

The electron transport chain is also called the **respiratory chain** because the oxygen we breathe is used in this process. One component of the electron transport chain, cytochrome oxidase, is inhibited by carbon monoxide. The deadly effects of carbon monoxide occur because the electron transport chain is shut down, preventing cells from making enough ATP for survival.

As shown in Figure 7.16, the movement of electrons results in the pumping of H^+ across the inner mitochondrial membrane to establish a large **H^+ electrochemical gradient** in which the concentration of H^+ is higher outside of the matrix, and an excess of positive charge exists outside the matrix. Because hydrogen ions consist of protons, the H^+ electrochemical gradient is also called the **proton-motive force**. NADH dehydrogenase, cytochrome b-c_1, and cytochrome oxidase are H^+ pumps.

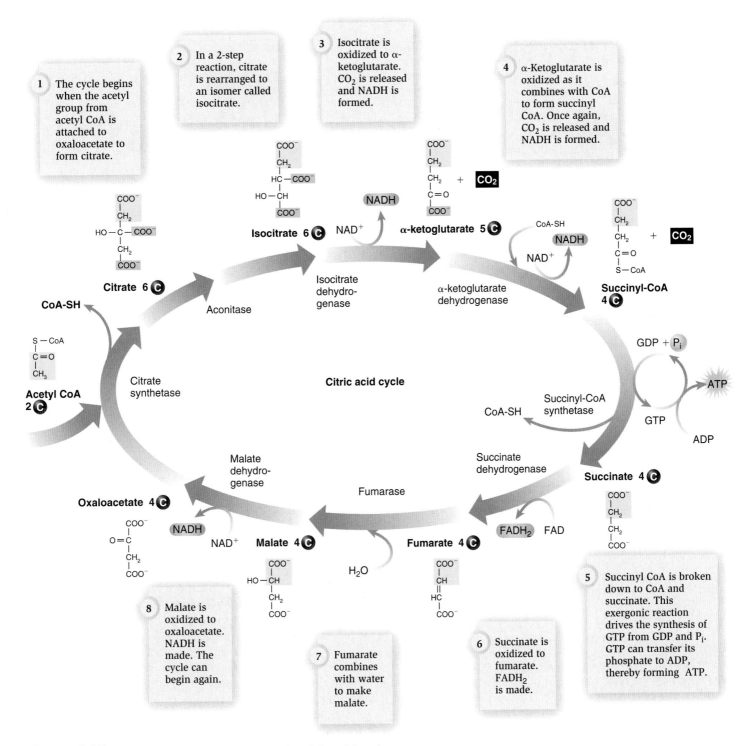

Figure 7.15 A detailed look at the steps of the citric acid cycle.

While traveling along the electron transport chain, electrons release free energy, and some of this energy is captured by these proteins to pump H^+ out of the matrix into the intermembrane space. Because the electrons from $FADH_2$ enter the chain at an intermediate step, fewer hydrogen ions are pumped out of the matrix compared to the release of electrons from NADH.

Why do electrons travel from NADH or $FADH_2$ to O_2? As you might expect, the answer lies in free energy changes. The electrons found on the energy intermediates have a high amount of potential energy. As they travel along the electron transport chain, free energy is released (**Figure 7.17**). The movement of one electron from NADH to O_2 results in a very negative free energy change of approximately -25 kcal/mole. That is why the process is spontaneous and proceeds in the forward direction. Because it is a highly exergonic reaction, some of the free energy can be harnessed to do cellular work. In this case, some energy is used to pump H^+ across the inner mitochondrial membrane and establish an H^+ electrochemical gradient.

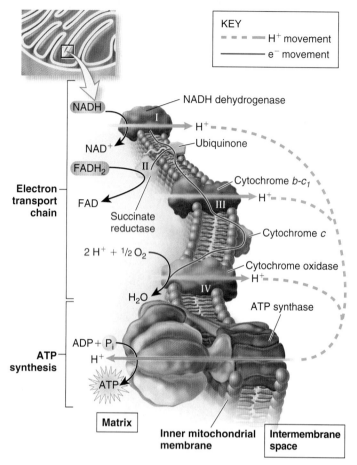

Figure 7.16 Oxidative phosphorylation. This process consists of two distinct events involving the electron transport chain and the ATP synthase. The electron transport chain removes electrons from NADH or $FADH_2$ and pumps H^+ across the inner mitochondrial membrane. The ATP synthase uses the energy in the H^+ electrochemical gradient to synthesize ATP.

Biological inquiry: Can you explain the name of cytochrome oxidase? Can you think of another appropriate name?

ATP Synthase The second event of oxidative phosphorylation is the synthesis of ATP by an enzyme called **ATP synthase**. The H^+ electrochemical gradient across the inner mitochondrial membrane is a source of potential energy. How is this energy used? The flow of H^+ back into the matrix is an exergonic process. The lipid bilayer is relatively impermeable to H^+. However, H^+ can pass through the membrane-embedded portion of the ATP synthase. This enzyme harnesses some of the free energy that is released as the ions flow through its membrane-embedded region to synthesize ATP from ADP and P_i (see Figure 7.16). This is an example of an energy conversion: energy in the form of an H^+ electrochemical gradient, or proton-motive force, is converted to chemical bond energy in ATP. The chemical synthesis of ATP by pushing H^+ across a membrane is called chemiosmosis (from the Greek *osmos*, to push), and the theory behind it was proposed by Peter Mitchell, a British chemist who was awarded the Nobel Prize in 1978.

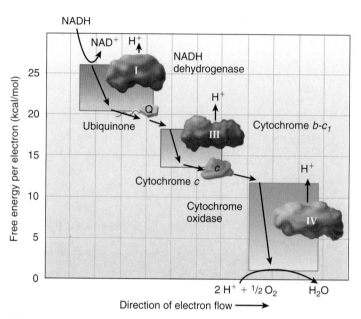

Figure 7.17 The relationship between free energy and electron movement along the electron transport chain. As electrons hop from one site to another along the electron transport chain, they release energy. Some of this energy is harnessed to pump H^+ across the inner mitochondrial membrane. The total energy released by a single electron is approximately −25 kcal/mole.

For each molecule of NADH that is oxidized and each molecule of ATP that is made, the two chemical reactions of oxidative phosphorylation can be represented as follows:

$$NADH + H^+ + 1/2\ O_2 \rightarrow NAD^+ + H_2O$$
$$ADP^{2-} + P_i^{2-} \rightarrow ATP^{4-} + H_2O$$

The oxidation of NADH to NAD^+ results in an H^+ electrochemical gradient in which more hydrogen ions are in the intermembrane space compared to the matrix. The synthesis of one ATP molecule is thought to require the movement of three to four ions into the matrix, down their H^+ electrochemical gradient.

When we add up the maximal amount of ATP that can be made by oxidative phosphorylation, most researchers agree that it is in the range of 30 to 34 ATP molecules for each glucose molecule that is broken down to CO_2 and water. However, the maximum amount of ATP is rarely achieved for two reasons. First, although 10 NADH and 2 $FADH_2$ are available to create the H^+ electrochemical gradient across the inner mitochondrial membrane, a cell may use some of these molecules for anabolic pathways. For example, NADH is used in the synthesis of organic molecules such as glycerol (a component of phospholipids) and lactic acid (which is secreted from muscle cells during strenuous exercise). Second, the mitochondrion may use some of the H^+ electrochemical gradient for other purposes. For example, the gradient is used for the uptake of pyruvate into the matrix via an H^+/pyruvate symporter. Therefore, the actual amount of ATP synthesis is usually a little less than the maximum number of 30 to 34. Even so, when we compare the amount of

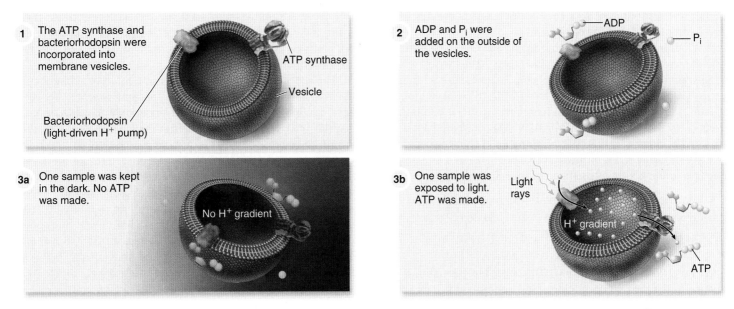

1 The ATP synthase and bacteriorhodopsin were incorporated into membrane vesicles.

ATP synthase

Vesicle

Bacteriorhodopsin (light-driven H$^+$ pump)

2 ADP and P$_i$ were added on the outside of the vesicles.

ADP

P$_i$

3a One sample was kept in the dark. No ATP was made.

No H$^+$ gradient

3b One sample was exposed to light. ATP was made.

Light rays

H$^+$ gradient

ATP

Figure 7.18   The Racker and Stoeckenius experiment showing that an H$^+$ electrochemical gradient drives ATP synthesis via the ATP synthase.

Biological inquiry: Is the functioning of the electron transport chain always needed to make ATP via the ATP synthase?

ATP that can be made by glycolysis (2), the citric acid cycle (2), and oxidative phosphorylation (30–34), we see that oxidative phosphorylation provides a cell with a much greater capacity to make ATP.

Experiments with Purified Proteins in Membrane Vesicles Verified Chemiosmosis

To show experimentally that the ATP synthase actually uses an H$^+$ electrochemical gradient to make ATP, researchers needed to purify the enzyme and study its function *in vitro*. In 1974, Ephraim Racker and Walther Stoeckenius purified the ATP synthase and another protein called bacteriorhodopsin, which is found in certain species of archaea. Previous research had shown that bacteriorhodopsin is a light-driven H$^+$ pump. Racker and Stoeckenius took both purified proteins and inserted them into membrane vesicles (**Figure 7.18**). The ATP synthase was oriented so that its ATP synthesizing region was on the outside of the vesicles. Bacteriorhodopsin was oriented so that it would pump H$^+$ into the vesicles. They added ADP and P$_i$ on the outside of the vesicles. In the dark, no ATP was made. However, when they shone light on the vesicles, a substantial amount of ATP was made. Because bacteriorhodopsin was already known to be a light-driven H$^+$ pump, these results convinced researchers that the ATP synthase uses an H$^+$ electrochemical gradient as an energy source to make ATP.

The ATP Synthase Is a Rotary Machine That Makes ATP as It Spins

The structure and function of the ATP synthase are particularly intriguing and have received much attention over the past few decades (**Figure 7.19**). The ATP synthase is a rotary machine.

The nonmembrane-embedded portion consists of 1 ε, 1 γ, 1 δ, 3 α, and 3 β subunits. Movement of H$^+$ through the c subunits causes the γ subunit to rotate. The rotation, in 120° increments, causes the β subunits to progress through a series of 3 conformational changes that lead to the synthesis of ATP from ADP and P$_i$.

The membrane-embedded portion consists of a ring of 9–12 c subunits, 1 a subunit, and 2 b subunits. H$^+$ move through the c subunits.

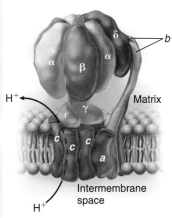

δ

b

α

β

α

H$^+$

Matrix

ε

γ

c c c

a

Intermembrane space

H$^+$

Figure 7.19   The subunit structure and function of the ATP synthase.

The membrane-embedded region is composed of three types of subunits called a, b, and c. Approximately 9 to 12 c subunits form a ring in the membrane. Each c subunit is an H$^+$ channel. One a subunit is bound to this ring, and two b subunits are attached to the a subunit and protrude out of the membrane. The nonmembrane-embedded subunits are designated with Greek letters. One ε and one γ subunit bind to the ring of c subunits. The γ subunit forms a long stalk that pokes into the center of another ring of three α and three β subunits. The β subunits are the catalytic site where ATP is made.

Finally, the δ subunit forms a connection between the ring of α and β subunits and the two *b* subunits.

When hydrogen ions pass through a *c* subunit, a conformational change causes the γ subunit to turn clockwise (when viewed from the intermembrane space). Each time the γ subunit turns 120° it changes its contacts with the three β subunits, which in turn causes the β subunits to change their conformations. How do these conformational changes promote ATP synthesis? The answer is that the conformational changes occur in a way that favors ATP synthesis and release. The conformational changes in the β subunits happen in the following order:

- Conformation 1: ADP and P_i bind with good affinity.
- Conformation 2: ADP and P_i bind so tightly that ATP is made.
- Conformation 3: ATP (and ADP and P_i) bind very weakly, and ATP is released.

Each time the γ subunit turns 120°, it causes a β subunit to change to the next conformation. After conformation 3, a 120° turn by the γ subunit returns a β subunit back to conformation 1, and the cycle of ATP synthesis can begin again. Because the ATP synthase has three β subunits, each subunit is in a different conformation at any given time.

Paul Boyer proposed the concept of a rotary machine in the late 1970s. In his model, the three β subunits alternate between three conformations, as described previously. Boyer's original idea was met with great skepticism, because the concept that part of an enzyme could spin was very novel, to say the least. John Walker and colleagues were able to determine the three-dimensional structure of the nonmembrane-embedded portion of the ATP synthase. The structure revealed that each of the three β subunits had a different conformation—one with ADP bound, one with ATP bound, and one without any nucleotide bound. This result supported Boyer's model. In 1997, Boyer and Walker shared the Nobel Prize for their work on the ATP synthase. As described in the Feature Investigation, researchers subsequently visualized the rotation of the γ subunit.

FEATURE INVESTIGATION

Yoshida and Kinosita Demonstrated That the γ Subunit of the ATP Synthase Spins

In 1997, Masasuke Yoshida, Kazuhiko Kinosita, and colleagues set out to experimentally visualize the rotary nature of the ATP synthase (**Figure 7.20**). The membrane-embedded region of the ATP synthase can be separated from the rest of the protein by treatment of mitochondrial membranes with a high concentration of salt, releasing the portion of the protein containing the one γ, three α, and three β subunits. The researchers adhered the $γα_3β_3$ complex to a glass slide so that the γ subunit was protruding upwards. Because the γ subunit is too small to be seen with a light microscope, it is not possible to visualize the rotation of the γ subunit directly. To circumvent this problem, the researchers attached a large, fluorescently labeled actin filament to the γ subunit via a linker protein. The fluorescently labeled actin filament is very long compared to the γ subunit and can be readily seen with a fluorescence microscope.

Figure 7.20   Evidence that the ATP synthase is a rotary machine.

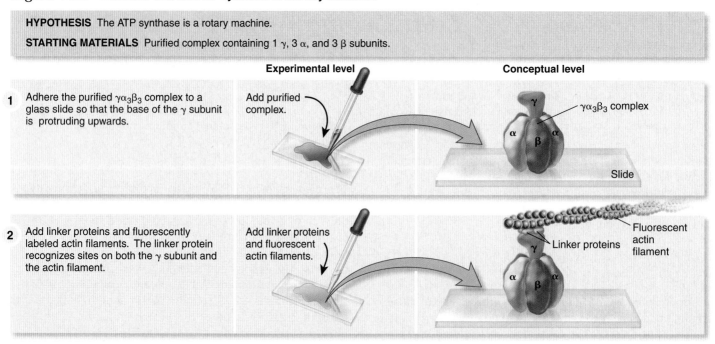

HYPOTHESIS The ATP synthase is a rotary machine.

STARTING MATERIALS Purified complex containing 1 γ, 3 α, and 3 β subunits.

Experimental level   **Conceptual level**

1 Adhere the purified $γα_3β_3$ complex to a glass slide so that the base of the γ subunit is protruding upwards.

Add purified complex.

$γα_3β_3$ complex

Slide

2 Add linker proteins and fluorescently labeled actin filaments. The linker protein recognizes sites on both the γ subunit and the actin filament.

Add linker proteins and fluorescent actin filaments.

Linker proteins

Fluorescent actin filament

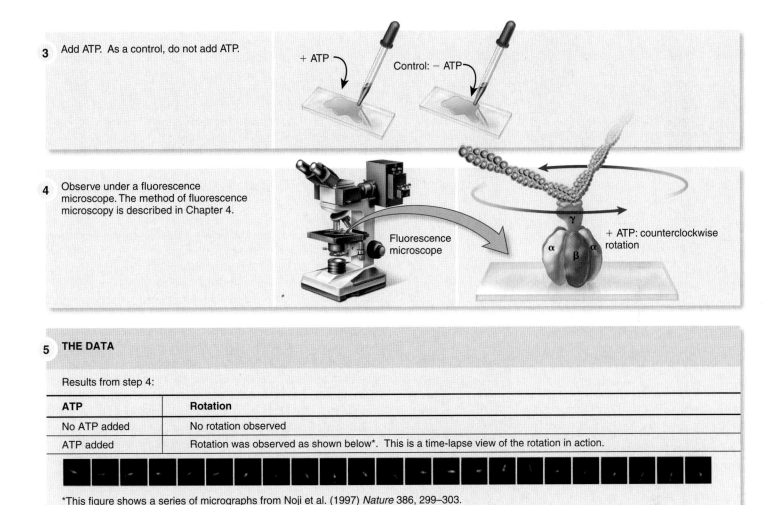

3 Add ATP. As a control, do not add ATP.

+ ATP   Control: − ATP

4 Observe under a fluorescence microscope. The method of fluorescence microscopy is described in Chapter 4.

Fluorescence microscope

γ
α   β   α
+ ATP: counterclockwise rotation

5 THE DATA

Results from step 4:

ATP	Rotation
No ATP added	No rotation observed
ATP added	Rotation was observed as shown below*. This is a time-lapse view of the rotation in action.

*This figure shows a series of micrographs from Noji et al. (1997) *Nature* 386, 299–303.

Because the membrane-embedded portion of the protein is missing, you may be wondering how the researchers could get the γ subunit to rotate. The answer is that they added ATP. Although the normal function of the ATP synthase is to make ATP, it can run backwards. In other words, the ATP synthase can hydrolyze ATP. As shown in the data for Figure 7.20, when the researchers added ATP, the fluorescently labeled actin fila- ment was observed to rotate in a counterclockwise direction, which is opposite to the direction that the γ subunit rotates when ATP is synthesized. In fact, actin filaments were observed to rotate for more than 100 revolutions in the presence of ATP. These results convinced the scientific community that the ATP synthase is indeed a rotary machine.

Metabolic Pathways for Carbohydrate Metabolism Are Interconnected to Pathways for Amino Acid and Fat Metabolism

Thus far, we have focused our attention on the stages of glucose breakdown that result in the release of CO_2 and the production of NADH, $FADH_2$ and ATP. In addition, cells use other organic molecules as a source of energy. When you eat a meal, it is likely to contain not only carbohydrates (including glucose) but also proteins and fats. Proteins and fats are also broken down by the enzymes involved with glucose metabolism.

As shown in **Figure 7.21**, proteins and fats can enter into glycolysis, or the citric acid cycle, at different points. Proteins are first acted upon by enzymes, either in digestive juices or within cells, that cleave the bonds connecting individual amino acids. Because the 20 amino acids differ in their side chains, amino acids and their breakdown products can enter at different points in the pathway. Breakdown products of amino acids can enter glycolysis, or an acetyl group can be removed from certain amino acids and become attached to CoA. Other amino acids can be modified and enter the citric acid cycle. Similarly, fats can be broken down to glycerol and fatty acids.

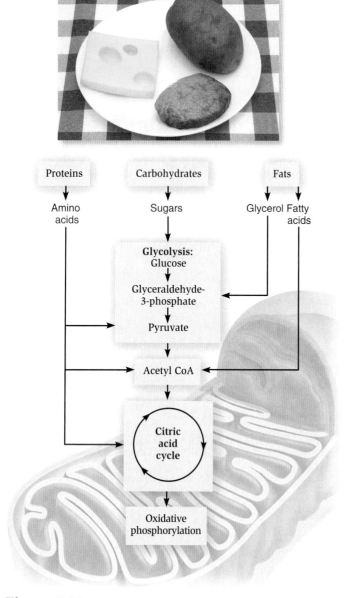

Figure 7.21   Integration of protein, carbohydrate, and fat metabolism.   Breakdown products of amino acids and fats can enter the same pathway that is used to break down carbohydrates.

Glycerol can be modified to glyceraldehyde-3-phosphate and enter glycolysis at step 5 (see Figure 7.12). Fatty acyl tails can have two carbon acetyl units removed, which bind to CoA and then enter the citric acid cycle. By utilizing the same pathways for the breakdown of sugars, amino acids, and fats, cells are more efficient because they can use the same enzymes for the breakdown of different starting molecules.

Likewise, carbohydrate metabolism is connected to the metabolism of other cellular components at the anabolic level. Cells may use carbohydrates to manufacture parts of amino acids, fats, and nucleotides. For example, glucose-6-phosphate

of glycolysis is used to construct the sugar and phosphate portion of nucleotides, while oxaloacetate of the citric acid cycle can be used as a precursor for the biosynthesis of purine and pyrimidine bases. Portions of amino acids can be made from products of glycolysis (for example, pyruvate) and components of the citric acid cycle (oxaloacetate). In addition, many other catabolic and anabolic pathways are found in living cells that connect the metabolism of carbohydrates, proteins, fats, and nucleic acids.

Anaerobic Respiration Involves the Breakdown of Organic Molecules in the Absence of Oxygen

In this section, we have primarily surveyed catabolic pathways that result in the complete breakdown of glucose in the presence of oxygen. It is also common for cells to metabolize organic molecules such as glucose without using oxygen, a process called **anaerobic respiration**. Some microorganisms, such as bacteria and fungi, exist in environments that lack oxygen and have to carry out anaerobic respiration to obtain sufficient amounts of energy. Examples include microbes living in your intestinal tract and those living deep in the soil. Similarly, when a person exercises strenuously, the rate of oxygen consumption by muscle cells may greatly exceed the rate of oxygen delivery. Under these conditions, the muscle cells become anaerobic and must use anaerobic respiration to maintain their level of activity.

Organisms have evolved two different strategies to carry out anaerobic respiration. One strategy is to use a substance other than O_2 as the final electron acceptor of the electron transport chain. In the electron transport chain shown in Figure 7.16, cytochrome oxidase recognizes O_2 and catalyzes its reduction to H_2O. The final electron acceptor of the chain is O_2. Many species of bacteria that live under anaerobic conditions have evolved enzymes that function similarly to cytochrome oxidase, but recognize molecules other than O_2 and use them as the final electron acceptor. For example, *Escherichia coli*, which is found in your intestinal tract, has an enzyme called nitrate reductase that can use nitrate (NO_3^-) as the final electron acceptor of the electron transport chain under anaerobic conditions, and thus oxidative phosphorylation can occur.

Other organisms, including yeast and mammals, can use only O_2 as the final electron acceptor of their electron transport chains. When confronted with anaerobic conditions, these organisms must have a different strategy for anaerobic respiration. Such organisms can still carry out glycolysis, which can occur under anaerobic or aerobic conditions. However, a key issue is that glycolysis uses NAD^+ and generates NADH. As discussed earlier in this chapter, NADH is a good electron donor, because it readily gives up its electrons. Under aerobic conditions, oxygen acts as a final electron acceptor, and the high-energy electrons from NADH can be used to make more ATP. However, this cannot occur under anaerobic conditions in these organisms and, as a result, NADH builds up. At high concentrations, NADH will haphazardly donate its electrons to other molecules and

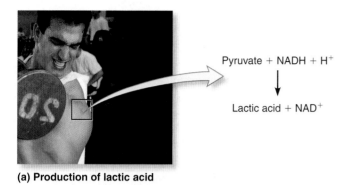

(a) Production of lactic acid

$$\text{Pyruvate} + \text{NADH} + \text{H}^+$$
$$\downarrow$$
$$\text{Lactic acid} + \text{NAD}^+$$

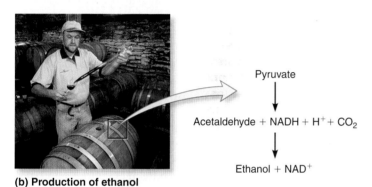

(b) Production of ethanol

$$\text{Pyruvate}$$
$$\downarrow$$
$$\text{Acetaldehyde} + \text{NADH} + \text{H}^+ + \text{CO}_2$$
$$\downarrow$$
$$\text{Ethanol} + \text{NAD}^+$$

Figure 7.22 **Examples of anaerobic respiration.** In these examples, NADH is produced by the oxidation of an organic molecule, and then the NADH is used up by donating electrons to a different organic molecule such as pyruvate (a) or acetaldehyde (b). Note: at neutral pH, lactic acid releases H^+ to form lactate.

promote the formation of free radicals, highly reactive chemicals that can damage DNA and cellular proteins. For this reason, cells of mammals and yeast that are exposed to anaerobic conditions must have a strategy to remove the excess NADH normally generated from the breakdown of organic molecules such as glucose. In addition, cells need to regenerate NAD^+ to keep glycolysis running.

In the case of muscle cells working under anaerobic conditions, the pyruvate from glycolysis is converted by NADH to lactate, also known as lactic acid (**Figure 7.22a**). When a person exercises strenuously, the buildup of lactic acid causes a burning sensation or even cramps that often prompt the individual to slow down. Products of anaerobic respiration, such as lactic acid, are eventually secreted from cells. Similarly, during wine making, a yeast cell metabolizes sugar under anaerobic conditions. The pyruvate is broken down to CO_2 and a two-carbon molecule called acetaldehyde. The acetaldehyde is then reduced by NADH to make ethanol (**Figure 7.22b**). In these examples, NADH is used up by donating its electrons to pyruvate and acetaldehyde, thereby creating lactic acid and ethanol, respectively. These reactions also regenerate NAD^+, which allows cells to metabolize more glucose and keep making ATP.

The term **fermentation** is used to describe the breakdown of organic molecules to produce energy without any net oxidation (that is, without any removal of electrons). The breakdown of glucose to lactic acid or ethanol are examples of fermentation. Although electrons are removed from an organic molecule such as glucose to make NADH and pyruvate, the electrons are donated back to an organic molecule in the creation of lactic acid or ethanol. Therefore, there is no net removal of electrons from an organic molecule. Compared with oxidative phosphorylation, fermentation produces far less ATP for two reasons. First, glucose is not oxidized completely to CO_2 and water. Second, the NADH that is made during glycolysis cannot be used to make more ATP. Overall, the complete breakdown of glucose in the presence of oxygen yields 34 to 38 ATP molecules. By comparison, the anaerobic breakdown of glucose to lactic acid or ethanol yields only two ATP molecules.

7.4 Secondary Metabolism

Primary metabolism is the synthesis and breakdown of molecules and macromolecules that are found in all forms of life and are essential for cell structure and function. These include compounds such as lipids, sugars, nucleotides, and amino acids and the macromolecules that are derived from them. Cellular respiration, which we considered earlier in this chapter, is an example of primary metabolism. By comparison, **secondary metabolism** involves the synthesis of molecules—**secondary metabolites**—that are not essential for cell structure and growth. Any given secondary metabolite is unique to one species or group of species and is not usually required for survival. Secondary metabolites, also called secondary compounds, are commonly made in plants, bacteria, and fungi, where they play a variety of roles. Many secondary metabolites taste bad. When produced in a plant, for example, such a molecule may prevent an animal from eating the plant. In some cases, secondary metabolites are toxic. Such molecules may act as a chemical weapon that inhibits the growth of nearby organisms. In addition, many secondary metabolites produce a strong smell or bright color that attracts or repels other organisms. For example, the scent from a rose is due to secondary metabolites. The scent attracts insects that aid in pollination. Alternatively, other secondary metabolites may smell bad and prevent an animal from ingesting a plant.

Biologists have discovered thousands of different secondary metabolites, though any given species tends to produce only one or a few types. As you will learn, many of these have been put to practical use by humans, including spices that are used in cooking and antibiotics that inhibit the growth of pathogenic microorganisms and are used to treat diseases. Plants are particularly diverse in the types of secondary metabolites they produce, perhaps because they need clever ways to defend themselves. Bacteria and fungi also produce a large array of these compounds, while animals tend to produce relatively few. In this section, we will survey four categories of secondary metabolites: phenolics, alkaloids, terpenoids, and polyketides.

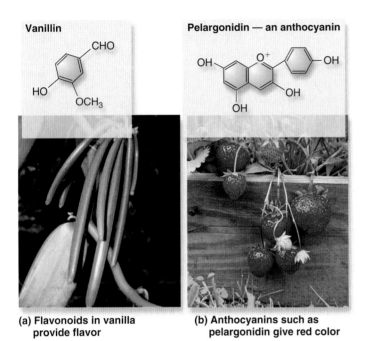

Figure 7.23 Phenolic compounds as secondary metabolites. The two examples shown here are flavonoids, which are a type of phenolic compound. (a) The flavor of vanilla is largely produced by flavonoids, an example of which is vanillin. Commercially, vanillin is extracted from the seed capsule of *Vanilla planifolia*. (b) Another group of flavonoids that causes red, blue, or purple color are anthocyanins. The red color of strawberries is caused by pelargonidin, an anthocyanin.

Phenolic Compounds Are Antioxidants That Have Intense Flavors and Bright Colors

The **phenolic** compounds all contain a cyclic ring of carbon with three double bonds, known as a benzene ring, within their structure. When a benzene ring is covalently linked to a single hydroxyl group, the compound is known as phenol.

Phenol is the simplest of the phenolic compounds, though free phenol is not significantly accumulated in living organisms. However, more complex molecules that are derived from phenol are made in cells. Such phenolic compounds are synthesized using the side groups of the amino acids phenylalanine (which has a benzene ring) or tyrosine (which has a phenol ring). Common categories of phenolics are the flavonoids, tannins, and lignins. The tannins and lignins are large polymeric molecules composed of many phenolic units.

Flavonoids are produced by many plant species and create a variety of flavors and smells. These can play a role as deterrents to eating a plant or as attractants that promote pollination. The flavors of chocolate and vanilla largely come from a mixture of flavonoid molecules. Vanilla is produced by several spe-

cies of perennial vines of the genus *Vanilla* native to Mexico and tropical America (**Figure 7.23a**). The primary source of commercial vanilla comes from *V. planifolia*. Vanilla extract is obtained from the seed capsules. Another role of flavonoids is pigmentation. Anthocyanins (from the Greek *anthos*, flower, and *kyanos*, blue) produce the red, purple, and blue colors of many flowers, fruits, and vegetables (**Figure 7.23b**).

Biochemists have discovered that flavonoids have remarkable antioxidant properties that prevent the formation of damaging free radicals. In plants, flavonoids are thought to act as powerful antioxidants helping to protect plants from UV damage. In recent times, nutritionists have advocated the consumption of fruits and vegetables that have high amounts of flavonoids, such as broccoli and spinach. Dark chocolate is also rich in these antioxidants!

Tannins are large phenolic polymers, so named because they combine with the protein of animal skins to form leather. This process, known as tanning, also imparts a tan color to animal skins. Tannins are found in many plant species and typically act as a deterrent to animals, either because of a bitter taste or due to toxic effects. They also can inhibit the enzymes found in the digestive tracts of animals, if consumed in large amounts. Tannins are found abundantly in grape skins and play a key role in the flavor of red wine. Aging breaks down tannins, making the wine less bitter.

Lignins are also large phenolic polymers synthesized by plants. Lignin is found in plant cell walls and makes up about one-quarter to one-third of the weight of dry wood. The lignins form polymers that bond with other plant wall components such as cellulose. This strengthens plant cells and enables a plant to better withstand the rigors of environmental stress. To make paper, which is much more malleable than wood, the lignin is removed.

Alkaloids Form a Large Group of Bitter-Tasting Molecules That Also Provide Defense Mechanisms

Alkaloids are a group of structurally related molecules that all contain nitrogen and usually have a cyclic, ringlike structure. More than 12,000 different alkaloids have been discovered. Their name is derived from the observation that they are basic or alkaline molecules. Alkaloids are usually synthesized from amino acids precursors. Alkaloids are commonly made in plant species and occasionally in fungi (mushrooms) and animals (shellfish). Familiar examples include caffeine, nicotine, atropine, morphine, ergot, and quinine.

Like phenolics, many alkaloids serve a defense function in plants. Alkaloids are bitter-tasting molecules and often have an unpleasant odor. These features may prevent an animal from eating a plant or its fruit. For example, an alkaloid in chile peppers called capsaicin elicits a burning sensation. This molecule is so potent that one-millionth of a drop can be detected by the human tongue. Capsaicin may serve to discourage mammals from eating the peppers. Interestingly, however, birds do not experience the burning sensation of capsaicin and serve to disperse the seeds.

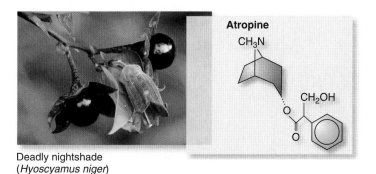

Deadly nightshade
(*Hyoscyamus niger*)

Figure 7.24 **Alkaloids as secondary metabolites.** Atropine is an alkaloid produced by the plant called deadly nightshade (*Hyoscyamus niger*). Atropine is toxic because it interferes with nerve transmission. In humans, atropine causes the heart to speed up to dangerous and possibly fatal rates.

Other alkaloids are poisonous, like the alkaloid **atropine**, a potent toxin derived from the deadly nightshade plant (**Figure 7.24**). Animals that eat this plant and consequently ingest atropine become very sick and may die. It is unlikely that an animal that eats deadly nightshade and survives would choose to eat it a second time. Atropine acts by interfering with nerve transmission. In humans, for example, atropine causes the heart to speed up to dangerous rates, because the nerve inputs that normally keep a check on heart rate are blocked by atropine. Other alkaloids are not necessarily toxic but can cause an animal that eats them to become overstimulated (caffeine), understimulated (any of the opium alkaloids like morphine), or simply nauseated because the compound interferes with nerves required for proper functioning of the gastrointestinal system.

Terpenoids Are Molecules with Intense Smells and Color

A third major class of secondary metabolites are the **terpenoids**, of which over 25,000 have been identified, more than any other family of naturally occurring products. Terpenoids are synthesized from five-carbon isoprene units (shown below) and are also called isoprenoids.

Isoprene units are linked to each other to form larger compounds with multiples of five-carbon atoms. In many cases, the isoprene units form cyclic structures.

Terpenoids have a wide array of functions in plants. Notably, because many terpenoids are volatile (they become gases), they are responsible for the odors emitted by many types of plants, such as menthol produced by mint. The odors of terpenoids may attract pollinators or repel animals that eat plants. In addition, terpenoids often impart an intense flavor to plant tissues. Many of the spices used in cooking are rich in different types of terpenoids. Examples include cinnamon, fennel, cloves, cumin, cara-

Flamingo (*Phoenicopterus ruber*)

Figure 7.25 **Terpenoids as secondary metabolites.** Carotenoids are a type of terpenoid with bright color. The example here is β-carotene, which gives many organisms an orange color. Flamingos (*Phoenicopterus ruber*) receive β-carotene in their diet, primarily from eating shellfish.

way, and tarragon. Terpenoids are found in many traditional herbal remedies and are under medical investigation for potential pharmaceutical effects.

Other terpenoids, like the carotenoids, are responsible for the coloration of many species. An example is β-carotene, which gives carrots their orange color. Carotenoids are also found in leaves, but their color is masked by chlorophyll, which is green. In the autumn, when chlorophyll breaks down, the color of the carotenoids becomes evident. Carotenoids give color to animals such as salmon, goldfish, and flamingos (**Figure 7.25**). Another role of terpenoids is cell signaling. All steroid hormones, which function as signaling molecules in animals and plants (as we will discuss in Chapter 9), are derived from terpenoids.

Polyketides Are Often Used as Chemical Weapons to Kill Competing Organisms

Polyketides are a group of secondary metabolites that are produced by bacteria, fungi, plants, insects, dinoflagellates, mollusks, and sponges. They are synthesized by the polymerization of acetyl (CH_3COOH) and propionyl (CH_3CH_2COOH) groups to create a diverse collection of molecules, often with many ringed structures. Polyketides are usually secreted by the organism that makes them and are often highly toxic to other organisms. For example, the polyketide known as streptomycin is made by the soil bacterium *Streptomyces griseus* (**Figure 7.26**). It is secreted by this bacterium and taken up by other species, where it disrupts protein synthesis and thereby inhibits their growth. In this way, *S. griseus* is able to kill or inhibit the growth of other species in its vicinity. This is an advantage for *S. griseus* because other species may be using limited resources that the bacterium could use for its own growth.

During the past several decades, over 10,000 polyketides have been identified and analyzed. Familiar examples include streptomycin, erythromycin, and tetracycline. The toxic effects of polyketides are often very selective, making them valuable medical tools. For example, streptomycin disrupts protein synthesis in many bacterial species, but it does not adversely affect protein synthesis in mammalian cells. Therefore, it has been used as an antibiotic to treat or prevent bacterial infections in humans and other mammals. Similarly, other polyketides inhibit the growth of fungi, parasites, and insects. More recently, researchers have even discovered that certain polyketides inhibit the growth of cancer cells. The production and sale of polyketides to treat and prevent diseases and as pesticides constitute an enormous industry, with annual sales in the U.S. at over $20 billion.

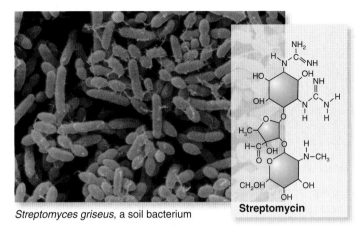

Streptomyces griseus, a soil bacterium · **Streptomycin**

Figure 7.26 **Polyketides as secondary metabolites.** Streptomycin, whose structure is shown here, is an antibiotic produced by *Streptomyces griseus*, a soil bacterium. The scanning electron micrograph shows *S. grisieus*.

CHAPTER SUMMARY

7.1 Energy, Chemical Reactions, and Enzymes

- The fate of a chemical reaction is determined by its direction and rate.

- Energy, the ability to promote change, exists in many forms. According to the first law of thermodynamics, energy cannot be created or destroyed but it can be converted from one form to another. The second law of thermodynamics states that energy interconversions involve an increase in entropy. (Figures 7.1, 7.2, Table 7.1)

- Free energy is the amount of available energy that can be used to do work. Spontaneous reactions release free energy, which means they have a negative free energy change. (Figure 7.3)

- An exergonic reaction has a negative free energy change, while an endergonic reaction has a positive change. Chemical reactions proceed until they reach a state of chemical equilibrium, where the rate of formation of products equals the rate of formation of reactants.

- Cells use energy intermediates such as ATP to drive endergonic reactions.

- Proteins that speed up the rate of a chemical reaction are called enzymes. They lower the activation energy that is needed to achieve a transition state. (Figure 7.4)

- Enzymes recognize the reactants, also called substrates, with a high specificity. Conformational changes are involved in lowering the activation energy for a chemical reaction. (Figure 7.5)

7.2 Overview of Metabolism

- Metabolism is the sum of the chemical reactions in a living organism. Enzymes often function in pathways that lead to the formation of a particular product. (Figure 7.6)

- Catabolic reactions involve the breakdown of larger molecules into smaller ones. These reactions regenerate small molecules that are used as building blocks to make new molecules. The small molecules are also broken down to make energy intermediates such as ATP and NADH. Such reactions are often redox reactions in which electrons are transferred from one molecule to another. (Figure 7.7)

- Anabolic reactions involve the synthesis of larger molecules and macromolecules.

- Estimates from genome analysis indicate that over 20% of a cell's proteins use ATP. (Table 7.2, Figure 7.8)

- Metabolic pathways are controlled by gene regulation, cell signaling, and feedback inhibition. (Figure 7.9)

7.3 Cellular Respiration

- Cells obtain energy via cellular respiration, which involves the breakdown of molecules.

- The breakdown of glucose occurs in four stages: glycolysis, pyruvate breakdown, citric acid cycle, and oxidative phosphorylation. (Figure 7.10)

- Glycolysis is the breakdown of glucose to two pyruvates, producing two ATP and two NADH. ATP is made by substrate-level phosphorylation. (Figures 7.11, 7.12)

- Pyruvate is broken down to CO_2 and an acetyl group that becomes attached to CoA. NADH is made during this process. (Figure 7.13)

- During the citric acid cycle, the acetyl group attached to CoA is broken down to two CO_2 molecules. Three NADH, one $FADH_2$, and one ATP are made during this process. (Figures 7.14, 7.15)

- Oxidative phosphorylation involves two events. The electron transport chain oxidizes NADH or $FADH_2$ and generates an H^+ electrochemical gradient. This gradient is utilized by the ATP synthase to make ATP via chemiosmosis. (Figures 7.16, 7.17)

- Racker and Stoeckenius showed that the ATP synthase uses an H^+ gradient by reconstituting the ATP synthase with a light-driven H^+ pump. (Figure 7.18)

- The ATP synthase is a rotary machine. The rotation is caused by the movement of H^+ through the c subunits that cause the γ subunit to spin, resulting in conformational changes in the β subunits that promote ATP synthesis. (Figure 7.19)

- Yoshida and Kinosita experimentally demonstrated rotation of the γ subunit by attaching a fluorescently labeled actin filament and watching it spin in the presence of ATP. (Figure 7.20)

- Proteins and fats can enter into glycolysis or the citric acid cycle at different points. (Figure 7.21)

- Anaerobic respiration occurs in the absence of oxygen. Either the final electron acceptor of the electron transport chain is not oxygen, or NAD^+ is regenerated by donating electrons to an organic molecule such as pyruvate (to make lactic acid). (Figure 7.22)

7.4 Secondary Metabolism

- Secondary metabolites are not usually necessary for cell structure and function, but they provide an advantage to an organism that may involve taste, smell, color, or poison. Four categories are phenolic compounds, alkaloids, terpenoids, and polyketides. (Figures 7.23, 7.24, 7.25, 7.26)

TEST YOURSELF

1. According to the second law of thermodynamics
   a. energy cannot be created or destroyed.
   b. each energy transfer decreases the disorder of a system.
   c. energy is constant in the universe.
   d. each energy transfer increases the level of disorder in a system.
   e. chemical energy is a form of potential energy.

2. _____ reactions release free energy.
   a. Exergonic   d. All of the above
   b. Spontaneous   e. Both a and b
   c. Endergonic

3. Enzymes speed up reactions by
   a. providing chemical energy to fuel a reaction.
   b. lowering the activation energy necessary to initiate the reaction.
   c. causing an endergonic reaction to become an exergonic reaction.
   d. substituting for one of the reactants necessary for the reaction.
   e. none of the above.

4. Which of the following factors will alter the function of enzymes?
   a. pH   d. all of the above
   b. temperature   e. b and c only
   c. cofactors

5. In biological systems, ATP functions by
   a. providing the energy necessary for an endergonic reaction by coupling it with an exergonic reaction.
   b. acting as an enzyme and lowering the activation energy of certain reactions.
   c. adjusting the pH of solutions to maintain optimal conditions for enzyme activity.
   d. regulating the speed at which endergonic reactions proceed.
   e. interacting with enzymes as a cofactor to stimulate chemical reactions.

6. During redox reactions, the molecule that donates an electron is said to be
   a. reduced.   d. catabolized.
   b. phosphorylated. e. methylated.
   c. oxidized.

7. Currently scientists are identifying proteins that use ATP as an energy source by
   a. determining whether those proteins function in anabolic or catabolic reactions.
   b. determining if the protein has a known ATP-binding site.
   c. predicting the free energy necessary for the protein to function.
   d. determining if the protein has an ATP synthase subunit.
   e. all of the above.

8. During glycolysis, ATP is produced by
   a. oxidative phosphorylation.
   b. substrate-level phosphorylation.
   c. redox reactions.
   d. all of the above.
   e. both a and b.

9. The energy necessary to produce ATP during oxidative phosphorylation is provided by
   a. the H^+ concentration gradient produced by the electron transport chain.
   b. GTP produced during the citric acid cycle.
   c. lactic acid metabolism.
   d. the release of CO_2 from the mitochondria.
   e. all of the above.

10. Secondary metabolites
   a. help deter predation of certain organisms by causing the organism to taste bad.
   b. help attract pollinators by producing a pleasant smell.
   c. help organisms compete for resources by acting as a poison to competitors.
   d. provide protection from DNA damage.
   e. all of the above.

CONCEPTUAL QUESTIONS

1. Distinguish between endergonic and exergonic reactions.

2. Define feedback inhibition.

3. The electron transport chain is so named because electrons are transported from one component to another. Describe the purpose of the electron transport chain.

EXPERIMENTAL QUESTIONS

1. The components of the ATP synthase are too small to be visualized by light microscopy. For the experiment of Figure 7.20, how did the researchers observe the movement of the ATP synthase?

2. In the experiment of Figure 7.20, what observation did the researchers make that indicated that the ATP synthase is a rotary machine? What was the control of this experiment? What did it indicate?

3. Were the rotations seen by the researchers in the data of Figure 7.20 in the same direction as expected in the mitochondria during ATP synthesis? Why or why not?

COLLABORATIVE QUESTIONS

1. Discuss several ways in which metabolic pathways are controlled or regulated.

2. Discuss the concept of secondary metabolism and give an example.

---

www.brookerbiology.com

This website includes answers to the Biological Inquiry questions found in the figure legends and all end-of-chapter questions.

8

PHOTOSYNTHESIS

A tropical rain forest in Akaka Falls State Park, Hawaii. Plant life in tropical rain forests carries out a large amount of the world's photosynthesis and supplies the atmosphere with a sizeable fraction of its oxygen.

Across the Earth, the most visible color on land is green. We often associate this color with emerging life, as in the growth of plants in the spring. The green color of plants is due to a pigment called chlorophyll. This pigment provides the starting point for the process of **photosynthesis**, in which the energy within light is captured and used to synthesize carbohydrates. Nearly all living organisms ultimately rely on photosynthesis for their nourishment. Photosynthesis is also responsible for producing the oxygen that makes up a large portion of the Earth's atmosphere. Therefore, all aerobic organisms ultimately rely on photosynthesis for respiration.

Organisms can be categorized as heterotrophs and autotrophs. **Heterotrophs** must eat food, organic molecules from their environment, to sustain life. Examples of heterotrophs include most species of bacteria and protists, as well as all species of fungi and animals. In Chapter 7, we learned how cells use food molecules such as glucose for their energy needs and as building blocks to make new cellular molecules and macromolecules. In this chapter, we turn to **autotrophs**, organisms that make organic molecules from inorganic sources, and focus on **photoautotrophs**, those organisms that use light as a source of energy. These include green plants, algae, and some prokaryotic species such as cyanobacteria.

We begin this chapter with an overview of photosynthesis, with an emphasis on how it occurs in green plants. We will then explore the two stages of photosynthesis: the light reactions, in which light energy is captured by the chlorophyll pigments within plants and converted to chemical energy in the form of two compounds, ATP and NADPH; and the Calvin cycle, a series of steps in which these compounds drive the incorporation of CO_2 into carbohydrates. We conclude with a consideration of the variations in photosynthesis that occur in plants existing in hot and dry conditions.

8.1 Overview of Photosynthesis

In the mid-1600s, a Flemish physician, Jan Baptista Van Helmont, conducted an experiment in which he transplanted the shoot of a young willow tree into a bucket of soil of known weight. He watered the tree and allowed it to grow for five years. After this time, the willow tree had added 164 pounds to its original weight, but the soil had lost only 2 ounces. Van Helmont correctly concluded that the willow tree did not get most of its nutrients from the soil. However, he incorrectly concluded that the material that made up the bark, wood, roots, and leaves came from the water he had added over the five years. Although water does contribute to the growth and mass of plants, we now know that CO_2 from the air is also critically important.

In 1771, Joseph Priestley, an English chemist, carried out an experiment in which he placed a burning candle in a closed chamber. The candle burned out very quickly. He conducted another experiment in which he placed a burning candle and a sprig of mint in a second chamber. Similarly, the candle quickly went out. After several days, Priestley was able to relight each candle without opening the two chambers by focusing a beam of sunlight onto the wicks with a mirror. However, only in the chamber with the sprig of mint could the candle burn again. Priestley hypothesized that plants restore to the air whatever burning candles remove. His results occurred because plants release oxygen as a result of photosynthesis.

Shortly thereafter, Jan Ingenhousz, a Dutch physician, immersed green plants underwater and discovered that they released bubbles of oxygen. Moreover, Inglenhousz determined that sunlight was necessary for oxygen production. During this same period, Jean Senebier, a Swiss botanist, found that CO_2 is required for plant growth and Nicolas-Théodore de Saussure, a Swiss chemist, showed that water is also required. With this accumulating information, Julius von Mayer, a German physicist, proposed in 1845 that plants convert light energy from the sun into chemical energy.

For the next several decades, plant biologists studied photosynthesis in prokaryotes, algae, and green plants. Researchers discovered that some photosynthetic bacteria could use hydrogen sulfide (H_2S) instead of water (H_2O) for photosynthesis and that these organisms released sulfur instead of oxygen. In the 1930s, based on this information, Dutch American microbiologist Cornelis van Niel proposed a general equation for photosynthesis that applies to plants, algae, and photosynthetic bacteria alike.

$$CO_2 + 2\ H_2A + \text{Light energy} \rightarrow CH_2O + 2A + H_2O$$

where A is oxygen (O) or sulfur (S) and CH_2O is the general formula for a carbohydrate. This is a redox reaction in which H_2A is oxidized and CO_2 is reduced.

In green plants, A is oxygen and 2A is a molecule of oxygen that is designated O_2. Therefore this equation becomes:

$$CO_2 + 2\ H_2O + \text{Light energy} \rightarrow CH_2O + O_2 + H_2O$$

When the carbohydrate that is produced is glucose, we multiply each side of the equation by six to obtain:

$$6\ CO_2 + 12\ H_2O + \text{Light energy} \rightarrow C_6H_{12}O_6 + 6\ O_2 + 6\ H_2O$$

Glucose

$$\Delta G = +685\ \text{kcal/mole}$$

In this redox reaction, CO_2 is reduced during the formation of glucose, and H_2O is oxidized during the formation of O_2. The free energy change required for the production of 1 mole of glucose from carbon dioxide and water is a whopping $+685$ kcal/mole! As we learned in Chapter 7, endergonic reactions are driven forward by coupling the reaction with an exergonic process, a process that releases free energy. In this case, the energy from light ultimately drives the synthesis of glucose.

In this section, we will survey the general features of photosynthesis as it occurs in green plants. Later sections will examine the various steps in this process.

Photosynthesis Powers the Biosphere

The term **biosphere** describes the regions on the surface of the Earth and in the atmosphere where living organisms exist. Life in the biosphere is largely driven by the photosynthetic power of green plants. For most species to exist, a key energy cycle involves the interplay between organic molecules (such as glucose) and inorganic molecules, namely, CO_2 and O_2. Life on Earth involves a cycle in which cells use organic molecules for energy and plants replenish those molecules via photosynthesis. As we examined in Chapter 7, cellular respiration involves the breakdown of organic molecules to produce energy intermediates such as ATP. When glucose is broken down to CO_2, the net reaction of cellular respiration in the presence of oxygen can be summarized as:

$$C_6H_{12}O_6 + 6\ O_2 \rightarrow 6\ CO_2 + 6\ H_2O + \textbf{Energy}$$

The net reaction of photosynthesis (in which only six net molecules of H_2O are consumed) can be viewed as the opposite of respiration.

$$6\ CO_2 + 6\ H_2O + \textbf{Energy} \rightarrow C_6H_{12}O_6 + 6\ O_2$$

The breakdown of glucose during cell respiration is an energy-releasing process that drives the synthesis of ATP. By comparison, the energy that is needed to synthesize glucose during photosynthesis ultimately comes from sunlight.

Plants make a large proportion of the Earth's organic molecules via photosynthesis. At the same time, they also produce O_2. These organic molecules are metabolized by the plants themselves as well as by heterotrophs such as animals and fungi. This metabolism generates CO_2, which is released into the atmosphere and can be used by plants to make more organic molecules like glucose. In this way, a cycle exists between photosynthesis and cellular respiration that sustains life on our planet.

In Plants, Photosynthesis Occurs in the Chloroplast

Chloroplasts are organelles found in plant cells and algae that carry out photosynthesis. These organelles contain large quantities of **chlorophyll**, a pigment that gives plants their green color. All green parts of a plant contain chloroplasts and are capable of photosynthesis, although the majority of photosynthesis occurs in the leaves (**Figure 8.1**). The central part of the leaf, called the **mesophyll**, contains cells that carry out the bulk of photosynthesis in plants. For photosynthesis to occur, the mesophyll cells must obtain water and carbon dioxide. The water is taken up by the roots of the plant and is transported to the leaves by small veins. Carbon dioxide gas enters the leaf, and oxygen exits, via pores called **stomata** (singular, *stoma*), from the Greek, meaning mouth. The anatomy of leaves will be examined further in Chapter 35.

Like the mitochondrion, a chloroplast contains an outer and inner membrane, with an intermembrane space lying between the two. A third membrane, called the **thylakoid membrane**, contains pigment molecules, including chlorophyll. The thylakoid membrane forms many flattened, fluid-filled tubules called the **thylakoids**, which enclose a single, convoluted compartment known as the **thylakoid lumen**. Thylakoids stack on top of each other to form a structure called a **granum** (plural, *grana*). The **stroma** is the fluid-filled region of the chloroplast between the thylakoid membrane and the inner membrane.

Photosynthesis Occurs in Two Stages

The process of photosynthesis can be divided into two stages called the **light reactions** and the **Calvin cycle**. The term photosynthesis is derived from the association between these two stages: The prefix photo refers to the light reactions that capture the energy needed for the synthesis of carbohydrates that occurs in the Calvin cycle. Each stage occurs at specific sites in the chloroplast: The light reactions take place at the thylakoid membrane, and the Calvin cycle occurs in the stroma (**Figure 8.2**).

The light reactions involve an amazing series of energy conversions, starting with light energy and ending with chemical energy in the form of covalent bonds. The light reactions produce three chemical products: ATP, NADPH, and O_2. ATP and NADPH are energy intermediates that provide the needed energy and electrons to drive the Calvin cycle. Like NADH, **NADPH (nicotinamide adenine dinucleotide phosphate)** is an electron carrier; its structure differs from NADH by the presence of an additional phosphate group. In the Calvin cycle, atmospheric carbon dioxide is incorporated into organic molecules, some of which are converted to carbohydrates.

O_2 is another important product of the light reactions. As described in Chapter 7, this molecule is vital to the process of aerobic respiration. Nearly all of the O_2 in the atmosphere is produced by photosynthesis from green plants and aquatic microorganisms. A large percentage of atmospheric oxygen is made by regions of the Earth that are rich in plant life, such as tropical rain forests. More than 20% of the world's oxygen is produced in the Amazon rain forest in South America alone.

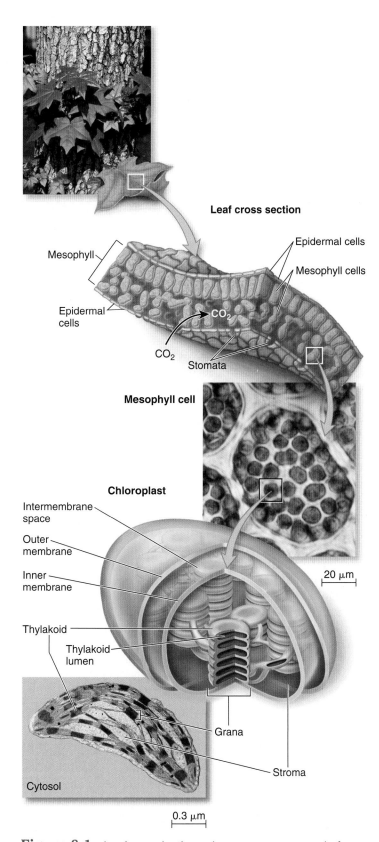

Figure 8.1 **Leaf organization.** Leaves are composed of layers of cells. The epidermal cells are on the outer surface, both top and bottom, with mesophyll cells sandwiched in the middle. The mesophyll cells in most plants are the primary sites of photosynthesis.

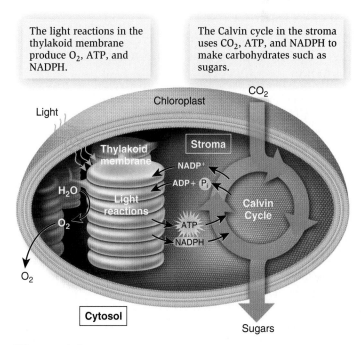

Figure 8.2 **An overview of the two stages of photosynthesis.** The light reactions, through which O_2, ATP, and NADPH are made, occur at the thylakoid membrane. The Calvin cycle, in which enzymes use ATP and NADPH to incorporate CO_2 into carbohydrate, occurs in the stroma.

Ecologists are alarmed about the rate at which such forests are being destroyed by human activities. Rain forests once covered 14% of the Earth's land surface but now occupy less than 6%. At their current rate of destruction, rain forests may be nearly eliminated in less than 40 years. Such an event may lower the level of oxygen in the atmosphere and thereby have a harmful impact on living organisms on a global scale.

8.2 Reactions That Harness Light Energy

Photosynthesis relies on the first law of thermodynamics. Recall from Chapter 7 that this law states that while energy cannot be created or destroyed, it can be transferred from one place to another and transformed from one type to another. During photosynthesis, energy in the form of light is transferred from the sun, some 92 million miles away, to a pigment molecule in a photosynthetic organism such as a plant. The next thing that happens is an interesting and complex series of energy transformations in which light energy is transformed into electrochemical energy and then into energy stored within chemical bonds.

In this section, we will explore this series of transformations, collectively called the light reactions of photosynthesis. We begin by examining the unique properties of light and then consider the features of chloroplasts that allow them to capture light energy. The remaining sections focus on how the light reactions of photosynthesis create three important products: O_2, ATP, and NADPH.

Light Energy Is a Form of Electromagnetic Radiation

Light is a critical phenomenon that is essential to support life on Earth. Light is a type of electromagnetic radiation, so named because it consists of energy in the form of electric and magnetic fields. Electromagnetic radiation travels as waves caused by the oscillation of the electric and magnetic fields. The **wavelength** is the distance between the peaks in a wave pattern. The **electromagnetic spectrum** encompasses all possible wavelengths of electromagnetic radiation, from relatively short wavelengths (gamma rays) to much longer wavelengths (radio waves) (**Figure 8.3**). Visible light is the range of wavelengths that are detected by the human eye, commonly in the range of 380–740 nm. As discussed later, visible light provides the energy to drive photosynthesis.

Physicists have also discovered that light exhibits behaviors that are characteristic of particles. Albert Einstein formulated the photon theory of light in which he proposed that light is composed of discrete particles called **photons**—massless particles each traveling in a wavelike pattern and moving at the speed of light. Each photon contains a specific amount of energy. An important difference between the various types of electro-

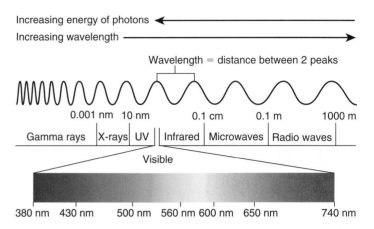

Figure 8.3   The electromagnetic spectrum.   The bottom portion of this figure emphasizes visible light, the wavelengths of electromagnetic radiation that are visible to the human eye. Light in the visible portion of the electromagnetic spectrum drives photosynthesis.

magnetic radiation described in Figure 8.3 is the amount of energy found in the photons. Shorter wavelength radiation carries more energy per unit of time than longer wavelength radiation. The photons of gamma rays carry more energy than those of radio waves.

The sun radiates the entire spectrum of electromagnetic radiation. The atmosphere prevents much of this radiation from reaching the Earth's surface. For example, the ozone layer forms a thin shield in the upper atmosphere, protecting life on Earth from much of the sun's ultraviolet rays. Even so, a substantial amount of electromagnetic radiation does reach the Earth's surface. The effect of light on living organisms is critically dependent on the energy of the photons. The photons found in gamma rays, X-rays, and UV rays have very high energy. When molecules in cells absorb such energy, the effects can be devastating. Such types of radiation can cause mutations in DNA and even lead to cancer. By comparison, the energy of photons found in visible light is much milder. Molecules can absorb this energy in a way that does not cause permanent harm. Let's now consider how molecules in living cells absorb the energy within visible light.

Photosynthetic Pigments Absorb Light Energy

When light strikes an object, one of three things can happen. First, light may simply pass through an object. Second, the object may change the path of light toward a different direction. A third possibility is that the object may absorb the light. The term **pigment** is used to describe a molecule that can absorb light energy. When light strikes a pigment, some of the wavelengths of light energy are absorbed, while others are reflected. For example, we perceive that leaves are green because they are reflecting radiant energy of the green wavelength. Various pigments in the leaves absorb the other light energy wavelengths.

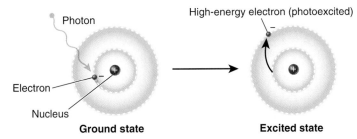

Figure 8.4 Absorption of light energy by an electron. When a photon of light of the correct amount of energy strikes an electron, the electron is boosted from the ground (unexcited) state to a higher energy level. When this occurs, the electron occupies an orbital that is farther away from the nucleus of the atom. At this farther distance, the electron is held less firmly and is considered unstable.

Biological inquiry: For an electron to drop down to a lower orbital, describe the three things that could happen.

At the extremes of color reflection are white and black. A white object reflects nearly all of the light energy falling on it, whereas a black object absorbs nearly all of the light energy.

What do we mean when we say that light energy is absorbed? In the visible spectrum, light energy is usually absorbed by boosting electrons to higher energy levels (**Figure 8.4**). Recall from Chapter 2 that electrons are located around the nucleus of an atom. The location that an electron is likely to be found is called its orbital. Electrons in different orbitals possess different amounts of energy. For an electron to absorb light energy and be boosted to an orbital with a higher energy, it must overcome the difference in energy between the orbital it is in and the orbital to which it is going. For this to happen, an electron must absorb a photon that contains precisely that amount of energy. Among different pigment molecules, there exist a variety of electrons that can be shifted to different energy levels. Therefore, the wavelength of light that a pigment absorbs depends on the amount of energy that is needed to boost an electron to a higher orbital.

After an electron absorbs energy, it is said to be in an excited state. Usually, this is an unstable condition. The electron may release the energy in one of two forms. When an excited electron drops back down to a lower energy level, it may release heat. For example, on a sunny day, the sidewalk heats up because it absorbs light energy that is released as heat. A second way that an electron can release energy is in the form of light. Certain organisms, such as jellyfish, possess molecules that make them glow. This glow is due to the release of light when electrons drop down to lower energy levels, a phenomenon called fluorescence.

In the case of photosynthetic pigments, however, a different event happens that is critical for the process of photosynthesis. At a particular step, an excited electron in a photosynthetic pigment is removed from that molecule and transferred to another molecule where the electron is more stable. When this occurs, the energy in that electron is said to be "captured" because the

electron does not readily drop down to a lower energy level and release heat or light.

In plants, several different pigment molecules absorb the light energy used to drive photosynthesis. Two types of chlorophyll pigments, termed **chlorophyll *a*** and **chlorophyll *b***, are found in green algae and plants. Their structure was determined in the 1930s by German chemist Hans Fischer (**Figure 8.5a**). In the chloroplast, both chlorophylls *a* and *b* are bound to integral membrane proteins in the thylakoid membrane. The chlorophylls contain a structure called a porphyrin ring that has a bound magnesium ion (Mg^{2+}). In this ring, an electron can follow a path in which it spends some of its time around several different atoms. These electrons, called delocalized electrons because they aren't restricted to a single atom, absorb light energy. Chlorophyll also contains a long hydrocarbon structure called a phytol tail. This tail is hydrophobic and anchors the pigment to the surface of proteins within the thylakoid membrane.

Carotenoids are another type of pigment found in chloroplasts (**Figure 8.5b**). These pigments impart a color that ranges from yellow to orange to red. Carotenoids are often the major pigments in flowers and fruits. In leaves, the more abundant chlorophylls usually mask the colors of carotenoids. In temperate climates where the leaves change colors, the quantity of chlorophyll in the leaf declines during autumn. The carotenoids become readily visible and produce the yellows and oranges of autumn foliage.

An **absorption spectrum** is a diagram that depicts the wavelengths of electromagnetic radiation that are absorbed by a pigment. Each of the pigments shown in **Figure 8.5c** absorbs light in different regions of the visible spectrum. The absorption spectra of chlorophylls *a* and *b* are slightly different, though both chlorophylls absorb light most strongly in the red and violet parts of the visible spectrum and absorb green light poorly. Carotenoids absorb light in the blue and blue-green regions of the visible spectrum.

Having different pigments allows plants to absorb light at many different wavelengths. In this way, plants are more efficient at capturing the energy in sunlight. This phenomenon is highlighted in an **action spectrum**, which describes the rate of photosynthesis plotted as a function of different wavelengths of light (**Figure 8.5d**). The highest rates of photosynthesis correlate with the wavelengths that are strongly absorbed by the chlorophylls and carotenoids. Photosynthesis is poor in the green region of the spectrum, because these pigments do not readily absorb this wavelength of light.

Photosystem II Captures Light Energy and Produces O₂

Photosynthetic organisms have the unique ability not only to absorb light energy but also to capture that energy in a stable way. Many organic molecules can absorb light energy. For example, on a sunny day, molecules in your skin absorb light energy and release the energy as heat. The heat that is released,

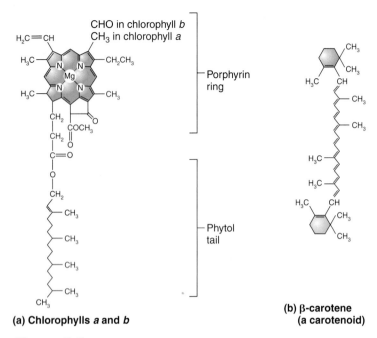

(a) Chlorophylls *a* and *b*

(b) β-carotene
(a carotenoid)

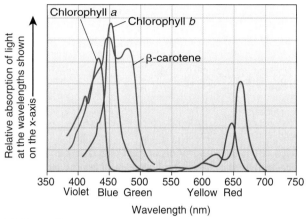

(c) Absorption spectra

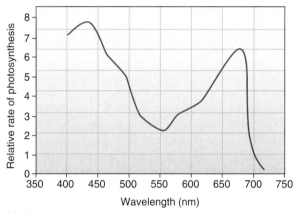

(d) Action spectrum

Figure 8.5 Structures and properties of pigment molecules.
(a) The structure of chlorophylls *a* and *b*. As indicated, chlorophylls *a* and *b* differ only at a single site, at which chlorophyll *a* has a —CH_3 group and chlorophyll *b* has a —CHO group. (b) The structure of β-carotene, an example of a carotenoid. The shaded areas are the regions where a delocalized electron can hop from one atom to another. (c) Absorption spectra that show the absorption of light by chlorophyll *a*, chlorophyll *b*, and β-carotene. (d) An action spectrum of photosynthesis depicting the relative rate of photosynthesis in green plants at different wavelengths of light.

however, cannot be harnessed to do useful work. A key feature of photosynthesis is the ability of pigments to capture light energy and transfer it to other molecules that can hold on to the energy in a stable fashion and ultimately produce energy intermediate molecules that can do cellular work.

Let's now consider how chloroplasts capture light energy. The thylakoid membrane contains two distinct complexes of proteins and pigment molecules called **photosystem I (PSI)** and **photosystem II (PSII)**. Photosystem I was discovered before photosystem II, but because photosystem II is the initial step in photosynthesis, we will examine its function first.

Photosystem II has two main components, a light-harvesting complex and a reaction center (**Figure 8.6**). In 1932, Robert Emerson and an undergraduate student, William Arnold, originally discovered the **light-harvesting complex** in the thylakoid membrane. It is composed of several dozen pigment molecules that are anchored to proteins. The role of the complex is to directly absorb photons of light. When a pigment molecule absorbs a photon, this boosts an electron to a higher energy level. As shown in Figure 8.6, the energy (not the electron itself) can be transferred to adjacent pigment molecules by a process called **resonance energy transfer**. Eventually, the energy may be transferred to a special pigment molecule designated P680, so called

because it is best at absorbing light at a wavelength of 680 nm. When an electron in P680 is excited, it is designated P680*. The P680 pigment molecule is located in the **reaction center** of PSII. The light-harvesting complex is also called the **antenna complex** because it acts like an antenna that absorbs energy from light and funnels that energy to P680 in the reaction center.

A high-energy (photoexcited) electron in a pigment molecule is relatively unstable. It may abruptly release its energy by giving off heat or light. Unlike the pigments in the antenna complex that undergo resonance energy transfer, P680* can actually release its high-energy electron. The role of the reaction center is to quickly remove the high-energy electron from P680* and transfer it to another molecule, where the electron will be more stable. This molecule is called the **primary electron acceptor** (Figure 8.6). The transfer of the electron from P680* to the primary electron acceptor is remarkably fast. It occurs in less than a few picoseconds! (One picosecond equals one-trillionth of a second, also noted as 10^{-12} s.) Because this occurs so quickly, the excited electron does not have much time to release its energy in the form of heat or light.

After the primary electron acceptor has received this high-energy electron, the light energy has been captured and can be used to perform cellular work. As we will discuss shortly, the

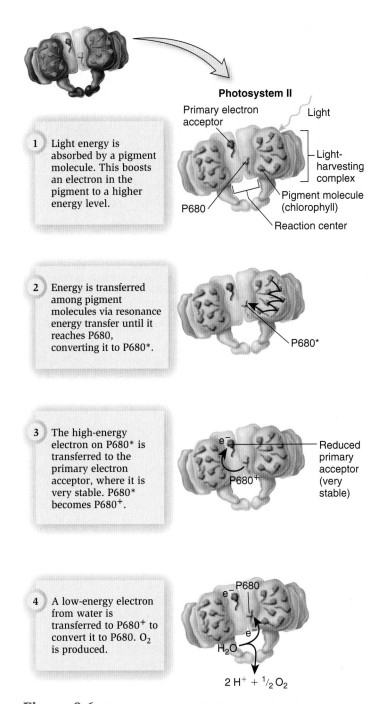

Photosystem II

Primary electron acceptor — Light

Light-harvesting complex

P680 — Pigment molecule (chlorophyll)

Reaction center

1. Light energy is absorbed by a pigment molecule. This boosts an electron in the pigment to a higher energy level.

2. Energy is transferred among pigment molecules via resonance energy transfer until it reaches P680, converting it to P680*.

P680*

3. The high-energy electron on P680* is transferred to the primary electron acceptor, where it is very stable. P680* becomes P680$^+$.

e$^-$ — Reduced primary acceptor (very stable)

P680$^+$

4. A low-energy electron from water is transferred to P680$^+$ to convert it to P680. O$_2$ is produced.

P680

e$^-$

e$^-$

H$_2$O

2 H$^+$ + $^1/_2$ O$_2$

Figure 8.6 The absorption of light energy by pigment molecules in the light-harvesting complex, and the path that leads to the capture of energy by the primary electron acceptor.

work that it first performs is to synthesize the energy intermediates ATP and NADPH. Later, these energy intermediates are used to make carbohydrates.

Before we examine the fate of the high-energy electron that was transferred to the primary electron acceptor, let's consider what happens to the P680 molecule after it has released its high-energy electron. Another function of the reaction center is to

replace the electrons that are removed from pigment molecules. They are replaced with electrons from water molecules (Figure 8.6). The reaction center of photosystem II removes electrons from water and transfers those electrons to oxidized pigment molecules (P680$^+$).

$$H_2O \rightarrow 1/2\ O_2 + 2\ H^+ + 2\ e^-$$

$$2\ P680^+ + 2\ e^- \rightarrow 2\ P680$$

(from water)

The oxidation of water results in the formation of oxygen gas (O$_2$). Photosystem II is the only known protein complex that can oxidize water, resulting in the release of O$_2$ into the atmosphere.

Photosystem II Is an Amazing Redox Machine

Redox reactions are fundamentally important for cells to store and utilize energy and to form covalent bonds in organic molecules. Photosystem II is a particularly remarkable example of a redox machine. As we have learned, this complex of proteins removes electrons from a pigment molecule and transfers them to a primary electron acceptor. Perhaps even more remarkable is that photosystem II can remove electrons from water, a very stable molecule that holds onto its electrons tightly. The removal of electrons is how O$_2$ is made.

Many approaches have been used to study how photosystem II works. In recent years, much effort has been aimed at determining the biochemical composition of the protein complex and the roles of its individual components. The number of protein subunits varies somewhat from species to species and may vary due to environmental changes. Typically, photosystem II contains around 19 different protein subunits. Two subunits, designated D1 and D2, contain the reaction center that carries out the redox reactions (**Figure 8.7a**). Two other subunits, called CP43 and CP47, bind the pigment molecules that form the light-harvesting complex. Many additional subunits regulate the function of photosystem II and provide structural support.

The oxidation of water occurs in a region called the **manganese cluster**. This site is located on the side of D1 that faces the thylakoid lumen. The manganese cluster has four Mn^{2+}, one Ca^{2+}, and one Cl$^-$. Two water molecules bind to this site. D1 catalyzes the removal of four electrons from the two water molecules to create four H$^+$ and O$_2$. The electrons are transferred, one at a time, to a tyrosine (Tyr) in D1 and then to an oxidized pigment molecule (P680$^+$) to produce P680. When the electron on P680 becomes excited, usually by resonance energy transfer, it then moves to the primary electron acceptor, which is an organic molecule called pheophytin (Pp) that is permanently bound to photosystem II. Pheophytin transfers its electron to a plastoquinone molecule, designated Q$_A$, which is also permanently bound to photosystem II. Next, the electron is transferred to another plastoquinone molecule designated Q$_B$, which can accept two high-energy electrons and bind two H$^+$. Q$_B$ can diffuse away from the reaction center.

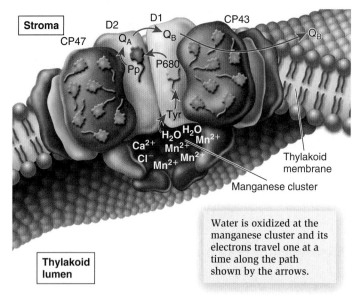

(a) The path of electron flow through photosystem II

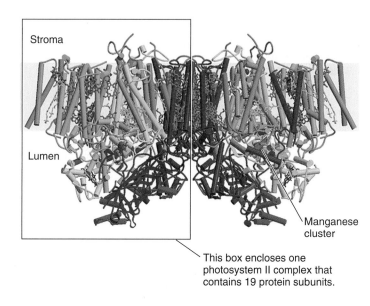

(b) Three-dimensional structure of photosystem II determined by X-ray crystallography

Figure 8.7   A closer look at the structure and function of photosystem II.   (a) Schematic drawing showing the path of electron flow from water to Q_B. The CP47 and CP43 protein subunits wrap around D1 and D2 so that pigments in CP47 and CP43 can transfer energy to P680 by resonance energy transfer. (b) The three-dimensional structure of photosystem II as determined by X-ray crystallography. In the crystal structure, the colors are CP47 (red), D2 (orange), D1 (yellow), and CP43 (green).

Biological inquiry: According to this figure, how many redox reactions does photosystem II catalyze?

In 2004, So Iwata, James Barber, and colleagues determined the three-dimensional structure of photosystem II using a technique called **X-ray crystallography**. In this method, researchers must purify a protein or protein complex and expose it to conditions that cause the proteins to associate with each other in an ordered array. In other words, the proteins form a crystal. When a crystal is exposed to X-rays, the resulting pattern can be analyzed mathematically to determine the three-dimensional structure of the crystal's components. Major advances in this technique over the last couple of decades have enabled researchers to determine the structures of relatively large macromolecular machines such as photosystem II and ribosomes. **Figure 8.7b** shows the three-dimensional structure of photosystem II. The structure shown here is a dimer; it has two PSII complexes each with 19 protein subunits. As seen in this figure, the intricacy of the structure of photosystem II rivals the complexity of its function.

Photosystems II and I Work Together to Produce ATP and NADPH

Let's now consider what happens to the high-energy electrons that are transferred to the primary electron acceptor in photosystem II (**Figure 8.8**). After electrons reach Q_B, they enter an electron transport chain located in the thylakoid membrane. The electron transport chain functions similarly to the one found in mitochondria. From Q_B, electrons go to a cytochrome complex, then to plastocyanin (Pc), a small protein, and then

to a pigment molecule in the reaction center of photosystem I. Along the journey from photosystem II to photosystem I, the electron releases some of its energy at particular steps and is transferred to the next component that has a higher electronegativity. The energy that is released is harnessed to move H^+ into the thylakoid lumen. One result of the electron movement is to establish an H^+ electrochemical gradient. Additionally, the splitting of water also adds H^+ into the thylakoid lumen. The synthesis of ATP in chloroplasts is achieved by a chemiosmotic mechanism similar to that used to make ATP in mitochondria.

The key role of photosystem I is to make NADPH. When light strikes the light-harvesting complex of photosystem I, this energy is also transferred to a reaction center, where a high-energy electron is removed from a pigment molecule, designated P700, and transferred to a primary electron acceptor. A protein called ferredoxin (Fd) can accept two high-energy electrons, one at a time, from the primary electron acceptor. Fd then transfers the two electrons to the enzyme NADP$^+$ reductase. This enzyme transfers the two electrons to NADP$^+$ and together with an H^+ creates NADPH. The formation of NADPH consumes one H^+ in the stroma and thereby contributes to the formation of an H^+ electrochemical gradient because it results in fewer H^+ in the stroma.

A key difference between photosystem II and photosystem I is how the oxidized forms of P680 and P700 receive electrons. As discussed earlier, P680$^+$ receives an electron from water. By comparison, P700$^+$—the oxidized form of P700—receives an electron from Pc. Therefore, photosystem I does not need to split water to reduce P700$^+$ and thus does not generate oxygen.

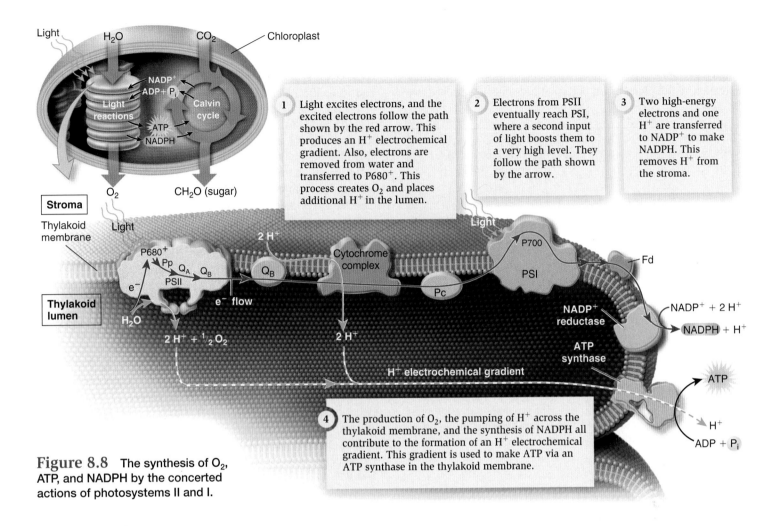

1. Light excites electrons, and the excited electrons follow the path shown by the red arrow. This produces an H^+ electrochemical gradient. Also, electrons are removed from water and transferred to $P680^+$. This process creates O_2 and places additional H^+ in the lumen.

2. Electrons from PSII eventually reach PSI, where a second input of light boosts them to a very high level. They follow the path shown by the arrow.

3. Two high-energy electrons and one H^+ are transferred to $NADP^+$ to make NADPH. This removes H^+ from the stroma.

4. The production of O_2, the pumping of H^+ across the thylakoid membrane, and the synthesis of NADPH all contribute to the formation of an H^+ electrochemical gradient. This gradient is used to make ATP via an ATP synthase in the thylakoid membrane.

Figure 8.8 The synthesis of O_2, ATP, and NADPH by the concerted actions of photosystems II and I.

In summary, the steps of the light reactions of photosynthesis produce three chemical products:

1. O_2 is produced in the thylakoid lumen by the oxidation of water by photosystem II. Two electrons are removed from water, which creates two H^+ and $1/2\ O_2$. The two electrons are transferred to $P680^+$ molecules.

2. ATP is produced in the stroma by an H^+ electrochemical gradient. This gradient results from three events: (1) the splitting of water, which places H^+ in the thylakoid lumen, (2) the movement of high-energy electrons from photosystem II to photosystem I, which pumps H^+ into the lumen, and (3) the formation of NADPH, which consumes H^+ in the stroma.

3. NADPH is produced in the stroma from high-energy electrons that start in photosystem II and are boosted a second time in photosystem I. Two high-energy electrons and one H^+ are transferred to $NADP^+$ to create NADPH.

The combined action of photosystem II and photosystem I is termed **noncyclic electron flow** because the electrons move linearly from PSII to PSI and ultimately to $NADP^+$.

The Use of Light Flashes of Specific Wavelengths Provided Experimental Evidence for the Existence of PSII and PSI

The use of light flashes at particular wavelengths has been an important experimental technique for helping researchers understand the light reactions of photosynthesis. In this method, pioneered by Robert Emerson, a photosynthetic organism is exposed to a particular wavelength of light, after which the rate of photosynthesis is measured by the amount of CO_2 consumed or the amount of O_2 produced. In the 1950s, Emerson performed a particularly intriguing experiment that greatly stimulated photosynthesis research (**Figure 8.9**). He subjected algae to light flashes of different wavelengths and obtained a mysterious result. When he exposed algae to a wavelength of 680 nm, he observed a low rate of photosynthesis. A similarly low rate of photosynthesis occurred when he exposed algae to a wavelength of 700 nm. However, when he exposed the algae to both wavelengths of light simultaneously, the rate of photosynthesis was more than double the rates observed at only one wavelength. This phenomenon was termed the **enhancement effect**. We know now that it occurs because 680-nm light can readily activate the pigment (P680) in the reaction center in photosystem II, but is not very efficient at activating pigments in photosystem I. In contrast, light of 700-nm wavelength is optimal at activating photosystem I but not very good at activating photosystem II. When algae are exposed to both wavelengths, however, maximal activation of the pigments in both photosystems is achieved.

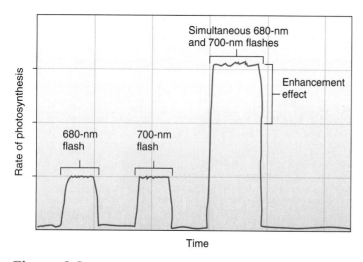

Figure 8.9   **The enhancement effect observed by Emerson.** When photosynthetic organisms such as green plants and algae are exposed to 680-nm and 700-nm light simultaneously, the rate of photosynthesis is much more than double the rate produced by each wavelength individually.

Biological inquiry: Would the enhancement effect be observed if two consecutive flashes of light occurred at 680 nm?

When researchers began to understand that photosynthesis results in the production of both ATP and NADPH, Robin Hill and Fay Bendall also proposed that photosynthesis involves two photoactivation events. According to their model, known as the **Z scheme**, an electron proceeds through a series of energy changes during photosynthesis. The Z refers to the zigzag shape of this energy curve. Based on our modern understanding of photosynthesis, we now know that these events involve increases and decreases in the energy of an electron as it moves from photosystem II to photosystem I (**Figure 8.10**). An electron on a nonexcited pigment molecule in photosystem II has the lowest energy. In photosystem II, light boosts an electron to a much higher energy level. As the electron travels from photosystem II to photosystem I, some of the energy is released. The input of light in photosystem I boosts the electron to an even higher energy than it attained in photosystem II. The electron releases a little energy before it is eventually transferred to NADP$^+$.

Cyclic Electron Flow Produces Only ATP

The mechanism of harvesting light energy, described in Figure 8.8, is called noncyclic electron flow because electrons begin at photosystem II and eventually are transferred to NADP$^+$. The electron flow is a linear process that produces ATP and NADPH in roughly equal amounts. However, as we will see, the Calvin cycle uses more ATP than NADPH. Therefore, in some photosynthetic organisms, excited electrons take an alternative path as a way to make more ATP. In 1959, Daniel Arnon discovered

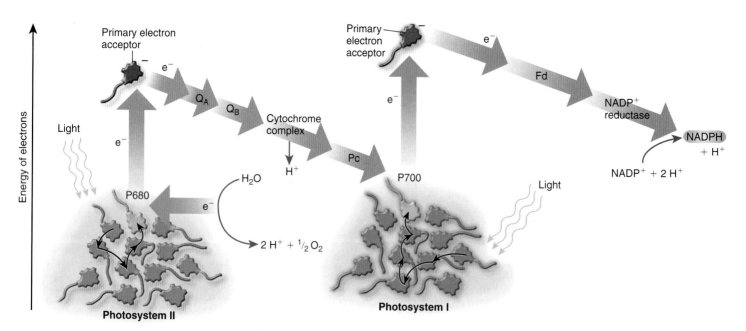

Figure 8.10   **The Z scheme, which depicts the energy of an electron as it moves from photosystem II to NADP$^+$.**   During its journey from photosystem II to NADP$^+$, an electron varies in the amount of energy it contains. As seen here, the input of light boosts the energy of the electron two times. At the end of the pathway, 2 electrons are used to make NADPH.

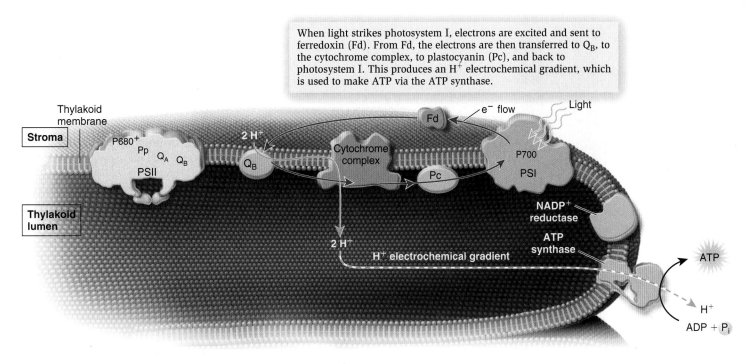

When light strikes photosystem I, electrons are excited and sent to ferredoxin (Fd). From Fd, the electrons are then transferred to Q_B, to the cytochrome complex, to plastocyanin (Pc), and back to photosystem I. This produces an H^+ electrochemical gradient, which is used to make ATP via the ATP synthase.

Figure 8.11 Cyclic photophosphorylation. As shown in this figure, an electron follows a cyclic path that is powered by photosystem I. This contributes to the formation of an H^+ electrochemical gradient, which is used to make ATP.

a pattern of electron flow that is cyclic and generates ATP alone (**Figure 8.11**). Arnon termed the process **cyclic photophosphorylation** because (1) the path of electrons is cyclic, (2) light energizes the electrons, and (3) ATP is made via the phosphorylation of ADP. Due to the path of electrons, the mechanism is also called **cyclic electron flow**.

When light strikes photosystem I, high-energy electrons are sent to the primary electron acceptor and then to ferredoxin (Fd). The key difference in cyclic photophosphorylation is that the high-energy electrons are transferred from ferredoxin to Q_B. From Q_B, the electrons then go the cytochrome complex, to plastocyanin (Pc), and back to photosystem I. As the electrons travel along this cyclic route, they release energy and some of this energy is used to transport H^+ into the thylakoid lumen. The resulting H^+ gradient drives the synthesis of ATP via the ATP synthase.

GENOMES & PROTEOMES

The Cytochrome Complexes of Mitochondria and Chloroplasts Have Evolutionarily Related Proteins in Common

A recurring theme in cell biology is that evolution has resulted in groups of genes that encode proteins that play similar but specialized roles in cells. When two or more genes are similar because they are derived from the same ancestral gene, they are called **homologous genes**. As discussed in Chapter 23, homologous genes encode proteins that have similar amino acid sequences and perform similar functions.

A comparison of the electron transport chains of mitochondria and chloroplasts reveals homologous genes. In particular, let's consider the cytochrome complex found in the thylakoid membrane of plants and algae, called cytochrome b_6-f (**Figure 8.12a**) and cytochrome b-c_1, which is found in the electron transport chain of mitochondria (**Figure 8.12b**; refer back to Figure 7.16). Both cytochrome b_6-f and cytochrome b-c_1 are composed of several protein subunits. One of those proteins is called cytochrome b_6 in cytochrome b_6-f and cytochrome b in cytochrome b-c_1. By analyzing the gene sequences, researchers discovered that cytochrome b_6 and cytochrome b are homologous. These proteins carry out similar functions: both of them accept electrons from a quinone (plastoquinone or ubiquinone) and both donate an electron to another protein within their respective complexes (cytochrome f or cytochrome $c1$). Likewise, both of these proteins function as H^+ pumps that capture some of the energy that is released from electrons to transport H^+ across the membrane. Thus, evolution has produced a family of cytochrome b-type proteins that play similar but specialized roles. Cytochrome b functions as a redox protein and H^+ pump in the electron transport chain of mitochondria, while cytochrome b_6 plays the same role in chloroplasts.

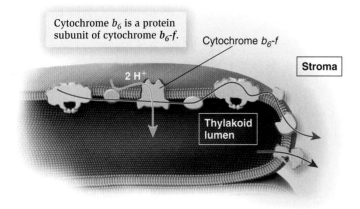

(a) Cytochrome b_6 in a chloroplast

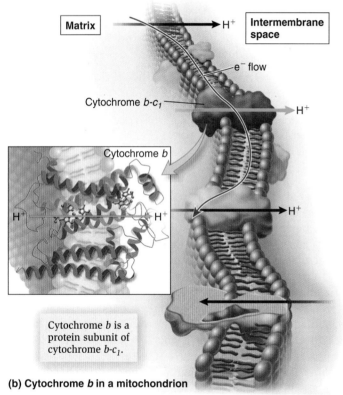

(b) Cytochrome b in a mitochondrion

Figure 8.12   **Homologous proteins in the electron transport chains of mitochondria and chloroplasts.**   **(a)** Cytochrome b_6, a subunit of the cytochrome b_6-f complex found in chloroplasts, and **(b)** cytochrome b, a subunit of the cytochrome b-c_1 complex found in mitochondria, are homologous proteins that play similar roles in their respective electron transport chains. The inset shows the three-dimensional structure of cytochrome b, which was determined by X-ray crystallography. It is an integral membrane protein with several transmembrane α helices and two heme groups, which are prosthetic groups involved in electron transfer. The structure of cytochrome b_6 has also been determined and found to be very similar. (Note: The orientation of cytochrome b in the inset is such that it would pump H^+ out of the matrix. The orientation of cytochrome b_6 is oriented so it would pump H^+ out of the stroma.)

Biological inquiry: Explain why the three-dimensional structures of cytochrome b and cytochrome b_6 are very similar.

8.3 Calvin Cycle

In the previous section, we learned how the light reactions of photosynthesis produce O_2, ATP, and NADPH. We will now turn our attention to the second phase of photosynthesis, the Calvin cycle, in which ATP and NADPH are used to make carbohydrates. The Calvin cycle consists of a series of steps that occur in a metabolic cycle somewhat similar to the citric acid cycle described in Chapter 7. However, while the citric acid cycle is catabolic, the Calvin cycle is an anabolic pathway leading to the biosynthesis of carbohydrates.

The Calvin cycle takes CO_2 from the atmosphere and incorporates the carbon into organic molecules, namely, carbohydrates. As mentioned earlier, carbohydrates are critical for two reasons. First, these organic molecules provide the precursors to make the organic molecules and macromolecules of nearly all living cells. The organic molecules in your body are ultimately derived from the operation of the Calvin cycle in algae and plants. The second key reason why the Calvin cycle is important involves the storage of energy. Recall that molecules such as glucose contain large amounts of chemical energy in their covalent bonds. The Calvin cycle produces carbohydrates, which store energy. These carbohydrates are accumulated inside plant cells. When a plant is in the dark and not carrying out photosynthesis, the stored carbohydrates can be used as a source of energy. Similarly, when an animal consumes a plant, it can use the carbohydrates as an energy source.

In this section, we will examine the three phases of the Calvin cycle and their components. We will also explore the experimental approach of Melvin Calvin and his colleagues that enabled them to elucidate these steps.

The Calvin Cycle Incorporates CO_2 into Carbohydrate

The Calvin cycle, also called the Calvin-Benson cycle, was determined by chemists Melvin Calvin and Andrew Adam Benson and their colleagues in the 1940s and 1950s. This cycle requires a massive input of energy. For every 6 carbon dioxide molecules that are incorporated into carbohydrate such as glucose, 18 ATP molecules are hydrolyzed and 12 NADPH molecules are oxidized.

$$6\ CO_2 + 12\ H_2O \rightarrow C_6H_{12}O_6 + 6\ O_2 + 6\ H_2O$$

Glucose

$$18\ ATP + 18\ H_2O \rightarrow 18\ ADP + 18\ P_i$$

$$12\ NADPH \rightarrow 12\ NADP^+ + 12\ H^+ + 24\ e^-$$

Although biologists commonly describe glucose as a product of photosynthesis, glucose is not directly made by the Calvin cycle. Instead, products of the Calvin cycle are used as starting materials for the synthesis of glucose and other molecules, including sucrose. After glucose molecules are made, they may be linked together to form a polymer of glucose called starch, which is

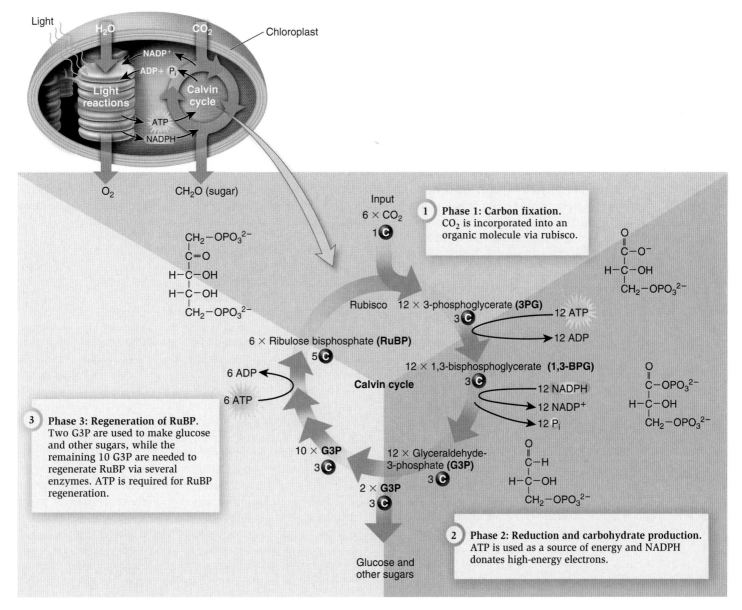

Figure 8.13 **The Calvin cycle.** This cycle has three phases: (1) carbon fixation, (2) reduction and carbohydrate production, and (3) regeneration of RuBP.

stored in the chloroplast for later use. Alternatively, the disaccharide sucrose may be made and transported out of the leaf to other parts of the plant.

The Calvin cycle can be divided into three phases: carbon fixation, reduction and carbohydrate production, and regeneration of RuBP (**Figure 8.13**).

Carbon Fixation (Phase 1) In **carbon fixation**, CO_2 becomes incorporated into ribulose bisphosphate (RuBP), a five-carbon sugar. The enzyme that catalyzes this step is named RuBP carboxylase/oxygenase, or **rubisco**. This enzyme, which constitutes the most abundant protein in chloroplasts, is perhaps the most abundant protein on Earth. The product of the reaction is a six-carbon intermediate that immediately splits in half to form two molecules of 3-phosphoglycerate (3PG).

Reduction and Carbohydrate Production (Phase 2) In the second phase, ATP is used to convert 3PG to 1,3-bisphosphoglycerate. Next, electrons from NADPH reduce 1,3-bisphosphoglycerate to glyceraldehyde-3-phosphate (G3P). G3P is a carbohydrate with three carbon atoms. The key difference between 3PG and G3P is that G3P has a C—H bond, while the analogous carbon in 3PG forms a C—O bond (Figure 8.13). The C—H bond can occur because the G3P molecule has been reduced by the addition of two electrons from NADPH. Compared to 3PG, the bonds in G3P store more energy and enable G3P to readily form larger organic molecules such as glucose.

Only some of the G3P molecules are used to make glucose or other carbohydrates. Phase 1 began with 6 RuBP molecules and 6 CO_2 molecules. Twelve G3P molecules are made at the end of phase 2. Two of these G3P molecules are used in carbohydrate production. As described next, the other 10 G3P molecules are needed to keep the Calvin cycle turning.

Regeneration of RuBP (Phase 3) In the last phase of the Calvin cycle, a series of enzymatic steps converts the 10 G3P molecules into 6 RuBP molecules, using 6 molecules of ATP. After the RuBP molecules are regenerated, they can serve as acceptors for CO_2, thereby allowing the cycle to continue.

As we have just seen, the Calvin cycle begins by using carbon from an inorganic source, that is, CO_2, and ends with organic molecules that will be used by the plant to make other compounds. You may be wondering why it is not possible to directly link the CO_2 molecules together to form these larger molecules. The answer lies in the number of electrons that orbit carbon atoms. In CO_2, the carbon atom is considered electron poor.

Oxygen is a very electronegative atom that monopolizes the electrons it shares with other atoms. In a covalent bond between carbon and oxygen, the shared electrons are closer to the oxygen atom.

By comparison, in an organic molecule, the carbon atom is electron rich. During the Calvin cycle, ATP provides energy and NADPH donates high-energy electrons so that the carbon originally in CO_2 has been reduced. Put simply, the Calvin cycle places additional electrons onto carbon atoms. Compared to the carbon in CO_2, the carbon in an organic molecule can readily form C—H and C—C bonds, which allows the eventual synthesis of larger essential molecules including glucose, amino acids, and so on. In addition, the covalent bonds within these molecules are capable of storing large amounts of energy.

FEATURE INVESTIGATION

The Calvin Cycle Was Determined by Isotope Labeling Methods

The steps in the Calvin cycle involve the conversion of one type of molecule to another, eventually regenerating the starting material, RuBP. In the 1940s and 1950s, Calvin and his colleagues used ^{14}C, a radioisotope of carbon, as a way to label and trace molecules produced during the cycle (**Figure 8.14**). They injected ^{14}C-labeled CO_2 into cultures of the green algae *Chlorella pyrenoidosa* grown in an apparatus called a "lollipop" (because of its shape). The *Chlorella* cells were given different lengths of time to incorporate the ^{14}C-labeled carbon, ranging from fractions of a second to many minutes. After this incubation period, the cells were abruptly placed into a solution of alcohol to inhibit enzymatic reactions and thereby stop the cycle.

The researchers separated the newly made radiolabeled molecules by a variety of methods. The most commonly used

method was two-dimensional paper chromatography. In this approach, a sample containing radiolabeled molecules was spotted onto a corner of the paper at a location called the origin. The edge of the paper was placed in a solvent, such as phenol-water, and the solvent would ascend to the top of the paper. As the solvent rose through the paper, so did the radiolabeled molecules. The rate at which they rose depended on their structures, which determined how strongly they interacted with the paper. This step separated the mixture of molecules spotted onto the paper at the origin. The paper was then dried, turned 90°, and then the edge was placed in a different solvent, such as butanol-propionic acid-water. Again, the solvent would rise through the paper, thereby separating molecules that may not have been adequately separated during the first separation step. After this second separation step, the paper was dried and exposed to X-ray film, a procedure called autoradiography. Radioactive emission from the ^{14}C-labeled molecules caused dark spots to appear on the film.

Figure 8.14   The determination of the Calvin cycle using labeling of CO_2 with ^{14}C.

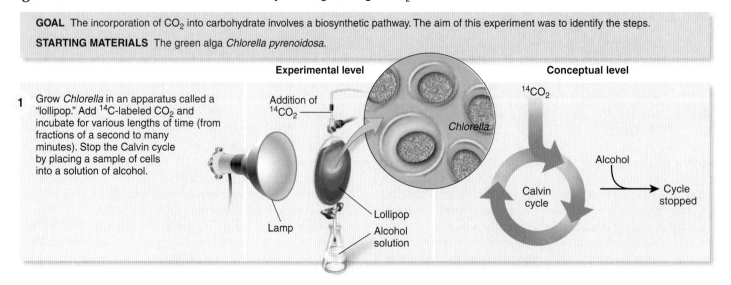

GOAL The incorporation of CO_2 into carbohydrate involves a biosynthetic pathway. The aim of this experiment was to identify the steps.

STARTING MATERIALS The green alga *Chlorella pyrenoidosa.*

Experimental level   Conceptual level

1   Grow *Chlorella* in an apparatus called a "lollipop." Add ^{14}C-labeled CO_2 and incubate for various lengths of time (from fractions of a second to many minutes). Stop the Calvin cycle by placing a sample of cells into a solution of alcohol.

Addition of $^{14}CO_2$

Chlorella

Lamp

Lollipop

Alcohol solution

$^{14}CO_2$

Alcohol

Calvin cycle

Cycle stopped

2 Take a sample of the internal cell contents and spot on the corner of chromatography paper. This spot is called the origin.

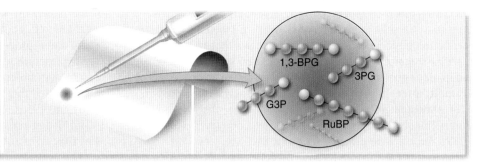

1,3-BPG

3PG

G3P

RuBP

3 Place edge of paper in a solvent, such as phenol-water, and allow time for solvent to rise and separate the mixture of molecules that were spotted at the origin.

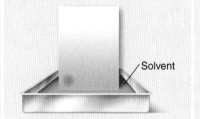

Solvent

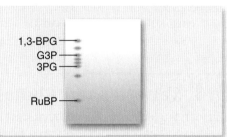

1,3-BPG
G3P
3PG

RuBP

4 Dry paper, turn 90°, and then place the edge in a different solvent such as butanol-propionic acid-water. Allow time for solvent to rise.

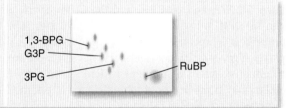

1,3-BPG
G3P

3PG

RuBP

5 Dry paper and place next to X-ray film. The developed film reveals dark spots where ^{14}C-labeled molecules were located. This procedure is called autoradiography.

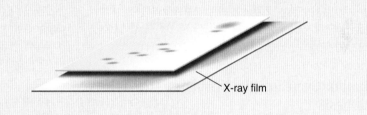

X-ray film

6 THE DATA

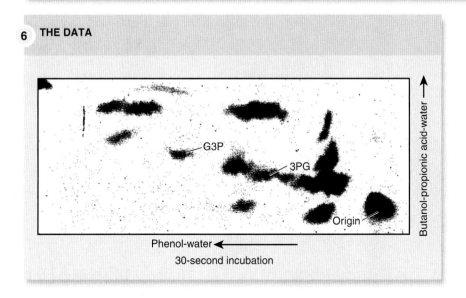

G3P

3PG

Origin

Butanol-propionic acid-water →

← Phenol-water

30-second incubation

The pattern of spots changed, depending on the length of time that the cells were incubated with ^{14}C-labeled CO_2. If the incubation period was short, only molecules that were made in the first steps of the Calvin cycle would be seen, while longer incubations revealed molecules synthesized in later steps. For example, after short incubations, 3-phosphoglycerate (3PG) and 1,3-bisphosphoglycerate (1,3-BPG) would be observed, while longer incubations would show glyceraldehyde-3-phosphate (G3P) and ribulose bisphosphate (RuBP).

A challenge for Calvin and his colleagues was to identify the chemical nature of each spot. This was achieved by a variety of chemical methods. For example, a spot could be cut out of the paper, the molecule within the paper could be washed out, or eluted, and then the eluted molecule could be subjected to the same procedure that included a radiolabeled molecule whose structure was already known. If the unknown molecule and known molecule migrated to the same spot in the paper, this indicated that they were the same molecule. During the late 1940s and 1950s, Calvin and his coworkers identified all of the ^{14}C-labeled spots and the order in which they appeared. In this way, they were able to determine the series of reactions of what we now know as the Calvin cycle. For this work, Calvin was awarded the Nobel Prize in 1961.

8.4 Variations in Photosynthesis

Thus far, we have considered the process of photosynthesis as it occurs in the chloroplasts of green plants and algae. Photosynthesis is a two-stage process in which the light reactions produce O_2, ATP, and NADPH, and the Calvin cycle uses the ATP and NADPH in the synthesis of carbohydrates. This two-stage process is a universal feature of photosynthesis in all green plants, algae, and cyanobacteria. However, certain environmental conditions such as light intensity, temperature, and water availability may influence both the efficiency of photosynthesis and the way in which the Calvin cycle operates. In this section, we begin by examining how hot and dry conditions may reduce the output of photosynthesis. We then explore two adaptations that certain plant species have evolved that conserve water and help to maximize photosynthetic efficiency in such environments.

Photorespiration Decreases the Efficiency of Photosynthesis

In the previous section, we learned that rubisco is a key enzyme of the Calvin cycle. Rubisco functions as a carboxylase because it adds a CO_2 molecule to RuBP, an organic molecule, to create two molecules of 3-phosphoglycerate (3PG).

$$RuBP + CO_2 \rightarrow 2\ 3PG$$

For most species of plants, the incorporation of CO_2 into RuBP is the only way for carbon fixation to occur. Because 3PG is a three-carbon molecule, these plants are called **C_3 plants**. Examples of C_3 plants include wheat and oak trees (**Figure 8.15**).

Researchers have discovered that the active site of rubisco can also function as an oxygenase. As mentioned earlier, that is why it is called rubisco, which stands for RuBP carboxylase/oxygenase. When rubisco adds an O_2 molecule to RuBP, this creates only one molecule of 3-phosphoglycerate and a two-carbon molecule called phosphoglycolate. The phosphoglycolate is then dephosphorylated to glycolate and released from the chloroplast. In a series of several steps, glycolate is eventually oxidized in other organelles to produce an organic molecule plus a molecule of CO_2.

$$RuBP + O_2 \rightarrow \text{3-phosphoglycerate} + \text{Phosphoglycolate}$$

$$\text{Phosphoglycolate} \rightarrow \text{Glycolate} \rightarrow\rightarrow\rightarrow CO_2$$

This process, called **photorespiration**, uses O_2 and liberates CO_2.

(a)

(b)

Figure 8.15 Examples of C_3 plants. The structures of (a) wheat and (b) white oak leaves are similar to that shown in Figure 8.1.

Photorespiration is considered wasteful because it reverses the effects of photosynthesis, thereby reducing the ability of a plant to make carbohydrates, which limits plant growth.

Photorespiration is more likely to occur when plants are exposed to a hot and dry environment. Under these conditions, the stomata of the leaves close, inhibiting the uptake of CO_2 from the air and trapping the O_2 that is produced by photosynthesis. When the level of CO_2 is low and O_2 is high, photorespiration is favored. If C_3 plants are subjected to hot and dry environmental conditions, as much as 25–50% of their photosynthetic work is reversed by the process of photorespiration.

Why do plants carry out photorespiration? The answer is not entirely clear. Photorespiration undoubtedly results in the disadvantage of lowering the efficiency of photosynthesis. One common view is that photorespiration does not offer any advantage and is an evolutionary relic. When rubisco first evolved some 3 billion years ago, the atmospheric oxygen level was low, so that phosphorespiration would not have been a problem. Another view is that photorespiration may have a protective advantage. On hot and dry days, CO_2 levels within a plant may fall and O_2 levels will rise. Under these conditions, highly toxic oxygen-containing molecules such as free radicals may be produced that could cause damage to the plant. Therefore, plant biologists have speculated that the role of photorespiration may be to protect the plant against the harmful effects of such toxic molecules by consuming O_2 and releasing CO_2. In addition, photorespiration may affect the metabolism of other compounds in plants. Recent research suggests that photorespiration may also help plants to assimilate nitrogen into organic molecules.

C_4 Plants Have Evolved a Mechanism to Minimize Photorespiration

Certain species of plants have developed an interesting way to prevent photorespiration. In the early 1960s, Hugo Kortschak discovered that the first product of photosynthesis in sugarcane is not 3-phosphoglycerate but instead is a compound with four carbon atoms. Species such as sugarcane are thus called **C_4 plants** because the first step in carbon fixation produces a four-carbon compound. Later, Marshall Hatch and Roger Slack confirmed this result and identified the compound as oxaloacetate. For this reason, the pathway is sometimes called the Hatch-Slack pathway.

C_4 plants employ an interesting cellular organization to avoid photorespiration (**Figure 8.16**). Unlike C_3 plants, an interior layer in the leaves of many C_4 plants has a two-cell organization composed of mesophyll cells and bundle-sheath cells. CO_2 from the atmosphere enters the mesophyll cells via stomata. Once inside, the enzyme **PEP carboxylase** adds CO_2 to phosphoenolpyruvate (PEP) to produce the four-carbon compound oxaloacetate. PEP carboxylase does not recognize O_2. Therefore, unlike rubisco, PEP carboxylase does not promote photorespiration when CO_2 is low and O_2 is high. Instead, PEP carboxylase continues to fix CO_2.

A key feature of these types of C_4 plants is that a four-carbon compound is transferred between cells. As shown in Figure 8.16, the compound oxaloacetate is converted to the four-carbon compound malate, which is transported into the bundle-sheath cell. Malate is then broken down into pyruvate and CO_2.

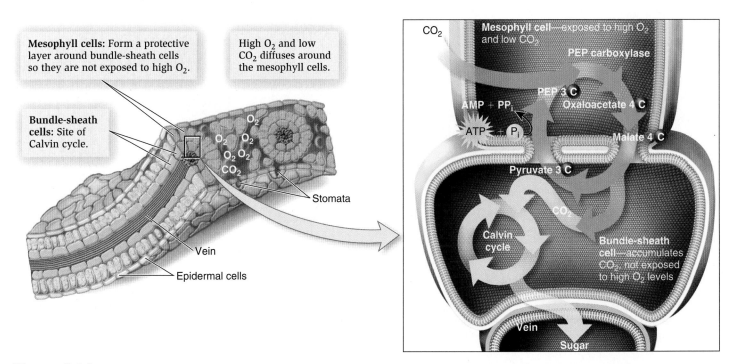

Figure 8.16   **Leaf structure and its relationship to the C_4 cycle.** C_4 plants have mesophyll cells that initially take up CO_2, and bundle-sheath cells, where much of the carbohydrate synthesis occurs. Compare this leaf structure with the structure of C_3 leaves shown in Figure 8.1.

The pyruvate returns to the mesophyll cell, where it is converted to PEP via ATP, and the cycle in the mesophyll cell can begin again. The main outcome of this C_4 cycle is that the mesophyll cell pumps CO_2 into the bundle-sheath cell. The Calvin cycle occurs in the chloroplasts of the bundle-sheath cell. Because the mesophyll cell supplies the bundle-sheath cell with a steady supply of CO_2, the concentration of CO_2 remains high in the bundle-sheath cell. This strategy minimizes photorespiration, which requires low CO_2 and high O_2 levels to proceed.

Which is better—being a C_3 or a C_4 plant? The answer is that it depends on the environment. In warm and dry climates, C_4 plants have an advantage because during the day they can keep their stomata partially closed to reduce water vaporization from the leaf and thereby conserve water. Furthermore, they can avoid photorespiration. C_4 plants are well adapted to habitats with high daytime temperatures and intense sunlight. Some examples of C_4 plants include crabgrass, corn, and sugarcane. In cooler climates, C_3 plants have the edge because it takes less energy for them to fix carbon dioxide. The process of carbon fixation that occurs in C_4 plants uses ATP to regenerate PEP from pyruvate (Figure 8.16), which C_3 plants do not have to expend. Biologists estimate that about 90% of the plant species on Earth are C_3 plants.

CAM Plants Are C_4 Plants That Take Up Carbon Dioxide at Night

We have just learned that certain C_4 plants prevent photorespiration by pumping CO_2 into the bundle-sheath cells, where the Calvin cycle occurs. Another strategy followed by other C_4 plants, called **CAM plants**, is to separate these processes in time. CAM stands for crassulacean acid metabolism, because the process was first studied in members of the plant family Crassulaceae. CAM plants are water-storing succulents such as cacti, bromeliads (including pineapple), and sedums. To avoid water loss, CAM plants keep their stomata closed during the day and open them during the night.

How, then, do CAM plants carry out photosynthesis? **Figure 8.17** compares CAM plants with the other type of C_4 plants we considered in Figure 8.16. During the night, the stomata of CAM plants open, thereby allowing the entry of CO_2 into mesophyll cells, which joins with PEP to form the four-carbon compound oxaloacetate. This is converted to malate, which accumulates during the night in the central vacuoles of the cells. In the morning, the stomata close to conserve moisture. The accumulated malate in the mesophyll cells leaves the vacuole and is broken down to release CO_2, which then drives the Calvin cycle during the daytime.

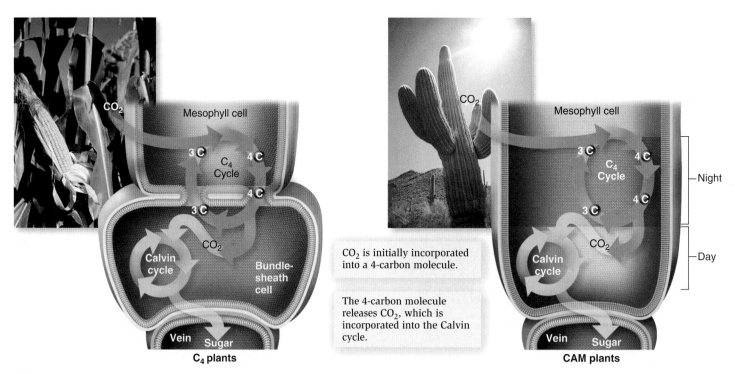

CO₂ is initially incorporated into a 4-carbon molecule.

The 4-carbon molecule releases CO_2, which is incorporated into the Calvin cycle.

C₄ plants

CAM plants

Figure 8.17   A comparison of C₄ and CAM plants.   The name C_4 plant describes those plants in which the first organic product of carbon fixation is a four-carbon compound. Using this definition, CAM plants are a type of C_4 plant because they produce a four-carbon molecule when CO_2 is initially taken up. CAM plants, however, do not separate the functions of making a four-carbon molecule and the Calvin cycle into different types of cells. Instead, they make a four-carbon molecule at night and break down that molecule during the day, so that the CO_2 can be incorporated via the Calvin cycle.

CHAPTER SUMMARY

- Photosynthesis is the process by which plants, algae, and cyanobacteria capture light energy to synthesize carbohydrates.

- Heterotrophs must obtain organic molecules in their food, while autotrophs can make organic molecules from inorganic sources. Photoautotrophs use the energy from light to make organic molecules.

8.1 Overview of Photosynthesis

- The general formula for photosynthesis is that carbon dioxide, water, and energy are needed to make carbohydrates and oxygen.

- In plants and algae, photosynthesis occurs within chloroplasts, which have an outer membrane, inner membrane, and thylakoid membrane. The stroma is found between the thylakoid membrane and inner membrane. In plants, the leaves are the major site of photosynthesis. (Figure 8.1)

- The light reactions of photosynthesis capture light energy to make ATP, NADPH, and O_2. These reactions occur at the thylakoid membrane. Carbohydrate synthesis happens in the stroma and uses ATP and NADPH from the light reactions. (Figure 8.2)

8.2 Reactions That Harness Light Energy

- Light is a form of electromagnetic radiation that travels in waves and is composed of photons with discrete amounts of energy. (Figure 8.3)

- Electrons can absorb light energy and be boosted to a higher energy level. (Figure 8.4)

- Photosynthetic pigments include chlorophylls a and b and carotenoids. These pigments absorb light energy in the visible spectrum. (Figure 8.5)

- Pigment molecules in photosystem II capture light energy, and that energy is transferred to the reaction center via resonance energy transfer. A high-energy electron from P680* is transferred to a primary electron acceptor. An electron from water is then used to replenish the electron that is lost from P680*. (Figures 8.6, 8.7)

- During noncyclic electron flow, electrons from photosystem II follow a pathway along an electron transport chain in the thylakoid membrane. This pathway generates an H^+ gradient that is used to make ATP. In addition, light energy striking photosystem I boosts an electron to a very-high-energy level that allows the synthesis of NADPH. (Figure 8.8)

- Emerson showed that, compared to single light flashes at 680 nm and 700 nm, light flashes at both wavelengths more than doubled the amount of photosynthesis. This occurred because these wavelengths activate pigments in PSII and PSI, respectively. (Figure 8.9)

- Hill and Bendall proposed the Z scheme for electron activation during photosynthesis. According to this scheme, an electron absorbs light energy twice, and it loses some of that energy as it flows along the electron transport chain in the thylakoid membrane. (Figure 8.10)

- During cyclic photophosphorylation, electrons are activated in PSI and flow from Fd to Q_B to the cytochrome complex to Pc and back to PSI. This cyclic electron route produces an H^+ gradient that is used to make ATP. (Figure 8.11)

- Cytochrome b in mitochondria and cytochrome b_6 in chloroplasts are homologous proteins, both of which are involved in electron transport and H^+ pumping. (Figure 8.12)

8.3 Calvin Cycle

- The Calvin cycle can be divided into three phases: carbon fixation, reduction and carbohydrate production, and regeneration of ribulose bisphosphate (RuBP). During this process, ATP is used as a source of energy and NADPH is used as a source of high-energy electrons so that CO_2 can be incorporated into carbohydrate. (Figure 8.13)

- Calvin and Benson determined the steps in the Calvin cycle by isotope labeling methods in which products of the Calvin cycle were separated by chromatography. (Figure 8.14)

8.4 Variations in Photosynthesis

- C_3 plants can only incorporate CO_2 into organic molecules via RuBP to make 3PG, a three-carbon molecule. (Figure 8.15)

- Photorespiration can occur under conditions of high O_2 and low CO_2, which occur under hot and dry conditions. During this process, some CO_2 is liberated and O_2 is used.

- Plants generally known as C_4 plants avoid photorespiration because the CO_2 is first incorporated, via PEP carboxylase, into a four-carbon molecule, which is pumped from mesophyll cells into bundle-sheath cells. This maintains a high concentration of CO_2 in the bundle-sheath cells, where the Calvin cycle occurs. The high CO_2 concentration minimizes photorespiration. (Figure 8.16)

- CAM plants prevent photorespiration by fixing CO_2 into a four-carbon molecule at night and then running the Calvin cycle during the day with their stomata closed. (Figure 8.17)

TEST YOURSELF

1. The water necessary for photosynthesis
   a. is split into H_2 and O_2.
   b. is directly involved in the synthesis of carbohydrate.
   c. provides the electrons to replace lost electrons in photosystem II.
   d. provides H^+ needed to synthesize G3P.
   e. none of the above.

2. The reaction center pigment differs from the other pigment molecules of the light-harvesting complex in that
   a. the reaction center pigment is a carotenoid.
   b. the reaction center pigment absorbs light energy and transfers that energy to other molecules without the transfer of electrons.
   c. the reaction center pigment transfers excited electrons to other molecules.
   d. the other pigments transfer high-energy electrons to other pigment molecules.
   e. the reaction center acts as an ATP synthase to produce ATP.

3. The cyclic electron flow that occurs in photosystem I produces
   a. NADPH.
   b. oxygen.
   c. ATP.
   d. all of the above.
   e. a and c only.

4. During the light reactions, the high-energy electron from P680
   a. eventually moves to NADP$^+$.
   b. becomes incorporated in water molecules.
   c. is pumped into the thylakoid space to drive ATP production.
   d. provides the energy necessary to split water molecules.
   e. falls back to the low-energy state in photosystem II.

5. During the first phase of the Calvin cycle, carbon dioxide is incorporated into ribulose bisphosphate by
   a. oxaloacetate.
   b. rubisco.
   c. RuBP.
   d. quinone.
   e. G3P.

6. The NADPH produced during the light reactions is necessary for
   a. the carbon fixation phase, which incorporates carbon dioxide into an organic molecule of the Calvin cycle.
   b. the reduction phase, which produces carbohydrates in the Calvin cycle.
   c. the regeneration of RuBP of the Calvin cycle.
   d. all of the above.
   e. a and b only.

7. The majority of the G3P produced during the reduction and carbohydrate production phase is used to produce
   a. glucose.
   b. ATP.
   c. RuBP to continue the cycle.
   d. rubisco.
   e. all of the above.

8. Photorespiration
   a. is the process where plants use sunlight to make ATP.
   b. is an inefficient way plants can produce organic molecules and in the process use O_2 and release CO_2.
   c. is a process that plants use to convert light energy to NADPH.
   d. occurs in the thylakoid space.
   e. is the normal process of carbohydrate production in cool, moist environments.

9. Photorespiration is avoided in C_4 plants because
   a. these plants separate the formation of a four-carbon molecule from the rest of the Calvin cycle in different cells.
   b. these plants only carry out anaerobic respiration.
   c. the enzyme PEP functions to maintain high CO_2 concentrations in the bundle-sheath cells.
   d. all of the above.
   e. a and c only.

10. Plants that are commonly found in hot and dry environments that carry out carbon fixation at night are
    a. oak trees.
    b. C_3 plants.
    c. CAM plants.
    d. all of the above.
    e. a and b only.

CONCEPTUAL QUESTIONS

1. Define photosynthesis. Explain the formula for photosynthesis.
2. Explain the function of NADPH.
3. Describe the parts of the chloroplast.

EXPERIMENTAL QUESTIONS

1. What was the purpose of the study conducted by Calvin and his colleagues?
2. In the experiment of Figure 8.14, why did the researchers use ^{14}C? Why did they examine samples at several different time periods? How were the different molecules in the samples identified?
3. What were the results of Calvin's study?

COLLABORATIVE QUESTIONS

1. Discuss the terms heterotroph and photoautotroph.
2. Discuss some of the differences between C_3 and C_4 plants.

---

www.brookerbiology.com

This website includes answers to the Biological Inquiry questions found in the figure legends and all end-of-chapter questions.

9

CELL COMMUNICATION AND REGULATION OF THE CELL CYCLE

CHAPTER OUTLINE

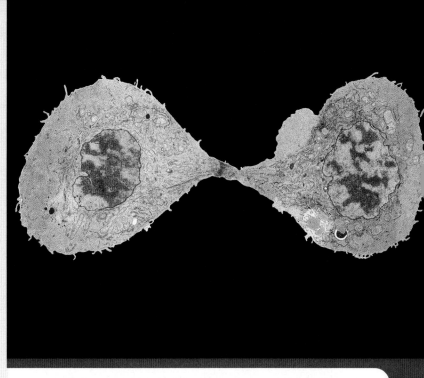

A micrograph of human skin cells dividing. The proper division of skin cells depends on signaling molecules, such as epidermal growth factor, that promote cell division. In addition, the division process is highly regulated to avoid mutations that could harm the resulting daughter cells.

In Chapter 5, we learned that all living cells are surrounded by a plasma membrane, which separates the internal cell contents from the extracellular environment. The plasma membrane enables cells to maintain an internal environment that is well ordered and carries out a variety of cell functions, as described throughout this unit. However, the plasma membrane also tends to isolate a cell from its surroundings. A cell cannot survive if it cannot sense changes in the extracellular environment and respond to them. For example, if the nutrient conditions change, such as a change from carbohydrates to fats, a cell needs to respond in a way that facilitates the uptake and metabolism of fats. If it cannot adapt to environmental changes, a cell is destined to die.

Cell communication is the process through which cells can detect and respond to signals in their extracellular environment. In multicellular organisms, cell communication is also needed to coordinate cellular activities within the whole organism. One of the most important reasons why cells must sense environmental conditions and communicate with each other is to promote cell division. For example, cells should divide only when they have sufficient nutrients to support the division process. The uptake of nutrients acts as a signal to stimulate cell division. In addition, the cells of multicellular organisms must communicate with each other so that cell division in one part of the body is coordinated with other parts. In animals, for example, signaling molecules are released at specific stages of development and promote the division of particular cells.

In this chapter, we will examine how cells respond to environmental signals and also produce signals so they can communicate with other cells. As you will learn, cell communication involves an amazing diversity of cellular proteins, lipids, and steroids that are devoted to this process. We will also consider the cell cycle, which in eukaryotic organisms is a series of events that result in cell division. This chapter focuses on the regulation of the cell cycle, which links cell communication and cell division. Chapter 15 will examine the steps of the cell division process as they pertain to the sorting of chromosomes.

9.1 General Features of Cell Communication

All living cells, including bacteria, fungi, protists, plant cells, and animal cells, are capable of cell communication, also known as cell signaling, a phenomenon that involves both incoming and outgoing signals. A **signal** is an agent that can influence the properties of cells. For example, on a sunny day, cells can sense their exposure to ultraviolet (UV) light and respond accordingly. In humans, UV light acts as an incoming signal to promote the synthesis of melanin, a protective pigment that helps to prevent the harmful effects of UV radiation. In addition, organisms can produce outgoing signals that influence the behavior of neighboring cells. Plant cells, for example, produce hormones that influence the pattern of cell elongation so that the plant grows toward light. Cells of all living organisms both respond to incoming signals and elicit outgoing signals. Cell communication is thus a two-way street.

Communication at the cellular level involves not only sending and receiving signals but also their interpretation. For this to occur, a signal must affect the conformation, or shape, of a cellular protein called a **receptor**. When a signal and receptor interact, a conformational change occurs in the receptor, eventually leading to some type of response in the cell. In this section, we begin by considering why cells need to respond to signals. We will then examine various forms of signaling, which differ in part based on the distance between the cells. Finally, we will examine the main steps that occur when a cell is exposed to a signal and elicits a response to it.

Cells Respond to Signals from Their Environment and from Other Cells

Before getting into the details of cell communication, let's take a general look at why cells need to respond to signals. The first reason is that cells need to respond to a changing environment. Changes in the environment are a persistent feature of life, and living cells are continually faced with alterations in temperature, nutrient availability, and availability of water. A cell may even be exposed to a toxic chemical in its environment. Being able to respond to change, a phenomenon called **adaptation**, is critical for the survival of all living organisms. Adaptation at the cellular level is also referred to as a **cellular response**. As an example, let's consider the response of a yeast cell to glucose in its environment (**Figure 9.1**). Some of the glucose acts as a signaling molecule that causes the cell to respond accordingly. In this case, the cell increases the number of glucose transporters that are needed to take glucose into the cell and also increases the number of enzymes that are required to metabolize glucose once it is inside. The cellular response has therefore allowed the cell to utilize glucose efficiently. We can say that the cell has become adapted to the presence of glucose in its environment.

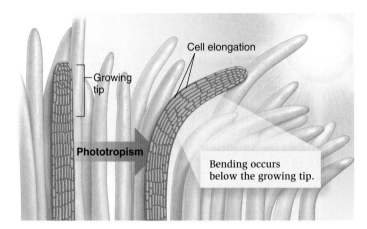

Figure 9.2 **Phototropism in plants.** This process involves a bend that occurs just beneath the actively growing tip. This bend is caused by cell elongation along the nonilluminated side. The amount of auxin is higher on the nonilluminated side.

Biological inquiry: Does auxin cause cells to elongate or shorten?

A second reason for cell signaling is the need for cells to communicate with each other—a process called cell-to-cell communication. In one of the earliest experiments demonstrating cell-to-cell communication, Charles Darwin and his son Francis Darwin studied phototropism, the phenomenon in which plants grow toward light (**Figure 9.2**). The Darwins observed that the actual bending occurs in a zone below the growing tip. They concluded that the transmission of a signal from the growing tip to cells below the tip had to take place for this to occur. Later research revealed that the signal is a molecule called auxin, which is transmitted from cell to cell. The higher amount of auxin present on the nonilluminated side promotes cell elongation on that side only, thereby causing the plant to bend toward the light source.

Cell-to-Cell Communication Can Occur Between Adjacent Cells and Between Cells That Are Long Distances Apart

Researchers have determined that organisms have evolved a variety of different mechanisms to achieve cell-to-cell communication. The mode of communication depends, in part, on the distance between the cells that need to communicate with each other. Let's first examine the various ways in which signals are transferred between cells. Later in this chapter, we will learn how such signals elicit a cellular response.

One way to categorize cell signaling is by the manner in which the signal is transmitted from one cell to another. Signals are relayed between cells in five common ways, all of which involve a cell that produces a signal and a target cell that receives the signal (**Figure 9.3**).

Direct Intercellular Signaling In a multicellular organism, cells that are adjacent to each other may have contacts, called

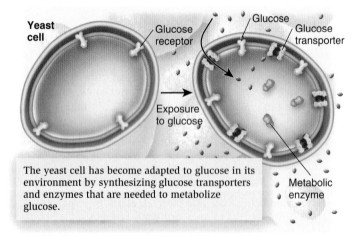

Figure 9.1 **Response of a yeast cell to glucose.** When glucose is absent from the extracellular environment, the cell is not well prepared to take up and metabolize this sugar. However, when glucose is present, some of that glucose binds to a receptor in the membrane, which changes the amounts and properties of intracellular and membrane proteins so that the cell can readily use glucose.

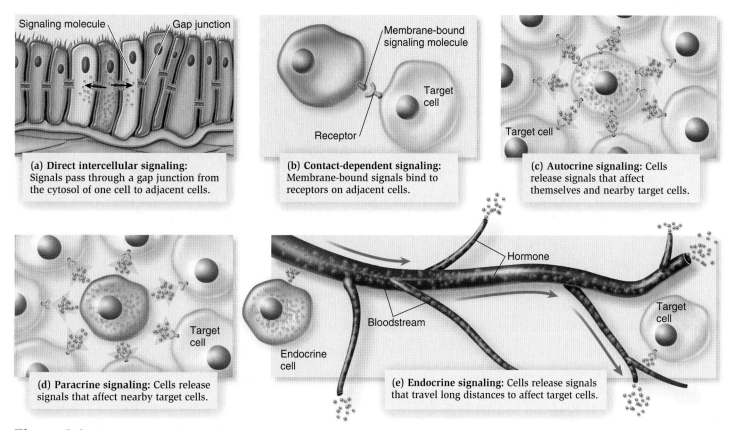

Figure 9.3 Examples of cell-to-cell communication based on the distance between cells.

cell junctions, that enable them to pass signaling molecules and other materials between the cytosol of one cell and the cytosol of another (Figure 9.3a). For example, certain cells that line your lungs have intercellular connections called gap junctions, which we will examine further in Chapter 10. One cell can transmit a signaling molecule to the cytosol of an adjacent cell and thereby affect that cell's behavior. This type of signaling influences the rhythmic movements of cilia on adjacent cells that sweep dust and other unwanted particles out of the lungs.

Contact-Dependent Signaling Not all signaling molecules can readily diffuse from one cell to another. Some molecules are bound to the surface of cells and provide a signal to other cells that make contact with the surface of that cell (Figure 9.3b). In this case, one cell has a membrane-bound signaling molecule that is recognized by a receptor on the surface of another cell. This occurs when portions of nerve cells grow and make contact with other nerve or muscle cells.

Autocrine Signaling In autocrine signaling, a cell secretes signaling molecules that bind to receptors on its own cell surface, stimulating a response (Figure 9.3c). In addition, the signaling molecule can affect neighboring cells of the same cell type. Autocrine signaling is often important for groups of cells to sense cell density. When cell density is high, the concentration of autocrine signals is also high.

Paracrine Signaling In paracrine signaling, a specific cell secretes a signaling molecule that does not affect the cell secreting the signal, but it does influence the behavior of target cells in close proximity (Figure 9.3d). Usually, the signal is broken down too quickly to be carried to other parts of the body and affect distant cells. A specialized form of paracrine signaling called **synaptic signaling** occurs in the nervous system of animals. Neurotransmitters—molecules made in nerve cells that transmit a signal to an adjacent cell—are released at the end of the nerve cell and traverse a narrow space called the synapse. The neurotransmitter then binds to a receptor in a target cell. We will discuss this mechanism of signaling in detail in Chapter 43.

Endocrine Signaling In contrast to the previous mechanisms of cell signaling, endocrine signaling occurs over long distances (Figure 9.3e). In both animals and plants, molecules involved in long-distance signaling are called **hormones**. They are usually longer lasting than signaling molecules involved in autocrine and paracrine signaling. In animals, endocrine signaling involves the secretion of hormones into the bloodstream that may affect virtually all cells of the body, including those that are far from the cells that secrete the signaling molecules. In plants, hormones move through vessels and can also move through adjacent cells. Some signaling molecules are even gases that are secreted into the air. Ethylene is a gas given off by plants that plays a variety of roles, such as the acceleration of fruit ripening.

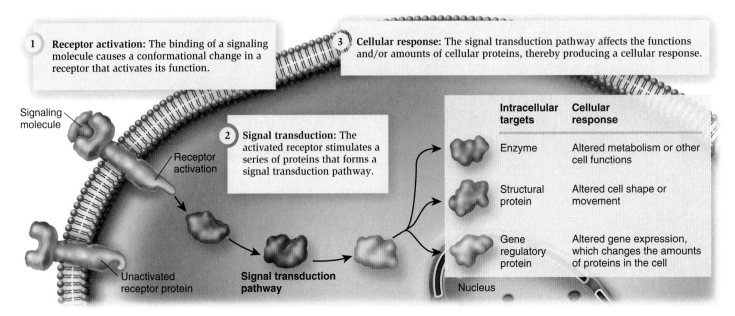

Figure 9.4   The three stages of cell signaling: receptor activation, signal transduction, and a cellular response.

Biological inquiry: For most signaling molecules, explain why a signal transduction pathway is necessary.

The Ability of Cells to Respond to Signals Is Usually a Three-Stage Process

Thus far, we have learned that signals influence the behavior of cells in close proximity or at long distances, usually interacting with receptors to elicit a cellular response. What events occur when a cell encounters a signal? In most cases, the binding of a signal to a receptor causes the receptor to activate a signal transduction pathway, which converts the signal to a cellular response. **Figure 9.4** diagrams the three stages of cell signaling: receptor activation, signal transduction, and a cellular response.

Stage 1: Receptor Activation   In the initial stage, a signaling molecule binds to a receptor, causing receptor activation. The binding of the signal causes a conformational change in the receptor that activates the receptor's function. In most cases, the activated receptor initiates a response by stimulating a sequence of changes in a series of proteins that collectively forms a signal transduction pathway, as described next.

Stage 2: Signal Transduction   During signal transduction, the initial signal is converted—or transduced—to a different signal inside the cell. This process is carried out by a group of proteins that form a **signal transduction pathway**. These proteins undergo a series of changes that may result in the production of another signaling molecule. For example, after a hormone binds to a receptor in the plasma membrane, the activated receptor may interact with intracellular proteins that produce new signals inside the cell.

Stage 3: Cellular Response   Cells can respond to signals in several different ways. Figure 9.4 shows three common cate-

gories of proteins that are controlled by cell signaling. Many signaling molecules exert their effects by altering the activity of one or more enzymes. For example, certain hormones provide a signal that the body needs energy. These hormones activate enzymes that are required for the breakdown of molecules such as carbohydrates.

A second way that cells respond to signals is by altering the functions of structural proteins in the cell. For example, when cells move during embryonic development or when an amoeba moves toward food, signals play a role in the rearrangement of actin filaments, which are components of the cytoskeleton. The coordination of signaling and changes in the cytoskeleton enable cells to move in the correct direction. In addition, changes in structural proteins may cause storage vesicles within a cell to fuse with the plasma membrane. Such vesicles may contain proteins or small molecules that are then secreted by the cell.

Cells may also respond to signals by changing the expression of genes. When exposed to sex hormones, cells can activate genes that change the properties of cells and even the characteristics of entire organisms. As discussed in Chapter 51, estrogens and androgens are responsible for the development of secondary sex characteristics in humans, including breast development in females and beard growth in males.

9.2 Cellular Receptors

As we have learned, signals are needed for cells to respond to environmental changes and to communicate with each other. Communication can occur between adjacent cells or over long distances. In most cases, the binding of a signaling molecule to its receptor activates a signal transduction pathway that ultimately leads to a cellular response. This response may involve effects on enzyme activities, the functions of structural proteins, and/or the transcription of genes.

In this section, we will take a closer look at receptors and how they interact with signaling molecules. We will focus on how these interactions affect the function of the receptor. As you will learn, cells contain many different types of receptors, and their molecular functions are quite diverse. In particular, we will look at differences among receptors based on whether they are located on the cell surface or inside the cell. In this chapter, our focus will be on receptors that respond to chemical signaling molecules. Other receptors discussed in Units 6 and 7 respond to mechanical motion (mechanoreceptors), temperature changes (thermoreceptors), and light (photoreceptors).

Signals Bind Specifically to Receptors and Alter Their Conformations

The ability of cells to respond to a signal usually requires precise recognition between a receptor and its signal. In many cases, the signal is a molecule—a steroid, peptide, or protein—that binds to the receptor. A signaling molecule binds to a receptor in much the same way that a substrate binds to the active site of an enzyme, as described in Chapter 7. The signaling molecule, which is called a **ligand**, binds noncovalently to the receptor molecule with a high degree of specificity. The binding occurs when the ligand and receptor collide in the correct orientation and with enough energy.

$$[Ligand] + [Receptor] \underset{k_{off}}{\overset{k_{on}}{\rightleftharpoons}} [Ligand \cdot Receptor\ complex]$$

The value k_{on} is the rate at which binding occurs. After a complex forms between the ligand and its receptor, the noncovalent interaction between a ligand and receptor remains stable for a finite period of time. The term k_{off} is the rate at which the ligand · receptor complex falls apart or dissociates.

In general, the binding and release between a ligand and its receptor are relatively rapid, and therefore an equilibrium is reached when the rate of formation of new ligand · receptor complexes equals the rate at which existing ligand · receptor complexes dissociate:

$$k_{on}\ [Ligand][Receptor] = k_{off}\ [Ligand \cdot Receptor\ complex]$$

Rearranging,

$$\frac{[Ligand]\ [Receptor]}{[Ligand \cdot Receptor\ complex]} = \frac{k_{off}}{k_{on}} = K_d$$

K_d is called the **dissociation constant** between a ligand and its receptor. Let's look carefully at the left side of this equation and consider what it means. At a ligand concentration where half of the receptors are bound to a ligand, the concentration of the ligand · receptor complex equals the concentration of receptor that doesn't have ligand bound. At this ligand concentration, [Receptor] and [Ligand · Receptor complex] cancel out of the

equation because they are equal. Therefore, at a ligand concentration where half of the receptors have bound ligand:

$$K_d = [Ligand]$$

When the ligand concentration is above the K_d value, most of the receptors are likely to have ligand bound to them. In contrast, if the ligand concentration is substantially below the K_d value, most receptors will not be bound by their ligand. The K_d values for many different ligands and their receptors have been experimentally determined. This information allows researchers to predict when a signaling molecule is likely to cause a cellular response. If the concentration of a signaling molecule is far below the K_d value, a cellular response is not likely because relatively few receptors will form a complex with the signaling molecule.

Unlike enzymes, which convert their substrates into products, receptors do not usually alter the structure of their ligands. Instead, the ligands alter the structure of their receptors, causing a conformational change. This concept is shown in **Figure 9.5**, in which the ligand is a hormone. Once the hormone binds, the receptor undergoes a conformational change. After binding, the hormone · receptor complex is called an activated receptor, because the binding of the hormone to its receptor has changed the receptor in a way that will activate its ability to initiate a cellular response.

Because cell communication is critical for cell survival, the evolution of organisms over the past 3.5 to 4.0 billion years has produced a variety of ways in which cells can respond to signals. Previously, we learned that one way to categorize cell communication is based on the distance that the signal travels. Another way to categorize cell signaling is based on the location and activity of the receptor, as we will explore next.

Cells Contain a Variety of Cell Surface Receptors That Respond to Signals in Different Ways

Most signals, either environmental agents or signals that are secreted from cells, are small hydrophilic molecules or large molecules that do not readily pass through the plasma membrane of cells.

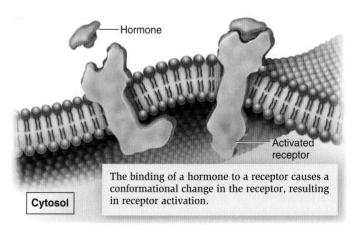

The binding of a hormone to a receptor causes a conformational change in the receptor, resulting in receptor activation.

Figure 9.5   A conformational change induced by a ligand binding to a receptor.

To respond to such signals, cells possess several different types of **cell surface receptors**—receptors that are found in the plasma membrane. A typical cell is expected to contain dozens or even hundreds of different cell surface receptors that enable the cell to respond to different kinds of signaling molecules.

By analyzing the functions of cell surface receptors from many different organisms, researchers have determined that most fall into one of three categories: enzyme-linked receptors, G-protein-coupled receptors, and ligand-gated ion channels.

Enzyme-Linked Receptors   Receptors known as **enzyme-linked receptors** are found in all living species. They typically have two important domains: an extracellular domain, which binds a signaling molecule, and an intracellular domain, which has a catalytic function (**Figure 9.6a**). When a signaling molecule binds to the extracellular domain, a conformational change is transmitted through the membrane-embedded portion of the protein that affects the conformation of the catalytic domain. In most cases, this conformational change causes the catalytic domain to become functionally active.

Most types of enzyme-linked receptors function as **protein kinases**, enzymes that transfer phosphate groups from ATP to a

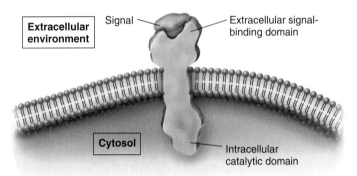

(a) Structure of enzyme-linked receptors

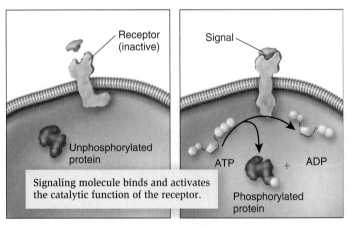

(b) A receptor that functions as a protein kinase

Figure 9.6   Enzyme-linked receptors.   (a) The enzyme-linked receptor protein has an extracellular domain, which binds a signaling molecule, and an intracellular domain, which has a catalytic function. (b) An enzyme-linked receptor can function as a protein kinase, which catalyzes the transfer of a phosphate group from ATP to an intracellular protein.

protein (**Figure 9.6b**). In the absence of a signaling molecule, the catalytic domain remains inactive. However, when a signal binds to the extracellular domain, this transmits a conformational change to the catalytic domain, making it active. Under these conditions, the cell surface receptor may phosphorylate itself or intracellular proteins. Later in this chapter, we will explore in more detail how this event leads to a cellular response.

G-Protein-Coupled Receptors   Receptors called **G-protein-coupled receptors (GPCRs)** are commonly found in the cells of eukaryotic species. GPCRs exhibit a typical structure in which the protein contains seven transmembrane segments that wind back and forth through the plasma membrane. The receptors interact with intracellular proteins called **G proteins**, which are so named because of their ability to bind guanosine triphosphate (GTP) and guanosine diphosphate (GDP). GTP is similar in structure to ATP except it has guanine as a base instead of adenine. In the 1970s, the existence of G proteins was first proposed by Martin Rodbell and colleagues, who found that GTP was needed for certain hormone receptors to cause an intracellular response. Later, Alfred Gilman and coworkers used genetic and biochemical techniques to identify and purify a G protein. In 1994, Rodbell and Gilman won the Nobel Prize for their pioneering work.

Figure 9.7 shows how a GPCR and G protein interact. At the cell surface, the binding of a signaling molecule to a GPCR activates the receptor by causing a conformational change. The activated receptor then binds to a membrane-bound G protein, causing the G protein to release GDP and bind GTP instead. GTP binding changes the conformation of the G protein, causing it to dissociate into its α subunit and a β/γ dimer. Eventually, the extracellular signaling molecule will be degraded, thereby lowering its concentration and resulting in the dissociation between the signaling molecule and the GPCR. When this occurs, the GPCR is no longer activated and the cellular response will be reversed, because the α subunit will eventually hydrolyze its bound GTP to GDP and P_i. When this occurs, the α and β/γ subunits reassociate with each other to form an inactive complex. Later in this chapter, we will examine how the α subunit and β/γ dimer interact with other proteins in a signal transduction pathway to elicit a cellular response.

Ligand-Gated Ion Channels   Ion channels are proteins that allow the diffusion of ions across cellular membranes. **Ligand-gated ion channels** are a third type of cell surface receptor found in the plasma membrane of animal and plant cells. When a signaling molecule (ligand) binds to this type of receptor, the channel opens and allows the flow of ions through the membrane (**Figure 9.8**).

In animals, ligand-gated ion channels are important in the transmission of signals between nerve and muscle cells and between two nerve cells. In addition, ligand-gated ion channels in the plasma membrane allow the uptake of Ca^{2+} into the cytosol. As discussed later in this chapter, changes in the cytosolic concentration of Ca^{2+} play a role in signal transduction.

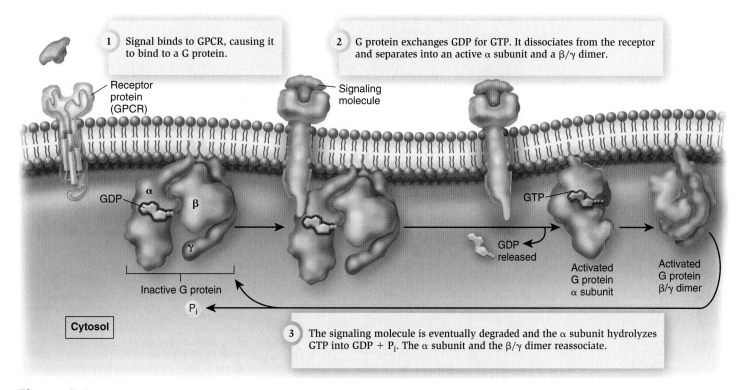

1 Signal binds to GPCR, causing it to bind to a G protein.

2 G protein exchanges GDP for GTP. It dissociates from the receptor and separates into an active α subunit and a β/γ dimer.

Receptor protein (GPCR)

Signaling molecule

GDP

α

β

γ

GTP

GDP released

Inactive G protein

Activated G protein α subunit

Activated G protein β/γ dimer

P_i

Cytosol

3 The signaling molecule is eventually degraded and the α subunit hydrolyzes GTP into GDP + P_i. The α subunit and the β/γ dimer reassociate.

Figure 9.7 The activation of G-protein-coupled receptors.

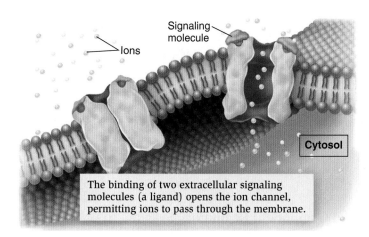

Signaling molecule

Ions

Cytosol

The binding of two extracellular signaling molecules (a ligand) opens the ion channel, permitting ions to pass through the membrane.

Figure 9.8 The function of a ligand-gated ion channel.

Some Signaling Molecules Pass Through the Plasma Membrane and Activate Intracellular Receptors

Although most receptors for signaling molecules are located in the plasma membrane, some are found inside the cell. In these cases, the signaling molecule must pass through the plasma membrane to gain access to its receptor. For example, two types of signaling molecules—steroids and auxins—diffuse into the cell, where they bind to internal receptors. As described in Chapter 51, steroid hormones, such as estrogens and androgens, are secreted into the bloodstream from cells of endocrine glands.

The behavior of estrogen is typical of many steroid hormones (**Figure 9.9a**). Because of its hydrophobic nature, estrogen is capable of passing through the plasma membrane of a target cell and binding to a receptor in the nucleus. Some steroids bind to receptors in the cytosol, which then travel into the nucleus, while other steroid hormones bind to receptors that are in the nucleus; estrogen is one of the latter. After binding, the estrogen • receptor complex undergoes a conformational change that enables it to form a dimer with another estrogen • receptor complex. The dimer then binds to the DNA and activates the transcription of specific genes. The estrogen receptor is an example of a transcription factor, a protein that regulates the transcription of genes.

A second example of an intracellular receptor is the receptor for a group of related plant hormones called auxins, which are important in many plant signaling pathways, including the growth of shoots toward light, the growth of roots into the soil, and the flowering process. In 2005, two research groups led by Ottoline Leyser and Mark Estelle determined that auxin binds to an intracellular receptor called TIR1 (TIR stands for transport inhibitor response, so named because mutations in this receptor alter the response of drugs that inhibit auxin transport in plants). The binding of auxin in the cytosol activates TIR1, and it travels into the nucleus. Like steroid receptors, TIR1 also causes the activation of specific genes. However, TIR1 does not do this directly. After auxin binds, the receptor causes the breakdown of a protein that inhibits several genes (**Figure 9.9b**). When this inhibitory protein is broken down, the gene inhibition is relieved and the genes are transcribed into mRNA.

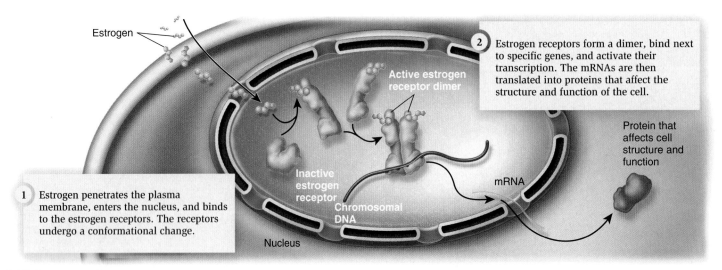

1 Estrogen penetrates the plasma membrane, enters the nucleus, and binds to the estrogen receptors. The receptors undergo a conformational change.

Estrogen

Active estrogen receptor dimer

Inactive estrogen receptor

Chromosomal DNA

Nucleus

2 Estrogen receptors form a dimer, bind next to specific genes, and activate their transcription. The mRNAs are then translated into proteins that affect the structure and function of the cell.

Protein that affects cell structure and function

mRNA

(a) Estrogen receptor

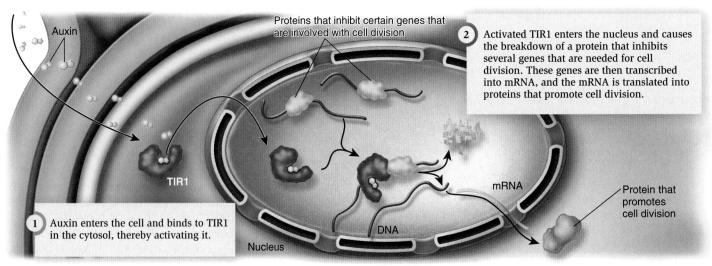

Auxin

Proteins that inhibit certain genes that are involved with cell division

TIR1

1 Auxin enters the cell and binds to TIR1 in the cytosol, thereby activating it.

Nucleus

DNA

2 Activated TIR1 enters the nucleus and causes the breakdown of a protein that inhibits several genes that are needed for cell division. These genes are then transcribed into mRNA, and the mRNA is translated into proteins that promote cell division.

mRNA

Protein that promotes cell division

(b) Auxin receptor

Figure 9.9 Examples of intracellular receptors.

9.3 Signal Transduction and the Cellular Response

In this section, we turn our attention to the intracellular events that enable a cell to respond to a signaling molecule that binds to a cell surface receptor. In most cases, the binding of a signaling molecule to its receptor stimulates a signal transduction pathway. We begin by examining the components of different signal transduction pathways, looking in detail at the two-component regulatory systems common to bacteria and the signaling transduction pathways involving molecules called second messengers. We will use the activities of the hormone epinephrine as a way to explore how signal transduction pathways affect cellular proteins in a way that leads to a cellular response. Lastly, we'll explore the reasons why different types of cells can respond in distinct ways to the same hormone.

Two-Component Regulatory Systems in Bacteria Sense Environmental Changes

The survival of bacteria is largely dependent on their ability to adapt to environmental changes. By studying many different bacterial species, researchers have discovered that a common way for bacteria to adapt to a changing environment is via **two-component regulatory systems**. In such systems, one component, an enzyme-linked receptor called a **sensor kinase**, recognizes a signal found in its environment. The sensor kinase also has the ability to hydrolyze ATP and phosphorylate itself. The phosphate group is then transferred to a second component, a protein called the **response regulator**, which is usually a protein that regulates the expression of many genes.

Figure 9.10 considers a two-component regulatory system, found in many species of bacteria, that senses the presence of

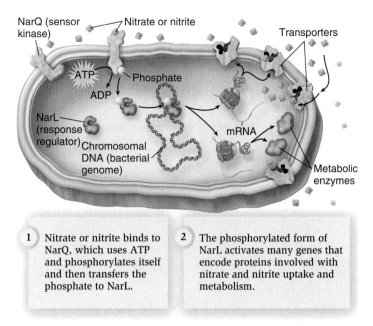

1 | Nitrate or nitrite binds to NarQ, which uses ATP and phosphorylates itself and then transfers the phosphate to NarL.

2 | The phosphorylated form of NarL activates many genes that encode proteins involved with nitrate and nitrite uptake and metabolism.

Figure 9.10 An example of a two-component regulatory system in bacteria. The system shown here regulates nitrate and nitrite metabolism. NarQ is a receptor, and NarL is a single component of a signal transduction pathway. When phosphorylated by NarQ, NarL functions as a transcriptional activator.

nitrate (NO_3^-) and nitrite (NO_2^-) in the environment. NarQ is a sensor kinase that recognizes either nitrate or nitrite. When either of these binds to NarQ, NarQ phosphorylates itself via ATP and then transfers a phosphate to the response regulator, NarL. The phosphorylated form of NarL activates the transcription of many genes involved in nitrate and nitrite metabolism and transport. Once these genes are transcribed into mRNA and then translated into specific proteins, the bacterium has become better adapted to the presence of nitrate or nitrite in its environment.

Two-component regulatory systems are also found in fungi and plants, but they do not appear to exist in animals. Why animals lack this form of signaling is not understood.

Second Messengers Are Key Components of Many Signal Transduction Pathways

Cell biologists call signals that bind to a cell surface receptor the first messengers. After first messengers bind to receptors, many signal transduction pathways lead to the production of **second messengers**, small molecules or ions that relay signals inside the cell. The following examples illustrate the roles of second messengers in signal transduction pathways.

Signal Transduction via cAMP As we saw earlier, the binding of a signaling molecule to a G-protein-coupled receptor (GPCR) activates an intracellular G protein by causing it to bind GTP and dissociate into an α subunit and a β/γ dimer (see Figure 9.7). Let's now follow the role of these subunits in signal

transduction pathways. The α subunit and the β/γ dimer can activate several different kinds of proteins that are components of signal transduction pathways.

Mammalian and plant cells make several different types of G protein α subunits. One type binds to **adenylyl cyclase**, an enzyme in the plasma membrane (**Figure 9.11a**). This stimulates adenylyl cyclase to synthesize **cyclic adenosine monophosphate (cAMP)** from ATP. The molecule, cAMP, is an example of a second messenger.

cAMP

One effect of cAMP is to activate protein kinase A (PKA), which is composed of four subunits: two catalytic subunits that phosphorylate specific cellular proteins, and two regulatory subunits that inhibit the catalytic subunits when they are bound to each other. Cyclic AMP binds to the regulatory subunits of PKA. The binding of cAMP separates the regulatory and catalytic subunits, which allows each catalytic subunit to be active.

The catalytic subunit of PKA then phosphorylates specific cellular proteins such as enzymes, structural proteins, and transcription factors. When a protein kinase attaches a phosphate group onto a protein, the shape and function of that protein is altered. Often, phosphorylation activates protein function. In 1955, Edmond Fischer and Edwin Krebs discovered that the phosphorylation of enzymes is important in regulating glycogen breakdown. Since that time, researchers have determined that phosphorylation is a widespread mechanism that regulates protein function in all species. For their key discovery, Fischer and Krebs were awarded the Nobel Prize in 1992.

Let's now consider how the effects of a signaling molecule are reversed. When the signaling molecule is no longer produced and its extracellular levels fall, the molecule dissociates from the receptor, because the binding to its receptor is a reversible process (**Figure 9.11b**). Once the signaling molecule is released, the receptor is no longer activated. Intracellularly, the α subunit hydrolyzes its GTP to GDP, and the α subunit and β/γ dimer reassociate to an inactive G protein. The levels of cAMP decrease due to the action of an enzyme called **phosphodiesterase**, which converts cAMP to AMP. As cAMP levels fall, the regulatory subunits of PKA release cAMP, and the regulatory and catalytic subunits reassociate, thereby inhibiting PKA. Finally, enzymes called **protein phosphatases** are responsible for removing phosphate groups from proteins, thereby reversing the effects of PKA.

In the 1950s, Earl Sutherland determined that many different hormones cause the formation of cAMP in a variety of cell types.

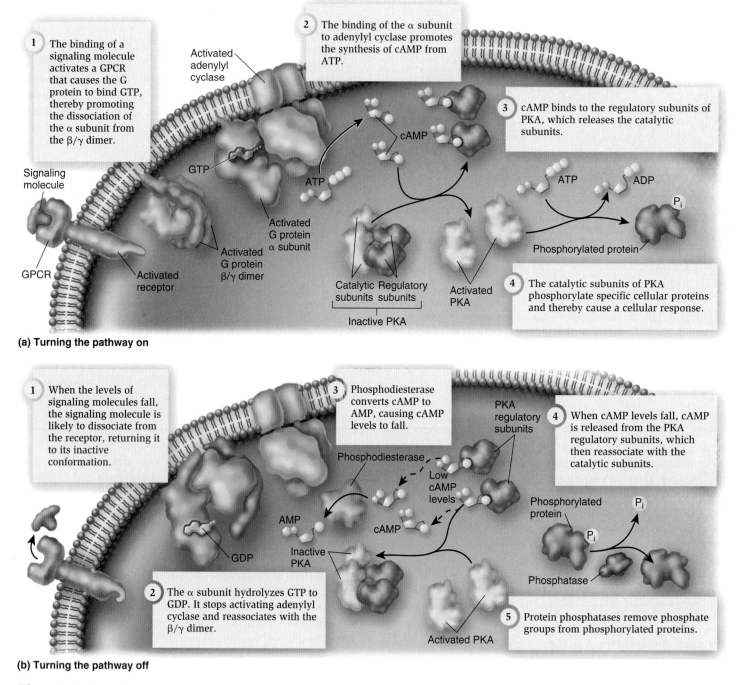

(a) Turning the pathway on

1. The binding of a signaling molecule activates a GPCR that causes the G protein to bind GTP, thereby promoting the dissociation of the α subunit from the β/γ dimer.

2. The binding of the α subunit to adenylyl cyclase promotes the synthesis of cAMP from ATP.

3. cAMP binds to the regulatory subunits of PKA, which releases the catalytic subunits.

4. The catalytic subunits of PKA phosphorylate specific cellular proteins and thereby cause a cellular response.

Activated adenylyl cyclase

Signaling molecule

GTP

ATP

cAMP

ATP   ADP

P_i

Activated G protein α subunit

Activated G protein β/γ dimer

GPCR

Activated receptor

Catalytic Regulatory subunits subunits

Inactive PKA

Activated PKA

Phosphorylated protein

(b) Turning the pathway off

1. When the levels of signaling molecules fall, the signaling molecule is likely to dissociate from the receptor, returning it to its inactive conformation.

2. The α subunit hydrolyzes GTP to GDP. It stops activating adenylyl cyclase and reassociates with the β/γ dimer.

3. Phosphodiesterase converts cAMP to AMP, causing cAMP levels to fall.

4. When cAMP levels fall, cAMP is released from the PKA regulatory subunits, which then reassociate with the catalytic subunits.

5. Protein phosphatases remove phosphate groups from phosphorylated proteins.

Phosphodiesterase

Low cAMP levels

AMP

cAMP

GDP

Inactive PKA

Activated PKA

PKA regulatory subunits

Phosphorylated protein

P_i

P_i

Phosphatase

Figure 9.11   **The signal transduction pathway involving cAMP.**   (a) The pathway leading to the formation of cAMP and subsequent activation of PKA, which is mediated by a G-protein-coupled receptor (GPCR). (b) The steps that shut the pathway off when the signaling molecule is no longer present in the environment.

This observation, for which he won the Nobel prize, stimulated great interest in the study of signal transduction pathways. Since Sutherland's discovery, the production of second messengers such as cAMP has been found to have two important advantages. One benefit is the amplification of the signal; the binding of a signal to a single receptor can cause the synthesis of many cAMP molecules that activate PKA (**Figure 9.12**). Likewise, each molecule of PKA can phosphorylate many proteins in the cell to promote a cellular response. In this way, a

signal can have a dramatic effect on the functioning of many proteins in a target cell.

A second advantage of second messengers such as cAMP is speed. Brian Bacskai and colleagues studied the response of nerve cells to a signaling molecule called serotonin, which is a neurotransmitter that binds to a GPCR. In humans, serotonin is believed to play a role in depression, anxiety, and sexual drive. To monitor cAMP levels, nerve cells grown in a laboratory were injected with a fluorescent protein that changes its fluorescence

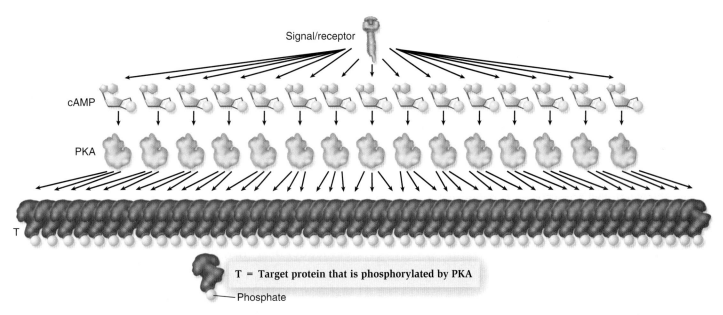

Signal/receptor

cAMP

PKA

T

T = Target protein that is phosphorylated by PKA

Phosphate

Figure 9.12 **Signal amplification.** An advantage of a signal transduction pathway is the amplification of a signal. In this case, a single signaling molecule can lead to the phosphorylation of many target proteins.

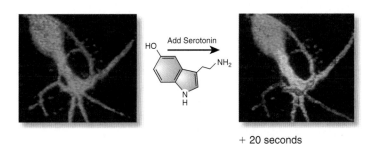

Add Serotonin

+ 20 seconds

Figure 9.13 **The rapid speed of cAMP production.** The micrograph on the *left* shows a nerve cell prior to its exposure to serotonin, while the micrograph on the *right* shows the same cell 20 seconds after exposure. Blue indicates a low level of cAMP, yellow is an intermediate level, and red/purple is a high level.

when cAMP is made. As shown in the micrograph on the right in **Figure 9.13**, a substantial amount of cAMP was made within 20 seconds after the addition of serotonin.

Signal Transduction via Ca²⁺ Cells use many different types of second messengers, and more than one type may be used at the same time. Calcium ions are another common second messenger. Cells maintain very large Ca^{2+} gradients (**Figure 9.14**). Two types of calcium pumps are found in the membranes of cells. Ca^{2+}-ATPases use the energy from ATP hydrolysis to pump Ca^{2+} against a gradient, while Na^+/Ca^{2+} and H^+/Ca^{2+} exchangers or antiporters use the energy within Na^+ or H^+ gradients to pump Ca^{2+} across the membrane. These pumps produce a cytosolic Ca^{2+} concentration that is very low, typically 0.1–1.0 μM. By comparison, the Ca^{2+} concentration found outside of cells and inside the endoplasmic reticulum (ER) lumen and mitochondrial matrix is far higher, as much as 1,000- to 10,000-fold higher!

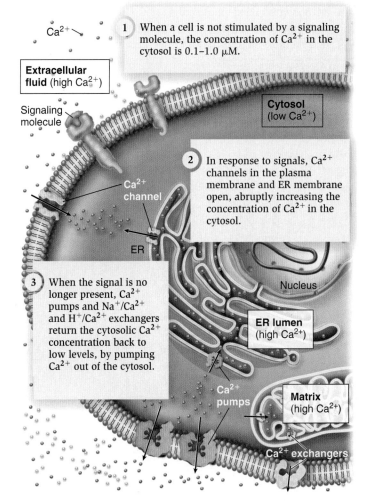

Ca^{2+}

1 When a cell is not stimulated by a signaling molecule, the concentration of Ca^{2+} in the cytosol is 0.1–1.0 μM.

Extracellular fluid (high Ca^{2+})

Cytosol (low Ca^{2+})

Signaling molecule

2 In response to signals, Ca^{2+} channels in the plasma membrane and ER membrane open, abruptly increasing the concentration of Ca^{2+} in the cytosol.

Ca^{2+} channel

ER

Nucleus

3 When the signal is no longer present, Ca^{2+} pumps and Na^+/Ca^{2+} and H^+/Ca^{2+} exchangers return the cytosolic Ca^{2+} concentration back to low levels, by pumping Ca^{2+} out of the cytosol.

ER lumen (high Ca^{2+})

Ca^{2+} pumps

Matrix (high Ca^{2+})

Ca^{2+} exchangers

Figure 9.14 Calcium levels inside and outside of eukaryotic cells.

Calcium channels that are found in the plasma membrane and ER membrane play a key role in the ability of calcium to act as a second messenger. When such channels open in response to signaling, the cytosolic concentration of Ca^{2+} can increase dramatically and quickly, in a matter of seconds. The increase in Ca^{2+} concentration in the cytosol acts as a second messenger that elicits a cellular response. In plants, calcium signaling is involved in many processes, including cell elongation in response to light, the opening and closing of stomata, and the ability to sense gravity. In animals, calcium-signaling pathways are also important in many cellular events such as nerve transmission, muscle contraction, and the secretion of digestive enzymes by the pancreas. As we will explore later, such responses are mediated by calcium-binding proteins that are activated when the cytosolic concentration of Ca^{2+} is increased.

The calcium channels that are found in the ER membrane are opened via a second messenger called inositol trisphosphate, a pathway that is described next.

Signal Transduction via Diacylglycerol and Inositol Trisphosphate   We have already examined how a G protein can activate adenylyl cyclase and thereby promote the synthesis of cAMP. Let's now consider a second way that an activated G protein can influence a signal transduction pathway. The α subunit can activate an enzyme called phospholipase C (**Figure 9.15**). When phospholipase C becomes active, it breaks a covalent bond in a plasma membrane phospholipid, which produces two second messengers, diacylglycerol (DAG) and inositol trisphosphate (IP_3). DAG binds to a membrane-bound enzyme called protein kinase C (PKC). IP_3 is released into the cytosol and binds to a ligand-gated Ca^{2+} channel in the ER membrane. The binding of IP_3 causes the channel to open, releasing Ca^{2+} into the cytosol.

Therefore, this pathway involves another messenger, the calcium ions that we considered previously.

Calcium ions can affect the behavior of cells in a variety of ways, two of which are shown in Figure 9.15. Ca^{2+} can bind to PKC, which, in combination with DAG, causes this enzyme to become activated. Once activated, PKC can phosphorylate specific cellular proteins. In addition, Ca^{2+} can bind to a protein called calmodulin, which is a calcium-modulated protein. The Ca^{2+}-calmodulin complex can then interact with specific cellular proteins and alter their functions. For example, calmodulin regulates proteins involved in carbohydrate breakdown in liver cells.

A Cellular Response Depends on Which Proteins Are Controlled by a Signal Transduction Pathway

As we have seen, signaling molecules exert their effects on eukaryotic cells via signal transduction pathways that control the activities and/or synthesis of specific proteins. In multicellular organisms, one of the amazing effects of signaling molecules such as hormones is their ability to coordinate cellular activities. One example is the hormone epinephrine (also called adrenaline), which is secreted from endocrine cells. Epinephrine is also called the fight-or-flight hormone because it quickly prepares the body for strenuous physical activity. In humans, for example, epinephrine is secreted into the bloodstream when someone is confronted with a stressful event or is exercising vigorously.

Epinephrine has different effects throughout the body (**Figure 9.16**). In the heart, it stimulates heart muscle cells so that the heart beats faster. In the liver, epinephrine promotes the release of glucose into the bloodstream so that an individual

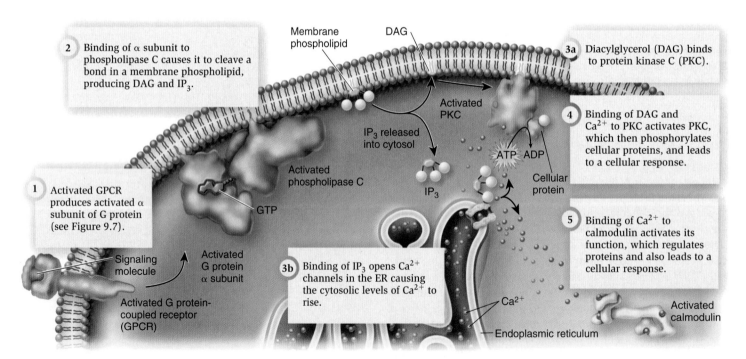

Figure 9.15   Signal transduction pathway involving diacylglycerol (DAG) and inositol trisphosphate (IP_3).

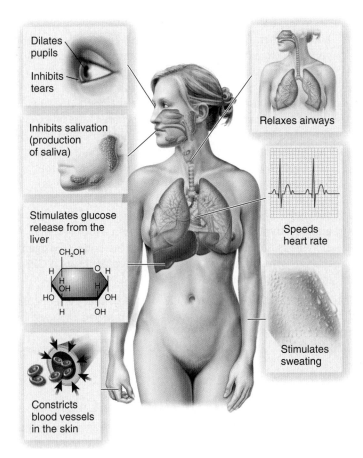

Figure 9.16   The effects of epinephrine in humans.

can use the glucose to produce energy (ATP) needed to fight or flee. Let's examine the cell's response to an extracellular signal by considering how epinephrine affects cells in the heart.

Cellular Response of Heart Muscle Cells to Epinephrine
Contraction of heart muscle is controlled by the level of Ca^{2+} in the cytosol. Calcium ions are stored inside an organelle found only in muscle cells called the sarcoplasmic reticulum, which is a specialized form of the endoplasmic reticulum. When a muscle cell is stimulated to contract, calcium ions are released from the sarcoplasmic reticulum into the cytosol, where the ions bind to a protein called troponin (**Figure 9.17a**). The binding of Ca^{2+} causes a conformational change in troponin that subsequently leads to muscle contraction. For the muscle to relax, the ions must be pumped back into the sarcoplasmic reticulum. A protein called phospholamban activates a Ca^{2+} pump, which stimulates the pumping of Ca^{2+} into the sarcoplasmic reticulum. This lowers the concentration of Ca^{2+} in the cytosol and causes the muscle to relax.

How does epinephrine increase the heart rate? In heart muscle cells, the primary effect of epinephrine is to activate adenylyl cyclase, which produces cAMP. This, in turn, activates PKA, which phosphorylates troponin and phospholamban (**Figure 9.17b**). When troponin is phosphorylated, this enhances Ca^{2+} binding and thereby increases the rate of contraction.

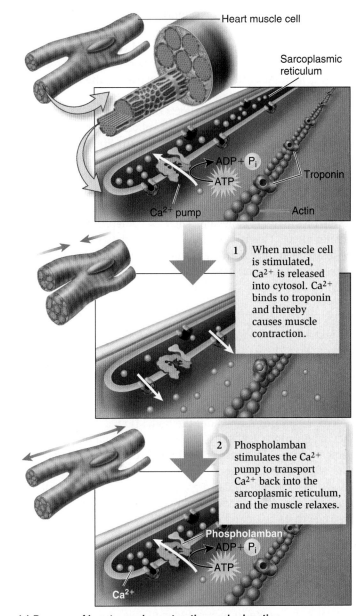

1   When muscle cell is stimulated, Ca^{2+} is released into cytosol. Ca^{2+} binds to troponin and thereby causes muscle contraction.

2   Phospholamban stimulates the Ca^{2+} pump to transport Ca^{2+} back into the sarcoplasmic reticulum, and the muscle relaxes.

(a) Process of heart muscle contraction and relaxation

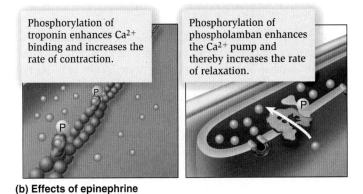

Phosphorylation of troponin enhances Ca^{2+} binding and increases the rate of contraction.

Phosphorylation of phospholamban enhances the Ca^{2+} pump and thereby increases the rate of relaxation.

(b) Effects of epinephrine

Figure 9.17   The contraction of heart muscle cells and the effects of epinephrine.   (a) The steps of muscle contraction and relaxation. (b) The effects of epinephrine. This hormone activates PKA, which phosphorylates troponin and phospholamban.

When phospholamban is phosphorylated, it stimulates the function of the Ca^{2+} pump. This promotes a faster pumping of Ca^{2+} back into the sarcoplasmic reticulum and thereby enhances the rate of relaxation. Taken together, the phosphorylation of these proteins increases the heart rate by increasing the rates of both contraction and relaxation.

Interestingly, one of the effects of caffeine can be explained by this mechanism. Caffeine inhibits phosphodiesterase, which converts cAMP to AMP (see Figure 9.11b). Phosphodiesterase functions to remove cAMP once a signaling molecule, such as epinephrine, is no longer present. When phosphodiesterase is inhibited by caffeine, cAMP persists for a longer period of time and thereby causes the heart to beat faster. Therefore, even low levels of signaling molecules such as epinephrine will have a greater effect. This is one of the reasons why drinks containing caffeine, including coffee and many energy drinks, provide a feeling of vitality and energy.

GENOMES & PROTEOMES

A Cell's Response to Signaling Molecules Depends on the Proteins It Makes

As Figure 9.16 shows, a hormone such as epinephrine produces diverse responses throughout the body. How do we explain the fact that various cell types can respond so differently to the same hormone? The answer lies in **differential gene regulation**. The transcription of genes is controlled by a variety of processes. As a multicellular organism develops from a fertilized egg, the cells of the body become differentiated into particular types, such as heart and liver cells. Although different cell types such as heart and liver cells contain the same set of genes, they are not expressed in the same pattern. Certain genes that are turned off in heart cells are turned on in liver cells, while some genes that are turned on in heart cells are turned off in liver cells. The pattern of gene regulation in any given cell type is critical in its ability to respond to signaling molecules. The following are examples of how differential gene regulation affects the cellular response:

1. *A cell may or may not express a receptor for a particular signaling molecule.* For example, not all cells of the human body express a receptor for epinephrine. These cells are not affected when epinephrine is released into the bloodstream.
2. *Different cell types have different cell surface receptors that recognize the same signaling molecule.* In humans, a signaling molecule called acetylcholine has two different types of receptors. One acetylcholine receptor is a ligand-gated ion channel that is expressed in skeletal muscle cells. Another acetylcholine receptor is a G-protein-coupled receptor (GPCR) that is expressed in heart muscle cells. Because of this, skeletal and heart muscle cells respond differently to acetylcholine.
3. *Two (or more) receptors may work the same way in different cell types but have different affinities for the same signaling molecule.* Two different GPCRs may recognize the same

hormone, but a receptor expressed in liver cells may have a higher affinity (that is, a lower K_d) for a hormone compared to a receptor expressed in muscle cells. In this case, the liver cells will respond to a lower hormone concentration than the muscle cells will.
4. *The expression of proteins involved in intracellular signal transduction pathways may vary in different cell types.* For example, one cell type may express the proteins that are needed to activate PKA, while another cell type may not.
5. *The expression of proteins that are controlled by signal transduction pathways may vary in different cell types.* In liver cells, the presence of epinephrine leads to the activation of glycogen phosphorylase kinase (GPK), an enzyme involved in glycogen breakdown. However, this enzyme is not expressed in all cells of the body. Glycogen breakdown will only be stimulated by epinephrine if GPK is expressed in that cell.

Taken together, these five examples of differential gene regulation help explain why different cell types respond to signaling molecules in a myriad of ways.

9.4 Regulation of the Cell Cycle

In this chapter, we have examined how cells receive signals and respond to them in meaningful ways. One of the most important ways that a cell may respond to a signal is to divide. Life is a continuum in which new living cells are formed by the division of pre-existing cells. The Latin axiom *Omnis cellula e cellula*, meaning "Every cell from a cell," was first proposed in 1858 by a German pathologist, Rudolf Virchow. From an evolutionary perspective, cell division is a cellular response with a very ancient origin. All living organisms, from unicellular bacteria to multicellular plants and animals, are products of repeated rounds of cell growth and division extending back to the beginnings of life nearly 4 billion years ago.

We now know that cell division is a process that involves remarkable accuracy and precise timing. A cell must be able to sense when conditions are appropriate for cell division to occur and then orchestrate a series of events that will ensure the production of healthy new cells. In Chapter 15, we will examine the mechanics of cell division, with an emphasis on how chromosomes are correctly sorted to new daughter cells. In this section, we will focus on the regulation of the cell cycle. We begin with a description of the phases of the cell cycle. We then explore the factors that affect the cell's decision to divide, and see how the cell cycle is controlled by proteins that carefully monitor the division process to ensure its accuracy.

The Cell Cycle Is a Series of Phases That Lead to Cell Division

Eukaryotic cells that are destined to divide progress through a series of stages known as the **cell cycle** (**Figure 9.18**). The phases consist of G_1 (first gap), S (synthesis of DNA, the genetic material), G_2 (second gap), and **M phase** (mitosis and cytokinesis).

The G_1 and G_2 phases were originally described as gap phases, to indicate a pause in activity between DNA synthesis and mitosis. However, we now know that these are critical stages of the cell cycle. In actively dividing cells, the G_1, S, and G_2 phases are collectively known as **interphase**. Alternatively, cells may exit the cell cycle and remain for long periods of time in a stage called **G_0**. The G_0 stage is a substitute for G_1. A cell in the G_0 phase has postponed making a decision to divide or, in the case of terminally differentiated cells (such as nerve cells in an adult animal), has made a decision to never divide again.

The length of the cell cycle varies considerably among different cells types, ranging from several minutes in quickly growing embryos to several months in slow-growing adult cells. For fast-dividing mammalian cells in adults, the length of the cycle is typically 24 hours. The various stages within the cell cycle also vary in length. G_1 is often the longest and also the most variable phase, while M phase is the shortest. For a cell that divides in 24 hours, the following lengths of time for each phase are typical:

- G_1 phase: 11 hours
- S phase: 8 hours
- G_2 phase: 4 hours
- M phase: 1 hour

The G_1 phase is a period in a cell's life when it may decide to divide. Depending on the environmental conditions and the presence of signaling molecules, a cell in the G_1 phase may accumulate molecular changes that cause it to progress through the rest of the cell cycle. When this occurs, cell biologists say that a cell has reached a special control point called the **restriction point**. Once past the restriction point, a cell is committed to advance to the S phase, during which the chromosomes are replicated. After replication, the two duplicated chromosomes are still joined to each other and referred to as a pair of **sister chromatids** (**Figure 9.19**). When S phase is completed, a cell actually has twice as many chromatids as the number of chromosomes in the G_1 phase. For example, a human cell in the G_1 phase has 46 distinct chromosomes, whereas the same cell in G_2 would have 46 pairs of sister chromatids, for a total of 92 chromatids.

During the G_2 phase, a cell synthesizes proteins that are necessary for chromosome sorting and cell division. It then progresses into the M phase of the cell cycle, when **mitosis** occurs. The primary purpose of mitosis is to divide one cell nucleus into two nuclei, distributing the duplicated chromosomes so that each daughter cell will receive the same complement of chromosomes. For example, a human cell in the G_2 phase has 92 chromatids, which are found in 46 pairs. During mitosis, these pairs of chromatids are separated and sorted so that each daughter cell will receive 46 chromosomes. Mitosis is the name given to this sorting process. In most cases, mitosis is followed by **cytokinesis**, which is the division of the cytoplasm to produce two distinct daughter cells.

The decision to divide is based on external factors, such as environmental conditions and signaling molecules, and internal controls, including cell cycle control molecules and checkpoints, as we will discuss next.

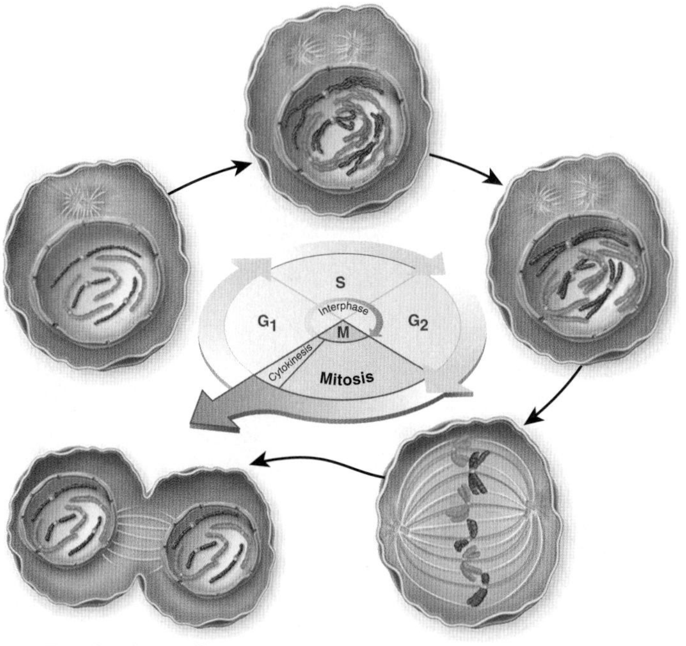

Two daughter cells

Figure 9.18 **The eukaryotic cell cycle.** Dividing cells progress through a series of stages denoted G_1, S, G_2, and M phases. This diagram shows the progression of a cell through the cell cycle to produce two daughter cells. The original diploid cell had three pairs of chromosomes, for a total of six individual chromosomes. During S phase, these have replicated to yield 12 chromatids. After mitosis is complete, two daughter cells each contain six chromosomes.

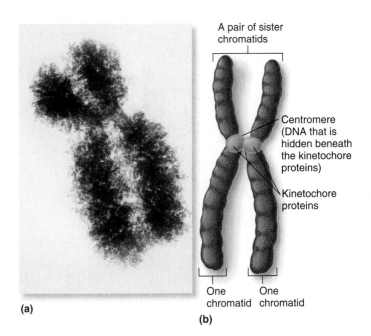

(a)

(b)

Figure 9.19 **Metaphase chromosomes.** (a) Metaphase is a step during mitosis when the chromosomes are highly compacted. This TEM shows a metaphase chromosome that exists in a form called a pair of sister chromatids. (b) A schematic drawing of sister chromatids. This structure has two chromatids that lie side by side. The two chromatids are held together by proteins called kinetochore proteins that bind to each other and to the centromeres on each chromatid.

Environmental Conditions and Signaling Molecules Affect the Decision to Divide

In unicellular organisms, the decision to divide is based largely on environmental conditions. For example, if yeast cells are supplied with a sufficient amount of nutrients and are exposed to the correct temperature and pH, they are likely to divide. In multicellular organisms such as plants and animals, the decision to divide is more complex. Although nutrient availability, temperature, and pH are important to the cells in a multicellular organism, other factors also influence the process of cell division. As development proceeds in a multicellular organism, genetic factors come into play. In mammals, for example, most nerve cells in the adult have lost the capacity to divide, due to a genetic program that begins during embryonic development. This is one reason why it is difficult to recover from certain injuries to the nervous system, such as those that affect the spinal cord.

Multicellular organisms rely on signaling molecules to coordinate cell division throughout the body. In plants, hormones play a key role in promoting cell division. For example, small molecules called **cytokinins**—so named because their presence causes cytokinesis—promote cell division in plants. These compounds have a structure that is similar to adenine. Cytokinins are secreted at the growing tips of plants. In animals, **growth factors**, a group of proteins that stimulate certain cells to grow and divide, are secreted into the bloodstream.

Several signaling pathways that promote cell division have been characterized at the molecular level. **Figure 9.20** describes a simplified signal transduction pathway for epidermal growth factor (EGF). This protein is secreted from endocrine cells and stimulates epidermal cells, such as skin cells, to divide (see chapter-opening photo). The pathway begins when two molecules of EGF bind to two EGF receptor subunits. The binding of EGF causes the subunits to dimerize and phosphorylate each other. The phosphorylated form of the EGF receptor is recognized by an intracellular protein called GRB2. This interaction changes the conformation of GRB2 so that it binds to the protein Sos, which also changes its conformation. The activation of Sos causes another protein called Ras to release GDP and bind GTP. The GTP form of Ras is the active form that binds to Raf-1, which is a protein kinase. This begins a **protein kinase cascade**, the sequential activation of several protein kinases in a row. Recall that protein kinases are enzymes that catalyze the phosphorylation of a target protein. This phosphorylation alters the activity and conformation of the target protein. Raf-1 phosphorylates MEK, which in turn phosphorylates MAPK. MAPK stands for mitogen-activated protein kinase. This kinase was first discovered because it is activated in the presence of mitogens—agents that cause a cell to proceed through mitosis. MAPK enters the nucleus and phosphorylates several proteins, including transcription factors such as Myc, Jun, and Fos, which are proteins that activate the transcription of genes involved in cell division.

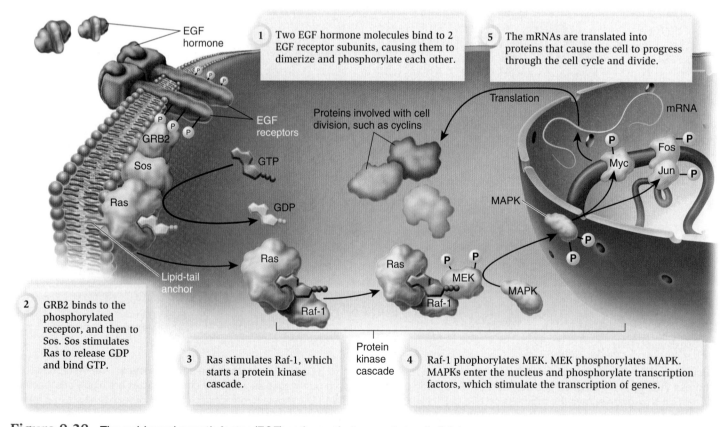

1 Two EGF hormone molecules bind to 2 EGF receptor subunits, causing them to dimerize and phosphorylate each other.

5 The mRNAs are translated into proteins that cause the cell to progress through the cell cycle and divide.

2 GRB2 binds to the phosphorylated receptor, and then to Sos. Sos stimulates Ras to release GDP and bind GTP.

3 Ras stimulates Raf-1, which starts a protein kinase cascade.

4 Raf-1 phophorylates MEK. MEK phosphorylates MAPK. MAPKs enter the nucleus and phosphorylate transcription factors, which stimulate the transcription of genes.

Figure 9.20   The epidermal growth factor (EGF) pathway that promotes cell division.

Biological inquiry: Certain mutations can alter the structure of the Ras protein so that it will not hydrolyze GTP. Such mutations cause cancer. Explain why.

Growth factors such as EGF cause a rapid increase in the expression of many genes in mammals, perhaps as many as 100. As we will discuss in Chapter 14, growth factor signaling pathways are often involved in cancer. Mutations that cause proteins in these pathways to become hyperactive result in cells that divide uncontrollably. These genes encode proteins that are necessary for a cell to divide, including proteins called cyclins, whose function is described next.

The Cell Cycle Is Controlled by Checkpoint Proteins

The progression through the cell cycle is a highly regulated process that ensures that the nuclear genome is intact and that the conditions are appropriate for a cell to divide. Proteins called **cyclins** and **cyclin-dependent kinases (cdks)** are responsible for advancing a cell through the phases of the cell cycle. Cyclins are so named because their amount is cyclical, fluctuating with the cell cycle. To be active, the kinases controlling the cell cycle must bind to (are dependent on) a cyclin. The number of cyclins and cdks varies from species to species.

Figure 9.21 gives a simplified description of how cyclins and cdks work together to advance a cell through G_1 and mitosis. During G_1, the amount of a particular cyclin termed G_1 cyclin increases. The G_1 cyclin binds to cdk to form an activated G_1 cyclin/cdk complex. This complex phosphorylates proteins that are needed to advance the cell to the next stage in the cell cycle. For example, certain proteins involved with DNA synthesis are phosphorylated and activated, thereby allowing the cell to carry on events in S phase. When the cell passes into the S phase, G_1 cyclin is degraded. Similar events advance the cell through other stages of the cell cycle. A different cyclin, called mitotic cyclin, accumulates late in G_2. It binds to cdk to form an activated mitotic cyclin/cdk complex. This complex phosphorylates proteins that are needed to advance into M phase.

Three critical regulatory points called **checkpoints** are found in the cell cycle of eukaryotic cells (Figure 9.21). At these checkpoints, a variety of proteins, referred to as checkpoint proteins, act as sensors to determine if a cell is in the proper condition to divide. The G_1 checkpoint, also called the restriction point, determines if conditions are favorable for cell division. In addition, G_1-checkpoint proteins can sense if the DNA has incurred damage. If so, these checkpoint proteins will prevent the formation of active cyclin/cdk complexes, and thereby stop the progression of the cell cycle. A second checkpoint exists in G_2. This checkpoint also checks the DNA for damage and ensures that all of the DNA has been replicated. In addition, the G_2 checkpoint monitors the levels of proteins that are needed to progress through M phase. A third checkpoint, called the metaphase checkpoint, senses the integrity of the spindle apparatus. As we will see in Chapter 15, the spindle apparatus is involved in chromosome sorting. Metaphase is a step in mitosis during which all of the chromosomes should be attached to the spindle apparatus. If a chromosome is not correctly attached, the metaphase checkpoint will stop the cell cycle. This checkpoint prevents cells from incorrectly sorting their chromosomes during division.

Checkpoint proteins delay the cell cycle until problems are fixed or even prevent cell division when problems cannot be fixed. A primary aim of checkpoint proteins is to prevent the division of a cell that may have incurred DNA damage or harbors abnormalities in chromosome number. When the functions of checkpoint genes are lost due to mutation, cell division may not be directly accelerated. However, as discussed in Chapter 14, the loss of checkpoint protein function increases the likelihood that undesirable genetic changes will occur that can cause mutation and cancerous growth.

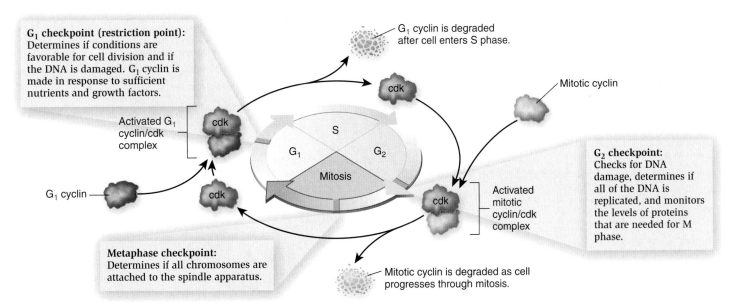

Figure 9.21 **Checkpoints in the cell cycle.** This is a general diagram of the eukaryotic cell cycle. Progression through the cell cycle requires the formation of activated cyclin/cdk complexes. There are different types of cyclin proteins, which are typically degraded after the cell has progressed to the next phase. The formation of activated cyclin/cdk complexes is regulated by checkpoint proteins.

FEATURE INVESTIGATION

Masui and Markert's Study of Oocyte Maturation Led to the Identification of Cyclin and Cyclin-Dependent Kinase

During the 1960s, researchers were intensely searching for the factors that promote cell division. In 1971, Yoshio Masui and Clement Markert developed a way to test whether a substance causes a cell to progress from one phase of the cell cycle to the next. They chose to study frog oocytes—cells produced by female frogs that develop or mature into egg cells. At the time of their work, researchers had already determined that frog oocytes naturally become dormant in the G_2 stage of the cell cycle for up to eight months (**Figure 9.22**). During mating season, female frogs produce a hormone called progesterone. After progesterone binds to receptors in dormant egg cells, they progress from G_2 to the beginning of M phase, where the chromosomes condense and become visible under the microscope. This phenomenon is called maturation. When a sperm fertilizes the egg, M phase is completed, and the zygote continues to undergo cellular divisions.

Because progesterone is a signaling molecule, Masui and Markert speculated that this hormone affects the functions and/or amounts of proteins that trigger the oocyte to undergo maturation. To test this hypothesis, they developed the procedure described in **Figure 9.23**, using the oocytes of the leopard frog (*Rana pipiens*). They began by exposing oocytes to progesterone *in vitro* and then incubating these oocytes for 2 hours or 12 hours. As a control, they also used oocytes that had not been exposed to progesterone. These three types of cells were called the donor oocytes.

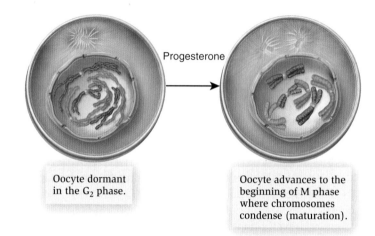

Figure 9.22 Oocyte maturation in certain species of frogs.

Next, they used a micropipette to transfer a small amount of cytosol from the three types of donor oocytes to recipient oocytes that had not been exposed to progesterone. As seen in the data, the recipient oocytes that had been injected with cytosol from the control donor oocytes or from oocytes that had been incubated with progesterone for only 2 hours did not progress to M phase. However, cytosol from donor oocytes that had been incubated with progesterone for 12 hours caused the recipient oocytes to advance to M phase. Masui and Markert concluded that a cytosolic factor, which required more than 2 hours to be synthesized after progesterone treatment, had been

Figure 9.23 The experimental approach used by Masui and Markert to identify cyclin and cyclin-dependent kinase (cdk).

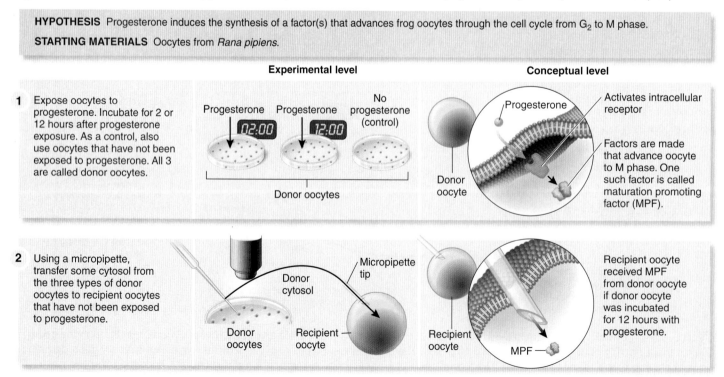

HYPOTHESIS Progesterone induces the synthesis of a factor(s) that advances frog oocytes through the cell cycle from G_2 to M phase.

STARTING MATERIALS Oocytes from *Rana pipiens*.

Experimental level · Conceptual level

1 Expose oocytes to progesterone. Incubate for 2 or 12 hours after progesterone exposure. As a control, also use oocytes that have not been exposed to progesterone. All 3 are called donor oocytes.

Progesterone Progesterone No progesterone (control)

02:00 12:00

Donor oocytes

Progesterone

Donor oocyte

Activates intracellular receptor

Factors are made that advance oocyte to M phase. One such factor is called maturation promoting factor (MPF).

2 Using a micropipette, transfer some cytosol from the three types of donor oocytes to recipient oocytes that have not been exposed to progesterone.

Donor cytosol

Micropipette tip

Donor oocytes Recipient oocyte

Recipient oocyte

MPF

Recipient oocyte received MPF from donor oocyte if donor oocyte was incubated for 12 hours with progesterone.

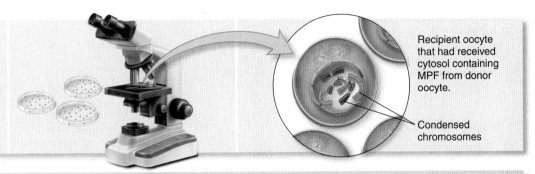

3 Incubate for several hours and observe the recipient oocytes under the microscope to determine if the recipient oocytes advance to M phase. Advancement to M phase can be determined by the condensation of the chromosomes.

Recipient oocyte that had received cytosol containing MPF from donor oocyte.

Condensed chromosomes

4 THE DATA

Donor oocytes	Recipient oocytes proceeded to M phase?
Control, no progesterone exposure	No
Progesterone exposure, incubation for 2 hours	No
Progesterone exposure, incubation for 12 hours	Yes

transferred to the recipient oocytes and induced maturation. The factor that caused the oocytes to progress (or mature) from G_2 to M phase was originally called the **maturation promoting factor (MPF)**.

After MPF was discovered in frogs, it was found in all eukaryotic species that researchers studied. MPF is important in the division of all types of cells, not just oocytes. It took another 17 years

before Manfred Lohka, Marianne Hayes, and James Maller were able to purify the components that make up MPF. This was a difficult undertaking because these components are found in very small amounts in the cytosol, and they are easily degraded during purification procedures. We now know that MPF is a complex made of mitotic cyclin and cyclin-dependent kinase (cdk), as described in Figure 9.21.

CHAPTER SUMMARY

9.1 General Features of Cell Communication

- A signal is an agent that can influence the properties of cells. Cell signaling is needed so that cells can sense environmental changes and communicate with each other.

- When a cell responds to an environmental signal, it has become adapted to its environment. (Figure 9.1)

- Cell-to-cell communication also allows cells to adapt, as when plants grow toward light. (Figure 9.2)

- Cell-to-cell communication can vary in the mechanism and distance that a signal travels. Signals are relayed between cells in five common ways: direct intercellular, contact-dependent, autocrine, paracrine, and endocrine signaling. (Figure 9.3)

- Cell signaling is usually a three-stage process involving receptor activation, signal transduction, and a cellular response. (Figure 9.4)

9.2 Cellular Receptors

- A signaling molecule, also called a ligand, binds to a receptor with an affinity that is measured as a K_d value. The binding of a ligand to a receptor is usually very specific and alters the conformation of the receptor. (Figure 9.5)

- Most receptors involved in cell signaling are found on the cell surface.

- Enzyme-linked receptors have some type of catalytic function. Many of them are protein kinases that can phosphorylate proteins. (Figure 9.6)

- G-protein-coupled receptors (GPCRs) interact with G proteins to initiate a cellular response. (Figure 9.7)

- Some receptors are ligand-gated ion channels that allow the flow of ions across cellular membranes (Figure 9.8)

- Some receptors, such as the estrogen receptor and auxin receptor, are intracellular receptors. (Figure 9.9)

9.3 Signal Transduction and the Cellular Response

- Two-component regulatory systems involve a sensor kinase and a response regulator. An example is NarQ and NarL, which regulate nitrate and nitrite utilization in bacteria. (Figure 9.10)

- Second messengers, such as cAMP, play a key role in signal transduction pathways. These pathways are reversible once the signal is degraded. (Figure 9.11)

- Second messenger pathways amplify the signal and occur with great speed. (Figures 9.12, 9.13)

- Changes in Ca^{2+} concentration play a key role in many signal transduction pathways. (Figure 9.14)

- Inositol trisphosphate (IP_3) and diacylglycerol (DAG) are other examples of second messengers involved in signal transduction. (Figure 9.15)

- Hormones such as epinephrine exert different effects throughout the body. (Figure 9.16)

- In heart muscle cells, epinephrine increases the rate of contraction due to signaling pathways that phosphorylate troponin and phospholamban. (Figure 9.17)

- The way in which any particular cell responds to a signaling molecule depends on the types of proteins that it makes. These include the types of receptors, proteins involved in signaling transduction pathways, and proteins that carry out the cellular response. The amounts of these proteins are controlled by differential gene regulation.

9.4 Regulation of the Cell Cycle

- The eukaryotic cell cycle consists of four phases called G_1 (first gap), S (synthesis of DNA), G_2 (second gap), and M phase (mitosis and cytokinesis). The G_1, S, and G_2 phases are collectively known as interphase. (Figure 9.18)

- Once a cell passes a restriction point in G_1, it is destined to duplicate its DNA and to divide. During S phase, chromosomes are replicated and form pairs of sister chromatids. (Figure 9.19)

- Signaling pathways influence whether or not a cell will divide. An example is the pathway that is stimulated by epidermal growth factor. (Figure 9.20)

- An interaction between cyclin and cyclin-dependent kinase is necessary for cells to progress through the cell cycle. Checkpoint proteins sense the environmental conditions and the integrity of the genome, and they control whether or not the cell progresses through the cell cycle. (Figure 9.21)

- Masui and Markert studied the maturation of frog oocytes to identify a substance that was necessary for oocytes to progress through the cell cycle. This substance was later identified as a complex of mitotic cyclin and cyclin-dependent kinase and called maturation promoting factor (MPF). (Figures 9.22, 9.23)

TEST YOURSELF

1. The ability of a cell to respond to changes in its environment is termed
   a. signaling.
   b. adaptation.
   c. irritability.
   d. cell communication.
   e. stimulation.

2. When a cell secretes a signaling molecule that binds to receptors on neighboring cells as well as the same cell, this is called _____ signaling.
   a. direct intercellular
   b. contact-dependent
   c. autocrine
   d. paracrine
   e. endocrine

3. Which of the following does not describe a typical cellular response to signaling molecules?
   a. activation of enzymes within the cell
   b. change in the function of structural proteins, which determine cell shape
   c. alteration of levels of certain proteins in the cell by changing the level of gene expression
   d. change in a gene sequence that encodes a particular protein
   e. all of the above are examples of cellular responses

4. A cell's ability to respond to a particular signal depends on
   a. whether or not the cell possesses the appropriate receptor for the signal.
   b. the chemical nature of the signal molecule.
   c. whether or not the signal molecule is water soluble.
   d. the concentration of ATP in the cell.
   e. none of the above.

5. _____ bind to receptors inside cells.
   a. Steroid hormones
   b. Ions
   c. Auxins
   d. All of the above
   e. Both a and c

6. Small molecules, such as cAMP, that relay signals within the cell are called
   a. secondary metabolites.
   b. ligands.
   c. G proteins.
   d. second messengers.
   e. transcription factors.

7. The benefit of second messengers in signal transduction pathways is
   a. an increase in the speed of a cellular response.
   b. duplication of the ligands in the system.
   c. amplification of the signal.
   d. all of the above.
   e. a and c only.

8. All cells of a multicellular organism may not respond in the same way to a particular signal that binds to a cell surface receptor. The difference in response may be due to
   a. the concentration of the signal molecule in the cytoplasm.
   b. the functional differences of the receptors.
   c. the structural differences that may occur in ligands.
   d. mutations that occur during development.
   e. none of the above.

9. Whether or not a cell divides depends on
   a. nutrient availability.
   b. environmental conditions.
   c. the presence of signal molecules that regulate cell division.
   d. cellular proteins that regulate cell division.
   e. all of the above.

10. Checkpoints during the cell cycle are important because they
    a. allow the organelle activity to catch up to cellular demands.
    b. ensure the integrity of the cell's DNA.
    c. allow the cell to generate sufficient ATP for cellular division.
    d. are the only time DNA replication can occur.
    e. all of the above.

CONCEPTUAL QUESTIONS

1. What are the two general reasons that cells need to communicate?
2. Explain the three stages of cell signaling.
3. What are protein kinases?

EXPERIMENTAL QUESTIONS

1. At the time of Masui and Markert's study shown in Figure 9.23, what was known about the effects of progesterone on oocytes?
2. What hypothesis did Masui and Markert propose to explain the function of progesterone? Explain the procedure used to test the hypothesis.
3. How did the researchers explain the difference between the results using 2-hour-exposed donor oocytes versus 12-hour-exposed donor oocytes?

COLLABORATIVE QUESTIONS

1. Discuss several different types of cell-to-cell communication.
2. Discuss how differential gene regulation enables various cell types to respond differently to the same signaling molecule.

www.brookerbiology.com
This website includes answers to the Biological Inquiry questions found in the figure legends and all end-of-chapter questions.

10

MULTICELLULARITY

An oak tree. The wood of an oak tree is largely composed of material that is outside of cells. This material connects cells to each other and provides structural support for the tree.

In unicellular species, an entire organism consists of a single cell. Prokaryotes, which include bacteria and archaea, are usually unicellular. Likewise, most protists are unicellular. As discussed in Chapter 22, multicellular organisms came into being approximately 1 billion years ago. In a species that is **multicellular**, a single organism is composed of more than one cell. Some species of protists are multicellular, as are most species of fungi. In this chapter we will focus on plants and animals, which are always multicellular organisms.

The main benefit of multicellularity arises from the division of labor between different cells of the body. For example, the intestinal cells of animals and the root cells of plants have become specialized for nutrient uptake. Other cells in a multicellular organism perform different roles, such as reproduction. In animals, most of the cells of the body are devoted to the growth, development, and survival of the organism, while specialized cells called gametes function in reproduction.

Multicellular species usually have much larger genomes than unicellular species. The increase in genome size is associated with an increase in proteome size; multicellular organisms produce a larger array of proteins than do unicellular species. The additional proteins play a role in three general phenomena. First, in a multicellular organism, cell communication is vital for the proper organization and functioning of cells. Many more proteins involved in cell signaling are made in multicellular species. Second, both the arrangement of cells within the body and the attachment of cells to each other require a greater variety of proteins in multicellular species than in unicellular species. Finally, additional proteins play a role in cell specialization because proteins that are needed for the structure and function of one cell type may not be needed in a different cell type, and vice versa.

In this chapter, we consider characteristics specific to the cell biology of multicellular organisms. We will begin by exploring the material that is produced by animal and plant cells and then secreted into the surrounding medium to form an extracellular matrix. This matrix plays many important roles in the organization and functioning of cells within multicellular organisms. We will then turn our attention to cell junctions, specialized structures that enable cells to make physical contact with one another. Cells within multicellular organisms form junctions that help to create a cohesive and well-organized body. Finally, we examine the organization and function of tissues, groups of cells that have a similar structure and function. In this chapter, we will survey the general features of tissues from a cellular perspective. Units VI and VII will explore the characteristics of plant and animal tissues in greater detail.

10.1 Extracellular Matrix

Organisms are not composed solely of cells. A large portion of an animal or plant consists of a network of material that is secreted from cells and forms a complex meshwork outside of cells called the **extracellular matrix (ECM)**. The ECM is a major component of certain parts of animals and plants. For example, bones and cartilage in animals and the woody portions of plants are composed largely of ECM. In fact, while the cells within wood eventually die, the ECM that they have produced provides a rigid structure that can support the plant for years or even centuries.

Over the past few decades, cell biologists have examined the synthesis, composition, and function of the ECM in animals and plants. In this section, we will begin by examining the structure and role of the ECM in animal cells, focusing on the function of the major ECM protein and carbohydrate macromolecules. We will then explore the cell wall, the extracellular component of plant cells, and consider how it differs in structure and function from the ECM of animal cells.

The Extracellular Matrix in Animals Supports and Organizes Cells and Plays a Role in Cell Signaling

Unlike the cells of bacteria, fungi, and plants, the cells of animals are not surrounded by a rigid cell wall that provides structure and support. However, animal cells secrete materials that form an extracellular matrix that serves a similar purpose. Certain animal cells are completely embedded within an extensive ECM, while other cells may only adhere to the ECM on one side. **Figure 10.1** illustrates the general features of the ECM and its relationship to cells. The major macromolecules of the ECM are proteins and polysaccharides. The most abundant proteins are those that form large fibers; the polysaccharides give the ECM a gel-like character.

As we will see, the ECM found in animals performs many important roles, including strength, structural support, organization, and cell signaling.

- **Strength:** The ECM is the "tough stuff" of animals' bodies. In the skin of mammals, the strength of the ECM prevents tearing. The ECM found in cartilage resists compression and provides protection to the joints. Similarly, the ECM protects the soft parts of the body, such as the internal organs.
- **Structural support:** The skeletons of many animals are composed primarily of ECM. Skeletons not only provide structural support but also facilitate movement via the functioning of the attached muscles.

- **Organization:** The attachment of cells to the ECM plays a key role in the proper arrangement of cells throughout the body. In addition, the ECM binds many body parts together, such as tendons to bones.
- **Cell signaling:** A newly discovered role of the ECM is cell signaling. One way that cells in multicellular organisms sense their environment is via changes in the ECM.

Let's now consider the synthesis and structure of ECM components found in animals.

Adhesive and Structural Proteins Are Major Components of the ECM of Animals

The idea that fibers are important components of living organisms has a long history. In the Middle Ages, living organisms were thought to be composed of fibers rather than cells. This belief was eventually debunked by the cell theory, which is described in Chapter 4. In the 1850s, Rudolf Virchow, who proposed that all cells come from pre-existing cells, also suggested that all extracellular materials are made and secreted by cells. Around the same time, biologists realized that gelatin and glue, which are produced by the boiling of animal tissues, must contain a common fibrous substance. This substance was named **collagen**, from the Greek for "glue producing." Since that time, the advent of experimental techniques in the areas of chemistry, microscopy, and biophysics has enabled scientists to probe the structure of the ECM. We now understand that the ECM contains a mixture of several different components, including proteins such as collagen, that form fibers.

The proteins that are found in the ECM can be grouped into adhesive proteins such as fibronectin and laminin, and structural proteins, such as collagen and elastin (**Table 10.1**). Fibronectin and laminin have multiple binding sites that bind to other components in the ECM such as protein fibers and carbohydrates. These same proteins also have binding sites for receptors on the surfaces of cells. Therefore, adhesive proteins are so named because they adhere cells to the ECM.

Structural proteins such as collagen and elastin form large fibers that give the ECM its strength and elasticity. As described in Chapter 6, proteins that are secreted from eukaryotic cells

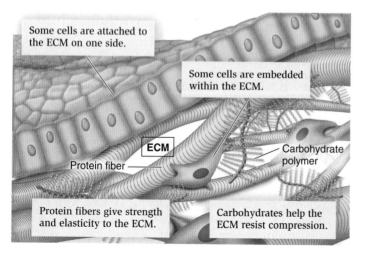

Figure 10.1   Animal cells and the extracellular matrix (ECM).

Some cells are attached to the ECM on one side.

Some cells are embedded within the ECM.

ECM

Protein fiber

Carbohydrate polymer

Protein fibers give strength and elasticity to the ECM.

Carbohydrates help the ECM resist compression.

Table 10.1	Proteins in the ECM of Animals	
General type	**Example**	**Function**
Adhesive	Fibronectin	Connects cells to the ECM and helps to organize components in the ECM.
	Laminin	Connects cells to the ECM and helps to organize components in the basal lamina, a specialized ECM found next to epithelial cells (described in Section 10.3).
Structural	Collagen	Forms large fibers and interconnected fibrous networks in the ECM. Provides tensile strength.
	Elastin	Forms elastic fibers in the ECM that can stretch and recoil.

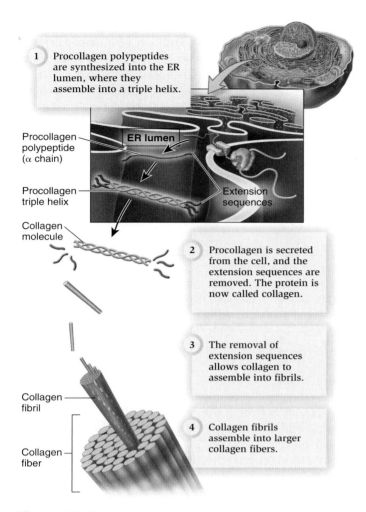

Figure 10.2 Formation of collagen fibers.

1. Procollagen polypeptides are synthesized into the ER lumen, where they assemble into a triple helix.

Procollagen polypeptide (α chain)

ER lumen

Procollagen triple helix

Extension sequences

Collagen molecule

2. Procollagen is secreted from the cell, and the extension sequences are removed. The protein is now called collagen.

3. The removal of extension sequences allows collagen to assemble into fibrils.

Collagen fibril

4. Collagen fibrils assemble into larger collagen fibers.

Collagen fiber

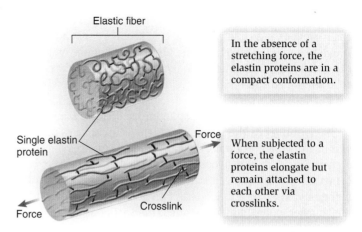

Elastic fiber

Single elastin protein

Force

Crosslink

Force

In the absence of a stretching force, the elastin proteins are in a compact conformation.

When subjected to a force, the elastin proteins elongate but remain attached to each other via crosslinks.

Figure 10.3 Structure and function of elastic fibers.

Biological inquiry: Let's suppose you started with an unstretched elastic fiber and treated it with a chemical that breaks the cross-links between adjacent elastin proteins. What would happen when the fiber is stretched?

are first directed to the endoplasmic reticulum (ER), then to the Golgi apparatus, and subsequently are secreted from the cell via vesicles that fuse with the plasma membrane. **Figure 10.2** depicts the synthesis and assembly of collagen. Individual procollagen polypeptides are first synthesized into the lumen (inside) of the ER. Three procollagen polypeptides then associate with each other to form a procollagen triple helix. The amino acid sequences at both ends of the polypeptides, termed extension sequences, serve to promote the formation of procollagen and prevent the formation of a much larger fiber. After procollagen is secreted out of the cell, extracellular enzymes remove the extension sequences. Once this occurs, the protein, now called collagen, can form larger structures. Collagen proteins assemble in a staggered way to form relatively thin collagen fibrils, which then align and create large collagen fibers.

A key function of collagen is to provide tensile strength, which is a measure of how much stretching force a material can bear without tearing apart. Collagen provides high tensile strength to many parts of the animal body. Collagen is the main protein found in bones, cartilage, tendons, and skin and is also found lining blood vessels and internal organs. In mammals, collagen consists of more than 25% of the total protein mass, much more than any other protein. Approximately 75% of the protein in

mammalian skin is composed of collagen. Leather is largely a pickled and tanned form of collagen.

In addition to tensile strength, elasticity is needed in regions of the body such as the lungs and blood vessels, which regularly expand and return to their original shape. In these places, the ECM contains an abundance of elastic fibers composed primarily of a protein called **elastin** (**Figure 10.3**). Elastin proteins form many covalent cross links to create a fiber. In the absence of a stretching force, each protein tends to adopt a compact conformation. When subjected to a stretching force, the compact proteins become more linear, with the covalent cross links holding the fiber together. When the stretching force has ended, the proteins naturally return to their compact conformation. In this way, elastic fibers behave much like a rubber band, stretching under tension and snapping back when the tension is released.

GENOMES & PROTEOMES

Collagens Are a Family of Proteins That Give Animal Cells a Variety of ECM Properties

As we have seen, proteins are important constituents of the ECM of animals. By analyzing genomes and the biochemical composition of cells, researchers have determined that many different types of collagen fibers are made. These are designated type I, type II, and so on. At least 27 different types of collagens have been identified in humans. Therefore, the human genome, as well as the genomes of other animals, has many different genes that encode collagen polypeptides.

Collagens have a common structure, in which three collagen polypeptides wind around each other to form a triple helix (see Figure 10.2). Each polypeptide is called an α chain. In some collagens, all three α chains are identical, while in others the α chains may be encoded by different collagen genes. Nevertheless, the triple helix structure remains common to all collagen proteins.

Each of the many different types of collagen polypeptides has a similar yet distinctive amino acid sequence that affects the structure and function of collagen fibers. For example, within the triple helix, the amino acid sequence of an α chain may cause collagen proteins to bind to each other very tightly, thereby creating a relatively stiff fiber. Such collagen fibers are found in bone and cartilage. In addition, amino acid side chains in the α chains influence the interactions between collagen proteins within a fiber. For example, the amino acid sequences of certain α chains may promote a looser interaction that produces a more bendable or thin fiber. More flexible collagen fibers support the lining of your lungs and intestines. In addition, domains within the collagen polypeptide may affect the spatial arrangement of collagen proteins. The collagen shown earlier in Figure 10.2 forms fibers in which the collagen proteins align themselves in parallel arrays. Not all collagen proteins form long fibers. For example, type IV collagen proteins interact with each other in a meshwork pattern. This meshwork acts as a filtration unit around capillaries.

Differential gene regulation controls which types of collagens are made throughout the body and in what amounts. Of the 27 types of collagens, **Table 10.2** considers types I to IV, each of which varies with regard to where it is primarily synthesized and its structure and function. Collagen genes are regulated so that collagen is made in the correct sites of the body. In skin cells, for example, the genes that encode the collagen polypeptides that make up collagen types I, III, and IV are turned on, while the synthesis of type II collagen is minimal.

The regulation of collagen synthesis has received a great deal of attention due to the phenomenon of wrinkling. As we age, the amount of collagen that is synthesized in our skin significantly decreases. The underlying network of collagen fibers, which provides scaffolding for the surface of our skin, loosens and unravels. This is one of the factors that cause the skin of older people to sink, sag, and form wrinkles. Various therapeu-

tic and cosmetic agents have been developed to prevent or reverse the appearance of wrinkles, most with limited benefits. One approach is collagen injections, in which small amounts of collagen (from cows) are injected into areas where the body's collagen has weakened, filling the depressions to the level of the surrounding skin. Because collagen is naturally broken down in the skin, the injections are not permanent and last only about three to six months.

Animal Cells Also Secrete Polysaccharides into the ECM

Polysaccharides are the second major component of the extracellular matrix of animals. Among vertebrates, the most abundant types of polysaccharides in the ECM are **glycosaminoglycans (GAGs)**. These molecules are long, unbranched polysaccharides containing a repeating disaccharide unit (**Figure 10.4a**). GAGs are highly negatively charged molecules that tend to attract positively charged ions and water. The majority of GAGs in the ECM are linked to core proteins, forming **proteoglycans** (**Figure 10.4b**).

Providing resistance to compression is the primary function of GAGs and proteoglycans. Once secreted from cells, these macromolecules form a gel-like component in the ECM. Due to its high water content, the ECM is difficult to compress and thereby serves to protect cells. GAGs and proteoglycans are abundantly found in regions of the body that are subjected to harsh mechanical forces, such as the joints of the human body.

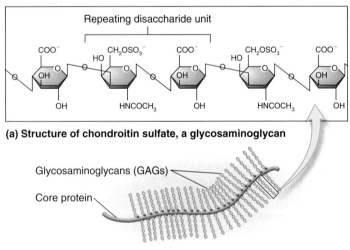

(a) Structure of chondroitin sulfate, a glycosaminoglycan

(b) General structure of a proteoglycan

Figure 10.4 Structures of glycosaminoglycans and proteoglycans.   (a) Glycosaminoglycans (GAGs) are composed of repeating disaccharide units. The length can range from several dozen to 25,000 disaccharide units. The GAG shown here is chondroitin sulfate, which is commonly found in cartilage. (b) Proteoglycans are composed of a long, linear core protein with many GAGs attached. Each GAG is typically 80 disaccharide units long.

Table 10.2	Examples of Collagen Types	
Type	**Sites of synthesis***	**Structure and function**
I	Tendons, ligaments, bones, and skin	Forms a relatively rigid and thick fiber. Very abundant, provides most of the tensile strength to the ECM.
II	Cartilage, disks between vertebrae	Forms a fairly thick and rigid fiber but is more flexible than type I. Permits smooth movements of joints.
III	Arteries, skin, internal organs, and around muscles	Forms thin fibers, often arranged in a netlike pattern. Allows for greater elasticity in tissues.
IV	Skin, intestine, and kidneys; also found around capillaries	Does not form long fibers. Instead, the proteins are arranged in a meshwork pattern that provides organization and support to cell layers. Functions as a filter around capillaries.

*The sites of synthesis denote where a large amount of the collagen type is made.

Two examples of GAGs are chondroitin sulfate, which is a major component of cartilage, and hyaluronic acid, which is found in the skin, eyes, and joint fluid.

Among many invertebrates, an important ECM component is **chitin**, a nitrogen-containing polysaccharide. Chitin forms the hard protective outer covering (called an exoskeleton) of insects, such as crickets and grasshoppers, and shellfish, such as lobsters and shrimp. In fact, the chitin exoskeleton is so rigid that as these animals grow, they must periodically shed this outer layer and secrete a new, larger one—a process called molting (look ahead to Figure 32.11).

The Cell Wall of Plants Provides Strength and Resistance to Compression

Let's now turn our attention to the extracellular matrix of plants. Plants cells are surrounded by an ECM called the **cell wall**, a protective layer that forms outside of the plasma membrane of the plant cell. Like animal cells, the cells of plants are surrounded by material that provides tensile strength and resistance to compression. The cell walls of plants, however, are usually thicker, stronger, and more rigid than the ECM found in animals. Plant cell walls provide rigidity for mechanical support, the maintenance of cell shape, and the direction of cell growth. As we learned in Chapter 5, the cell wall also prevents expansion when water enters the cell. During the evolution of plants, these structural features of the plant cell wall may have been key factors that caused plants to thrive in a sedentary lifestyle.

The cell walls of plants are composed of a primary cell wall and a secondary cell wall, so named according to the timing of their synthesis (**Figure 10.5**). The **primary cell wall** is made before the secondary cell wall. During cell division, the primary cell wall develops between two newly made daughter cells. It is usually very flexible and allows new cells to increase in size. The main macromolecule of the primary cell wall is **cellulose**, a polymer made of repeating molecules of glucose attached end to end. These glucose polymers associate with each other via

hydrogen bonding to form microfibrils that provide great tensile strength (**Figure 10.6**).

Cellulose was discovered in 1838 by the French chemist Anselme Payen, who was the first scientist to try to separate wood into its component parts. After treating different types of wood with nitric acid, Payen obtained a fibrous substance that was also found in cotton and other plants. His chemical analysis revealed that the fibers were made of the carbohydrate glucose. Payen called this substance cellulose, which means consisting of cells. Cellulose is probably the single most abundant organic molecule on Earth. Wood consists mostly of cellulose, and cotton and paper (including the page you are reading now) are almost pure cellulose.

In addition to cellulose, other components found in the primary cell wall include hemicellulose, glycans, and pectins (see Figure 10.5). Hemicellulose is another linear carbohydrate with a structure similar to that of cellulose, but it contains sugars other than glucose in its structure and usually forms thinner microfibrils. Glycans, carbohydrates with branching structures, are also important in cell wall structure. The cross-linking glycans bind to cellulose and provide organization to the cellulose microfibrils. Pectins, which are highly negatively charged, attract water and have a gel-like character that provides the cell wall with the ability to resist compression. Besides carbohydrates, the primary cell wall also contains small amounts of protein. Some of these proteins may increase the strength of the cell wall, while others are enzymes involved in the synthesis and organization of the carbohydrate polymers. The mechanism of cellulose synthesis via extracellular enzymes is described in Chapter 30.

The **secondary cell wall** is synthesized and deposited between the plasma membrane and the primary cell wall after a plant cell matures and has stopped increasing in size. It is made in layers by the successive deposition of cellulose microfibrils and other components. While the primary wall structure is relatively similar in nearly all cell types and species, the structure of the secondary cell wall is more variable. The secondary cell wall

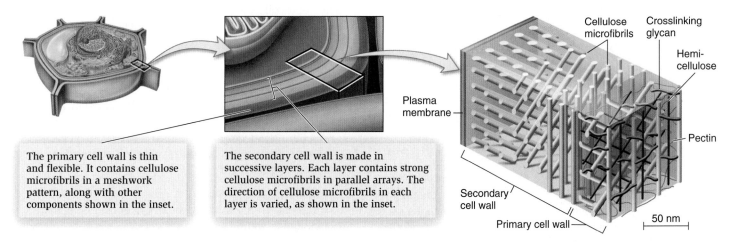

The primary cell wall is thin and flexible. It contains cellulose microfibrils in a meshwork pattern, along with other components shown in the inset.

The secondary cell wall is made in successive layers. Each layer contains strong cellulose microfibrils in parallel arrays. The direction of cellulose microfibrils in each layer is varied, as shown in the inset.

Plasma membrane

Cellulose microfibrils

Crosslinking glycan

Hemi-cellulose

Pectin

Secondary cell wall

Primary cell wall

50 nm

Figure 10.5 **Structure of the plant cell wall.** The primary cell wall is relatively thin and flexible. The secondary cell wall, which is produced only by certain plant cells, is made after the primary cell wall and is synthesized in successive layers.

Biological inquiry: With regard to cell growth, what would happen if the secondary cell wall was made too soon?

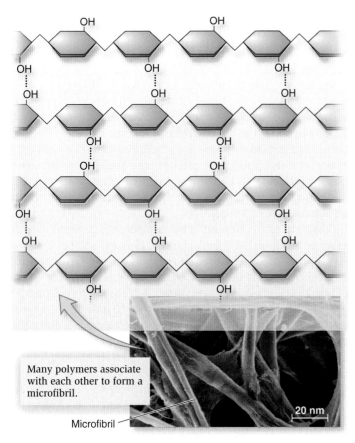

Many polymers associate with each other to form a microfibril.

Microfibril

20 nm

Figure 10.6 Structure of cellulose. Cellulose is made of repeating glucose units linked end to end that hydrogen-bond to each other to form microfibrils (SEM).

Table 10.3	Common Types of Cell Junctions
Type	**Description**
Animals	
Anchoring junctions	Cell junctions that hold adjacent cells together or bond cells to the ECM. Anchoring junctions are mechanically strong.
Tight junctions	Junctions between adjacent cells that prevent the leakage of material between cell layers.
Gap junctions	Channels that permit the direct exchange of ions and small molecules between the cytosol of adjacent cells.
Plants	
Middle lamella	A carbohydrate layer that cements together the cell walls of adjacent cells.
Plasmodesmata	Open passageways between the cell walls of adjacent cells that permit the direct diffusion of ions and molecules between cells.

often contains components in addition to those found in the primary cell wall. For example, phenolic compounds called lignins are very hard and impart considerable strength to the secondary wall structure. Lignin, a type of secondary metabolite described in Chapter 7, is found in the woody parts of plants.

10.2 Cell Junctions

Thus far, we have learned that the cells of animals and plants create an extracellular matrix that provides strength, support, and organization. For an organism to become a multicellular unit, cells within the body must be linked to each other and to the ECM. In animals and plants, this is accomplished by specialized structures called **cell junctions** (Table 10.3). In this section, we will examine different types of cell junctions in animal and plant cells.

Animal cells, which lack the structural support provided by the cell wall, have a more varied group of junctions than plant cells. In animal cells, junctions called anchoring junctions play a role in anchoring cells to each other or to the extracellular matrix. In other words, they hold cells in their proper place in the body. Other junctions, termed tight junctions, seal cells together to prevent small molecules from leaking through one

cell layer into another. Still another type of junction known as a gap junction allows cells to communicate directly with each other. In this section, we will examine all three of these types of junctions.

In plants, cellular organization is somewhat different because plants cells are surrounded by a rigid cell wall. As you will learn, plants cells are connected to each other by a component called the middle lamella, which cements their cell walls together. They also have junctions termed plasmodesmata that allow adjacent cells to communicate with each other.

Anchoring Junctions Link Animal Cells to Each Other and to the ECM

The advent of electron microscopy allowed researchers to explore the types of junctions that occur between cells and within the extracellular matrix. In the 1960s, Marilyn Farquhar, George Palade, and colleagues conducted several studies showing that various types of cellular junctions connect cells to each other. Over the past few decades, researchers have begun to unravel the functions and molecular structures of these junctions, called **anchoring junctions**, which attach cells to each other and to the extracellular matrix. Anchoring junctions rely on the functioning of membrane proteins called **cell adhesion molecules (CAMs)**. Two types of CAMs are cadherin and integrin.

Anchoring junctions are grouped into four main categories, according to their functional roles and their connections to cellular components (**Figure 10.7**)

1. **Adherens junctions** connect cells to each other via cadherins. In many cases, these junctions are organized into bands around cells. In the cytosol, adherens junctions bind to cytoskeletal filaments called actin filaments.
2. **Desmosomes** also connect cells to each other via cadherins. They are spotlike points of intercellular contact that rivet

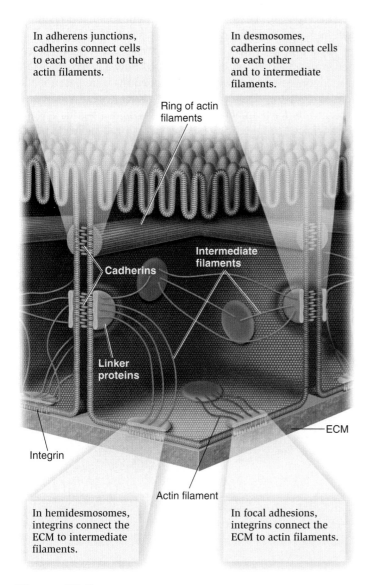

Figure 10.7 Types of anchoring junctions.

In adherens junctions, cadherins connect cells to each other and to the actin filaments.

In desmosomes, cadherins connect cells to each other and to intermediate filaments.

Ring of actin filaments

Intermediate filaments

Cadherins

Linker proteins

ECM

Integrin

Actin filament

In hemidesmosomes, integrins connect the ECM to intermediate filaments.

In focal adhesions, integrins connect the ECM to actin filaments.

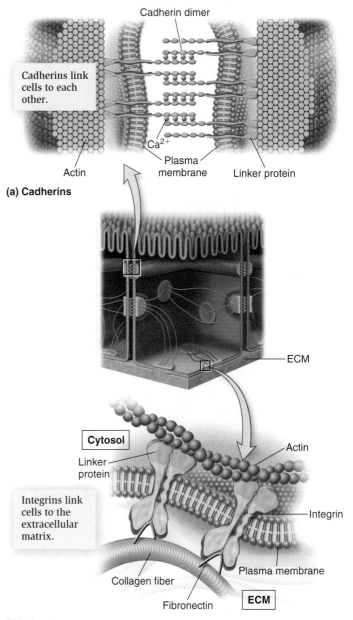

Cadherin dimer

Cadherins link cells to each other.

Actin   Ca²⁺   Linker protein
Plasma membrane

(a) Cadherins

ECM

Cytosol

Linker protein

Actin

Integrin

Integrins link cells to the extracellular matrix.

Collagen fiber   Plasma membrane

Fibronectin   **ECM**

(b) Integrins

Figure 10.8 Types of cell adhesion molecules (CAMs). (a) A cadherin in one cell binds to a cadherin of an identical type in an adjacent cell. The binding requires Ca^{2+}. In the cytosol, cadherins bind to the actin or intermediate filaments of the cytoskeleton. (b) Integrins link cells to the extracellular matrix and form intracellular connections to actin or intermediate filaments.

cells together. Desmosomes are connected to cytoskeletal filaments called intermediate filaments.

3. **Focal adhesions** connect cells to the extracellular matrix via integrins. In the cytosol, focal adhesions bind to actin filaments.

4. **Hemidesmosomes** also connect cells to the extracellular matrix via integrins. Like desmosomes, they interact with intermediate filaments.

Let's now consider the molecular components of anchoring junctions. **Cadherins** are CAMs that create cell-to-cell junctions (**Figure 10.8a**). Each cadherin is a dimer of identical subunits. The extracellular domains of two cadherin dimers, each in adjacent cells, bind to each other to promote cell-to-cell adhesion. This binding requires the presence of calcium ions, which change the conformation of cadherin, so that cadherins in adjacent cells can bind to each other. On the inside of the cell, linker proteins connect cadherins to actin or intermediate filaments

of the cytoskeleton. This promotes a more stable interaction between two cells because their strong cytoskeletons are connected to each other.

Cadherins are the major CAMs in vertebrate species. The genomes of vertebrates contain several different cadherin genes, which encode slightly different cadherin proteins. Having different types of cadherins allows different types of cells to recognize each other. Dimer formation follows a homophilic, or like-to-like, binding mechanism. To understand the concept of homophilic binding, let's consider an example. One cadherin is called E-cadherin and another is N-cadherin. E-cadherin in one cell will bind to E-cadherin but not to N-cadherin in an adjacent cell. Similarly, N-cadherin will bind to N-cadherin but not to E-cadherin in an adjacent cell. By expressing only certain types of cadherins, each cell will bind only to other cells that express the same cadherin types. This phenomenon is important in the proper arrangement of cells throughout the body.

Integrins, a group of cell-surface receptor proteins, are a second type of CAM, one that creates connections between cells and the extracellular matrix. In the example shown in **Figure 10.8b**, an integrin is bound to fibronectin, an ECM protein that binds to other ECM components such as collagen fibers. Like cadherins, integrins also bind to actin or intermediate filaments in the cytosol of the cell, via linker proteins, to promote a strong association between the cytoskeleton of a cell and the extracellular matrix. Thus, integrins have an extracellular domain for the binding of ECM components and an intracellular domain for the binding of cytosolic proteins.

When these CAMs were first discovered, researchers imagined that cadherins and integrins played only a mechanical role in cell biology. In other words, their functions were described as holding cells together or to the ECM. More recently, however, experiments have shown that cadherins and integrins are important in cell communication. When cell-to-cell and cell-to-ECM junctions are formed or broken, this affects signaling pathways within the cell. Similarly, intracellular signaling pathways can affect cadherins and integrins in ways that alter intercellular junctions and the binding of cells to ECM components.

With regard to cell signaling, integrins are particularly interesting because they are capable of both outside-in and inside-out signaling (**Figure 10.9**). Integrins are so named because they integrate changes in the ECM to changes in the cytoskeleton. When the extracellular domain of an integrin binds to components of the ECM, this causes a conformational change

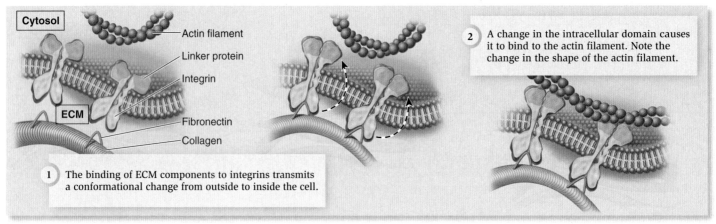

(a) Outside-in signaling

① The binding of ECM components to integrins transmits a conformational change from outside to inside the cell.

② A change in the intracellular domain causes it to bind to the actin filament. Note the change in the shape of the actin filament.

(labels: Cytosol, Actin filament, Linker protein, Integrin, ECM, Fibronectin, Collagen)

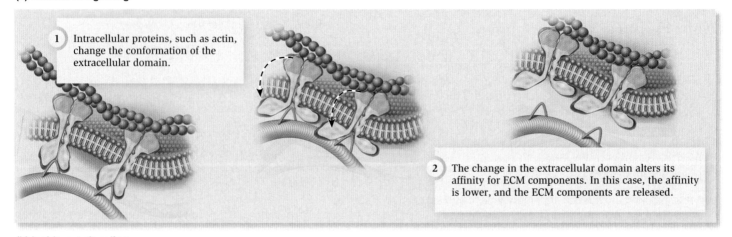

(b) Inside-out signaling

① Intracellular proteins, such as actin, change the conformation of the extracellular domain.

② The change in the extracellular domain alters its affinity for ECM components. In this case, the affinity is lower, and the ECM components are released.

Figure 10.9   Cell signaling via integrins.   (a) Outside-in signaling occurs when an integrin binds to a component in the ECM, which transmits a signal to the cytosol, thereby affecting activities inside the cell. (b) Inside-out signaling occurs when the cytosol affects the structure of an integrin and thereby changes the integrin's ability to bind to components in the ECM. In the example shown here, the effect is to lower the affinity for an ECM component, causing it to be released from the integrin.

Biological inquiry: When an animal receives a wound, this causes outside-in signaling. Explain how.

that affects the structure of the intracellular domain, altering its interaction with cytoskeletal proteins. This outside-in signaling regulates cell adhesion (the ability of cells to adhere to the ECM), cell growth, and cell migration. In addition, signals generated inside the cell can alter integrins and affect their ability to bind to components in the ECM, either lowering or increasing their affinity. This phenomenon, termed inside-out signaling, is also important for cell adhesion and migration, and it provides a way for cells to contribute to the organization of the ECM.

Abnormalities in CAMs such as integrins are often associated with the ability of cancer cells to metastasize, that is, to move to other parts of the body. Cell adhesion molecules are critical for keeping cells in their correct locations. When their function becomes abnormal due to cancer-causing mutations, cells lose their proper connections with the ECM and adjacent cells and may spread to other parts of the body. This topic is considered in more detail in Chapter 14.

Tight Junctions Prevent the Leakage of Materials Across Animal Cell Layers

In animals, **tight junctions**, or occluding junctions, are a second type of junction, one that forms a tight seal between adjacent cells and thereby prevents extracellular material from leaking between cells. As an example, let's consider the intestine. The cells that line the intestine form a sheet that is one cell thick; one side faces the intestinal lumen, while the other faces the blood (**Figure 10.10**). Tight junctions between these cells ensure that nutrients pass through the plasma membranes of the intestinal cells before entering the blood and prevent the transport of materials from the blood into the intestine.

Tight junctions are made by membrane proteins, called occludin and claudin, that form interlaced strands in the plasma membrane (see inset to Figure 10.10). These strands of proteins,

each in adjacent cells, bind to each other and thereby form a tight seal between cells. Occluding junctions are not mechanically strong like anchoring junctions because they do not have strong connections with the cytoskeleton. Therefore, adjacent cells that have occluding junctions also have anchoring junctions to hold them in place.

The amazing ability of tight junctions to prevent the leakage of material across cell layers has been demonstrated by dye-injection studies. In 1972, Daniel Friend and Norton Gilula injected lanthanum, which is electron dense and can be visualized under the electron microscope, into the bloodstream of a rat. A few minutes later, a sample of a cell layer in the digestive tract was removed and visualized by electron microscopy. As seen in the micrograph in **Figure 10.11**, lanthanum diffused into the region between the cells that faces the blood, but it could not move past the tight junction to the side of the cell layer facing the lumen of the intestine.

Gap Junctions in Animal Cells Provide a Passageway for Intercellular Transport

A third type of junction found in animals is called a **gap junction** because a small gap occurs between the plasma membranes of cells connected by these junctions (**Figure 10.12**). In vertebrates, gap junctions are composed of a membrane protein called connexin. Invertebrates have a structurally similar protein called innexin. Six connexin proteins in one cell align with six connexin proteins in an adjacent cell to form a channel called a **connexon** (see inset to Figure 10.12).

The connexons allow the passage of ions and small molecules with a molecular mass that is less than 1,000 Daltons,

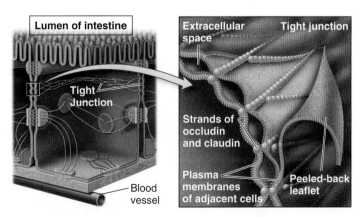

Figure 10.10 Tight junctions between adjacent intestinal cells. In this example, tight junctions form a seal that prevents the movement of material between cells, from the intestinal lumen into the blood, and vice versa. The inset shows the interconnected network of occludin and claudin that forms the tight junction.

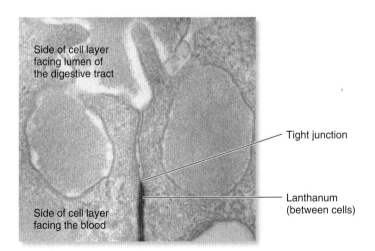

Figure 10.11 An experiment demonstrating the function of a tight junction. When lanthanum was injected into the bloodstream of a rat, it diffused between the cells in the region up to a tight junction, but could not diffuse past the junction to the other side of the cell layer.

Biological inquiry: What results would you expect if a rat was fed lanthanum and then a sample of intestinal cells was observed under the EM?

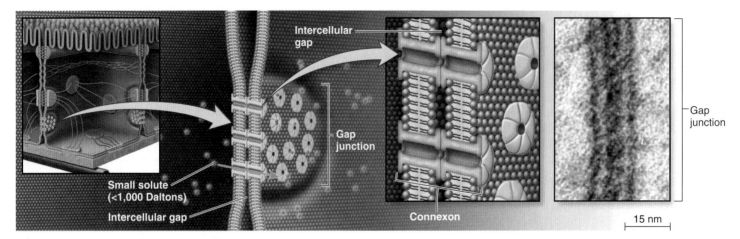

Figure 10.12 **Gap junctions between adjacent cells.** Gap junctions form intercellular channels that allow the passage of small solutes with masses less than 1,000 Daltons. A transmembrane channel called a connexon consists of 12 proteins called connexins, 6 in each cell. The micrograph shows a gap junction between intestinal cells.

including amino acids, sugars, and signaling molecules like cAMP and IP_3. In this way, gap junctions allow adjacent cells to share metabolites and directly signal each other. At the same time, gap-junction channels are too small to allow the passage of RNA, proteins, or large carbohydrates. Therefore, cells that communicate via gap junctions still maintain their own distinctive set of macromolecules.

Because gap junctions allow the passage of ions, electrical changes in one cell are easily transmitted to an adjacent cell that is connected via gap junctions. In 1959, Edwin Furshpan and David Potter first postulated the existence of gap junctions. Their results, which showed that certain cells in the crayfish are electrically coupled, indicated that ions can directly move from the cytosol of one cell to the cytosol of an adjacent cell.

FEATURE INVESTIGATION

Loewenstein and Colleagues Followed the Transfer of Fluorescent Dyes to Determine the Size of Gap-Junction Channels

As we have seen, gap junctions allow the passage of small molecules, those with a mass up to about 1,000 Daltons. This property of gap junctions was determined in experiments involving the transfer of fluorescent dyes. During the 1960s, several research groups began using fluorescent dyes to study cell morphology and function. As discussed in Chapter 4, the location of fluorescent dyes within cells can be seen via fluorescence microscopy. In 1964, Werner Loewenstein and colleagues observed that a fluorescent dye could move from one cell to an adjacent cell, which prompted them to investigate this phenomenon further.

In the experiment shown in **Figure 10.13**, Loewenstein and colleagues grew rat liver cells in the laboratory, where they formed a single layer (a monolayer). The adjacent cells formed

Figure 10.13 Use of fluorescent molecules to determine the size of gap-junction channels.

HYPOTHESIS Gap-junction channels allow the passage of ions and molecules, but there is a limit to how large the molecules can be.

STARTING MATERIALS Rat liver cells grown in laboratory.

1 Grow rat liver cells in a laboratory on solid growth media until they become a monolayer. At this point, adjacent cells have formed gap junctions.

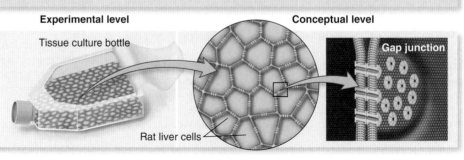

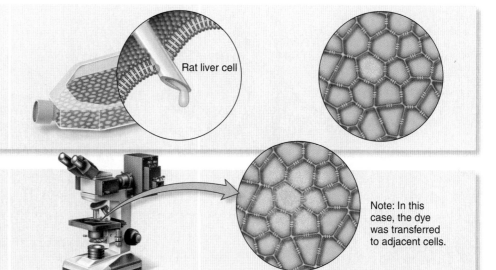

2   Inject 1or 2 cells in the monolayer with fluorescently labeled amino acids or peptides. Note: Several dyes with different molecular masses were tested.

Rat liver cell

3   Incubate for various lengths of time (for example, 40–45 minutes). Observe cell layer under the fluorescence microscope to determine if the dye has moved to adjacent cells.

Note: In this case, the dye was transferred to adjacent cells.

4   **THE DATA**

Mass of Dye	Transfer to adjacent cells *	Mass of Dye	Transfer to adjacent cells *
376	+ + + +	851**	–
464	+ + + +	901	+ + +
536	+ + +	946	–
559	+ + + +	1004	–
665	+	1158	–
688	+ + + +	1678	–
817	+ + +	1830	–

* The number of pluses indicates the relative speed of transfer. Four pluses denote fast transfer, while one plus is slow transfer. A minus indicates that transfer between cells did not occur. ** In some cases, molecules with less mass did not pass between cells compared to molecules with a higher mass. This may be due to differences in their structures (e.g., charges) that influence whether or not they can easily penetrate the channel.

gap junctions. The cells were injected with various dyes composed of fluorescently labeled amino acids or peptide molecules with different masses and then observed via fluorescence microscopy. As shown in the data, dyes with a molecular mass up to 901 Daltons were observed to pass from cell to cell. Larger dyes, however, did not move intercellularly. Loewenstein and other researchers subsequently investigated dye transfer in other cell types and species. Though some variation is found when comparing different cell types and species, the researchers generally observed that molecules with a mass greater than 1,000 Daltons do not pass through gap junctions.

The Middle Lamella Cements Adjacent Plant Cell Walls Together

In animal cells, we have seen that cell-to-cell contact, via anchoring junctions, tight junctions, and gap junctions, involves interactions between membrane proteins in adjacent cells. In plants, cell junctions are quite different. Rather than using membrane proteins to form cell-to-cell connections, an additional component in the ECM is made called the **middle lamella**. When plant cells are dividing, the middle lamella is the first layer that is formed. Next, the primary cell wall is made inside the middle lamella (**Figure 10.14**). The middle lamella is rich in pectins, negatively charged carbohydrate polymers that are also found in the primary cell wall (see Figure 10.5). These polymers attract water and make a hydrated gel. Ca^{2+} and Mg^{2+} interact with the negative charges in the carbohydrates and cement the cell walls of adjacent cells together.

The process of fruit ripening illustrates the importance of pectins in holding plant cells together. An unripened fruit, such as a green tomato, is very firm because the rigid cell walls of adjacent cells are firmly attached to each other. During ripening, the cells secrete a group of enzymes called pectinases, which digest pectins in the middle lamella as well as pectins in the primary cell wall. As this process continues, the attachments between cells are broken, and the cell walls become less rigid. For this reason, a red ripe tomato is much less firm than an unripe tomato.

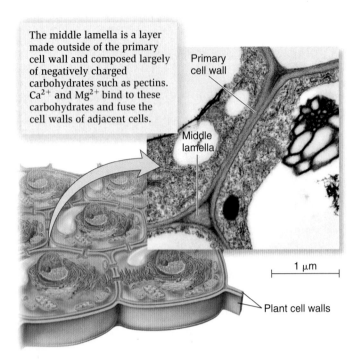

The middle lamella is a layer made outside of the primary cell wall and composed largely of negatively charged carbohydrates such as pectins. Ca^{2+} and Mg^{2+} bind to these carbohydrates and fuse the cell walls of adjacent cells.

Primary cell wall

Middle lamella

1 μm

Plant cell walls

Figure 10.14   Cell-to-cell junctions known as middle lamella.

Plasmodesmata Are Channels Connecting the Cytoplasm of Adjacent Plant Cells

In 1879, Eduard Tangl, a Russian botanist, observed intercellular cytoplasmic connections in the seeds of the strychnine tree and hypothesized that the cytoplasm of adjacent cells is connected by ducts in the cell walls. He first proposed the concept that direct cell-to-cell communication integrates the functioning of plant cells. The ducts or intercellular channels that Tangl observed are now known as **plasmodesmata** (singular, *plasmodesma*).

Plasmodesmata are functionally similar to gap junctions in animal cells, in that they allow the passage of ions, water, sugars, amino acids, and signaling molecules between cells. However, the structure of plasmodesmata is quite different from that of gap junctions. As shown in **Figure 10.15**, plasmodesmata are open channels in the cell walls of adjacent cells. At these sites, the plasma membrane of one cell is continuous with the plasma membrane of the other cell, which permits the diffusion of molecules from the cytosol of one cell to the cytosol of the other. In addition to a cytosolic connection, plasmodesmata also have a central tubule, called a desmotubule, connecting the ER membranes of adjacent cells.

10.3 Tissues

A **tissue** is a part of an animal or plant consisting of a group of cells having a similar structure and function. Because tissues are fundamental units within multicellular organisms, understanding the characteristics of tissues is essential to many areas of biology, particularly plant and animal development. For example,

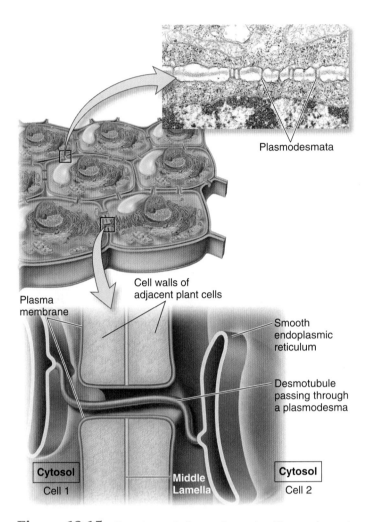

Plasmodesmata

Cell walls of adjacent plant cells

Plasma membrane

Smooth endoplasmic reticulum

Desmotubule passing through a plasmodesma

Cytosol Cell 1

Middle Lamella

Cytosol Cell 2

Figure 10.15   Structure of plasmodesmata. Plasmodesmata are cell junctions connecting the cytosol of adjacent plant cells, allowing water and small molecules to pass from cell to cell. At these sites, the plasma membrane of one cell is continuous with the plasma membrane of an adjacent cell. In addition, the ER from one cell is connected to that of the adjacent cell via a desmotubule.

geneticists want to know how genes play a role in the formation and arrangement of tissues to create an entire organism. Likewise, plant and animal biologists are interested in understanding the genetic and morphological changes that occur as the tissues of young plants and animals develop from fertilized eggs into an adult organism. These topics will be examined in Chapters 19, 39, and 52.

In this section, we will view tissues from the perspective of cell biology. Animals and plants contain many different types of cells. Humans, for example, contain over 200 different cell types, each with a specific structure and function. Even so, these cells can be grouped into a few general categories. For example, muscle cells found in your heart (cardiac muscle cells), in your biceps (skeletal muscle cells), and around your arteries (smooth muscle cells) look somewhat different under the microscope and have unique roles in the body. Yet due to structural and functional similarities, all three types can be categorized as muscle tissue cells. In this section, we will begin by surveying the basic processes that cells undergo in order to create tissues. Next, we will examine the main categories of both animal and plant tissues. We will conclude by taking a more in-depth look at some similarities and differences between selected animal and plant tissues, focusing in particular on the functions of the ECM and cell junctions.

Six Basic Cell Processes Create Tissues and Organs

A multicellular organism such as a plant or animal contains many cells. For example, an adult human has somewhere between 10 trillion and 100 trillion cells in her or his body. Cells are organized into tissues, and tissues are organized into organs. An **organ** is a collection of two or more tissues that performs a specific function or set of functions. The heart is an organ found in the bodies of complex animals, while a leaf is an organ found in plants. We will examine the structures and functions of organs in Units VI and VII.

To create tissues and organs, cells undergo six basic processes that influence their morphology, arrangement, and number:

1. *Cell division*: As discussed in Chapters 9 and 15, eukaryotic cells progress through a cell cycle that leads to cell division.
2. *Cell growth*: Following cell division, cells take up nutrients and usually expand in volume.
3. *Differentiation*: Due to gene regulation, cells differentiate into specialized types of cells. Cell differentiation is described in Chapter 19.
4. *Migration*: During embryonic development in animals, cells migrate to their appropriate positions within the body. Cell migration does not occur during plant development.
5. *Apoptosis*: Cell death, also known as apoptosis, is necessary to produce certain morphological features of the body. For example, during development in mammals, the formation of individual fingers and toes requires the removal, by apoptosis, of the skin cells between them.
6. *Cell connections*: In the first two sections of this chapter, we learned that cells secrete an extracellular matrix that provides strength and support. In animals, the ECM serves to organize cells within tissues and organs. In plants, the cell wall forms the ECM that shapes plant tissues. Different types of cell junctions in both animal and plant cells enable cells to make physical contact and communicate with one another.

Animals Are Composed of Epithelial, Connective, Muscle, and Nervous Tissues

The body of an animal contains four general types of tissue—epithelial, connective, muscle, and nervous tissue—that serve very different purposes (**Figure 10.16**).

Epithelial Tissue Epithelial tissue is composed of cells that are joined together via tight junctions and form continuous

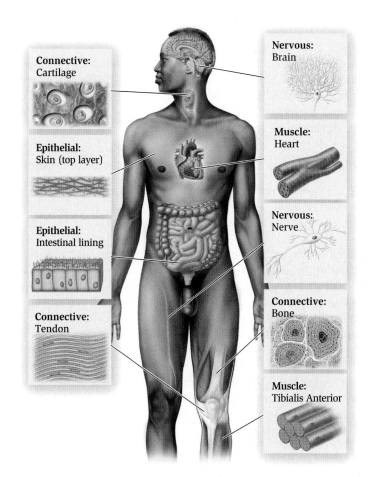

Figure 10.16 Examples of the four general types of tissues—epithelial, connective, muscle, and nervous—found in animals.

sheets. Epithelial tissue covers or forms the lining of all internal and external body surfaces. For example, epithelial tissue lines organs such as the lungs and digestive tract. In addition, epithelial tissue forms skin, a protective surface that shields the body from the outside environment.

Connective Tissue Most connective tissue provides support to the body and/or helps to connect different tissues to each other. Connective tissue is rich in extracellular matrix. In some cases, the tissue contains only a sparse population of cells that are embedded in the ECM. Examples of connective tissue include cartilage, tendons, bone, fat tissue, and the inner layers of the skin. Blood is also considered a form of connective tissue because it provides liquid connections to various regions of the body.

Muscle Tissue Muscle tissue can generate a force that facilitates movement. Muscle contraction is needed for bodily movements such as walking and running, and also plays a role in the movement of materials throughout the body. For example, contraction of heart muscle propels blood through your body. The properties of muscle tissue in animals are examined in Chapter 46.

Nervous Tissue Nervous tissue receives, generates, and conducts electrical signals throughout the body. In vertebrates, these electrical signals are integrated by nervous tissue in the brain and transmitted down the spinal cord to the rest of the body. Chapter 43 considers the cellular basis for nerve signals, known as action potentials, and Chapters 44 and 45 examine the organization of nervous systems in animals.

Plants Contain Dermal, Ground, and Vascular Tissues

The bodies of most plants contain three general types of tissue—dermal, ground, and vascular—each with a different structure suited to its functions, as shown in **Figure 10.17**.

Dermal Tissue The **dermal tissue** forms a covering on various parts of the plant. The **epidermis** refers to the newly made tissue on the surfaces of leaves, stems, and roots. Surfaces of leaves are usually coated with a waxy cuticle to prevent water loss and often have hairs, or trichomes, which are specialized types of epidermal cells that have diverse functions, including the secretion of oils and leaf protection. Epidermal cells called guard cells form pores in leaves known as stomata that permit gas exchange. The function of the root epidermis is the absorption of water and nutrients. The root epidermis does not have a waxy cuticle, because such a cuticle would inhibit water and nutrient absorption.

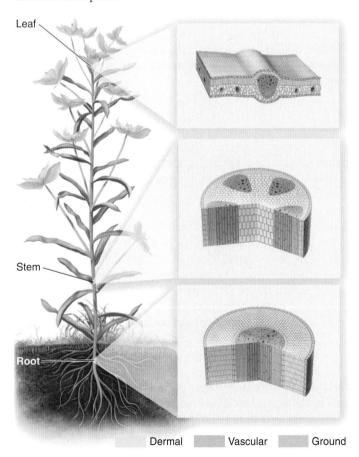

Figure 10.17 Locations of the three general types of tissues—dermal, ground, and vascular—found in plants.

Ground Tissue Most of a plant's body is made of **ground tissue**, which has a variety of functions, including photosynthesis, storage of carbohydrates, and support. Ground tissue can be subdivided into three types: parenchyma, collenchyma, and sclerenchyma. Let's look briefly at each of these types of ground tissue.

1. Parenchyma tissue is very active metabolically. The mesophyll, the central part of the leaf, which contains the cells that carry out the bulk of photosynthesis, is parenchyma tissue. Parenchyma tissue also functions in the storage of carbohydrates. The cells of parenchyma tissue usually lack a secondary cell wall or, if present, it is very thin.
2. Collenchyma tissue provides structural support to the plant body, particularly to growing regions such as the periphery of the stems and leaves. Collenchyma cells tend to have thick, secondary cell walls but do not contain much lignin. Therefore, they provide support but are also able to stretch.
3. Sclerenchyma tissue also provides structural support to the plant body, particularly to those parts that are no longer growing. The secondary cell walls of sclerenchyma cells tend to have large amounts of lignin and thereby provide rigid support. In many cases, sclerenchyma cells are dead at maturity but their cell walls continue to provide structural support during the life of the plant.

Vascular Tissue Most plants are vascular plants. In these species, which include ferns and flowering plants, the vascular tissue is composed of cells that are interconnected and form conducting vessels for water and nutrients. Two vascular tissues are found in flowering plants: xylem and phloem. The xylem transports water and mineral ions from the root to the rest of the plant, while the phloem distributes the products of photosynthesis and a variety of other nutrients throughout the plant. Some types of plants, such as mosses, are nonvascular plants that lack conducting vessels. These plants tend to be small and live in damp, shady places.

Plant and Animal Tissues Have Striking Differences and Similarities

Because plants and animals appear strikingly different, it is not too surprising that their cells and tissues show conspicuous differences. For example, the vascular tissue of plants (which transports water and nutrients) does not resemble any one tissue in animals. The blood vessels of animals (which transport blood carrying oxygen and nutrients throughout the body) are hollow tubes that contain both connective and muscle tissue. In addition, animals have two tissue types that are not found in plants: muscle and nervous tissue. Even so, plants are capable of movement and the transmission of signals via action potentials. For example, the Venus flytrap (*Dionaea muscipula*) has two modified leaves that resemble a clamshell. When an insect touches the surface of these leaves, an action potential is triggered across the leaf cells that causes the leaves to move closer to each other, thereby trapping the unsuspecting insect.

Although cellular differences are prominent between plants and animals, certain tissues show intriguing similarities. The epithelial tissue of animals and the dermal tissue of plants both form a protective covering over the organism. Also, the connective tissue of animals and the ground tissue of plants both play a role in structural support. Let's take a closer look at the similarities between these tissues in animals and plants.

A Comparison of Epithelial and Dermal Tissues Both the epithelial tissue in animals (also called an **epithelium**) and dermal tissue in plants form layers of cells. An epithelium can be classified according to its number of layers. Simple epithelium is one cell layer thick, while stratified epithelium has several layers (**Figure 10.18**). In both cases, the epithelium has a polarity, which is due to an asymmetry to its organization. The outer or apical side of an epithelium is exposed to air or to a watery fluid such as the lumen of the intestine. The inner or basal side rests on some type of support, such as another type of tissue or on a form of ECM called the basal lamina.

A hallmark of epithelial cells is that they form many connections with each other. For example, in the simple epithelium lining the intestine (**Figure 10.19**), adjacent cells form anchoring junctions with each other and with the basal lamina. These anchoring junctions hold the cells firmly in place. Tight junctions, found near the apical surface, prevent the leakage of materials from the lumen of the intestine into the blood. Instead, as described in Chapter 41, nutrients are selectively transported from the intestinal lumen into the cytosol of the epithelial cell and then are exported across the basal side of the cell into the blood. This phenomenon, called transepithelial transport, allows the body to take up the nutrients it needs, while preventing unwanted materials from getting into the bloodstream. Epithelial cells are also connected via gap junctions, which allow the exchange of nutrients and signaling molecules throughout the epithelium.

In flowering plants, the epidermis covers all of the newly made parts of a plant. For example, the upper and lower sides of leaves are covered by epidermis, which is usually a single layer of closely packed cells (**Figure 10.20a**). Epidermal cells have a thick primary cell wall and are tightly interlocked by their middle lamella.

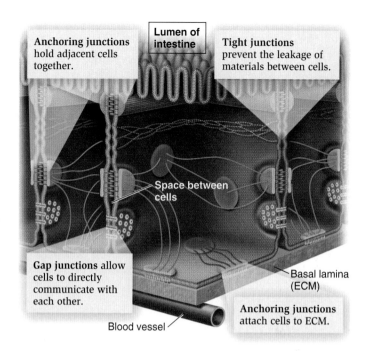

Figure 10.19 A closer look at a simple epithelium that lines the intestine. This figure emphasizes that the three major types of cell junctions are common in epithelial tissue.

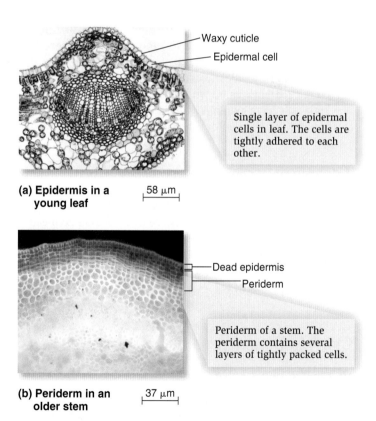

Figure 10.20 Dermal tissues in plants. (a) Epidermis in a young leaf. (b) Periderm in an older stem.

Biological inquiry: Do you notice any parallels between simple epithelium and epidermis, and between stratified epithelium and periderm?

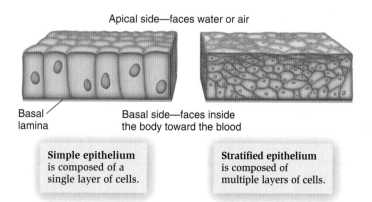

Figure 10.18 Simple and stratified epithelia.

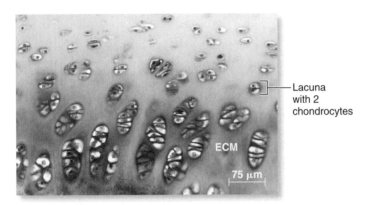

Lacuna
with 2
chondrocytes

ECM

75 μm

Figure 10.21   An example of connective tissue in animals that is rich in extracellular matrix.   This micrograph of cartilage shows chondrocytes in the ECM. The chondrocytes, which are responsible for making the components of cartilage, are found in cavities called lacunae.

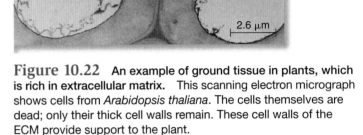

Secondary
cell wall

2.6 μm

Figure 10.22   An example of ground tissue in plants, which is rich in extracellular matrix.   This scanning electron micrograph shows cells from *Arabidopsis thaliana*. The cells themselves are dead; only their thick cell walls remain. These cell walls of the ECM provide support to the plant.

Thus, plant epidermal cells are tightly woven together, much like epithelial cell layers in animals. In leaves, the cells are often polygonal in shape, which means they are flattened cells that have several angles. The epidermal cells of new stems tend to have a more rectangular shape.

As a plant ages, the epidermis may be replaced by another type of dermal tissue called the periderm (**Figure 10.20b**). In woody plants, an example of periderm is the bark on trees. The tissue protects the plant from pathogens, prevents excessive water loss, and provides insulation. The periderm consists of interconnected cork cells, which may be several layers thick. The cork cells have extremely thick cell walls. When cork cells reach maturity, they die, but the cell walls continue to provide support.

A Comparison of Connective and Ground Tissue In contrast to epithelial tissue, which is almost entirely composed of cells, the connective tissue of animals is largely composed of extracellular matrix and has relatively few cells. In animal connective tissue, cell-to-cell contact is somewhat infrequent. Instead, cells are usually adhered to the ECM via integrins, as shown earlier in Figure 10.8b. In some cases, the primary function of cells within

connective tissue is to synthesize the components of the ECM. For example, let's consider cartilage, a connective tissue found in joints such as your knees. The cells that synthesize cartilage, known as chondrocytes, actually represent a small proportion of the total volume of cartilage. As shown in **Figure 10.21**, the chondrocytes are found in small cavities within the cartilage called lacunae (singular, *lacuna*). In some types of cartilage, the chondrocytes represent only 1–2% of the total volume of the tissue! Chondrocytes are the only cells found in cartilage; they are solely responsible for the synthesis of protein fibers, such as collagen, as well as glycosaminoglycans and proteoglycans.

Similar to connective tissue in animals, ground tissue in plants provides structural support and is also rich in ECM. **Figure 10.22** shows a scanning electron micrograph of sclerenchyma cells found in *Arabidopsis thaliana*, a model plant studied by plant biologists. At maturity, the cells are dead, but the thick secondary cell walls continue to provide rigid support for the stem. However, not all ground tissue in plants is rich in ECM. For example, mesophyll cells are a type of parenchymal cell in the leaf that carry out photosynthesis. Because a thick cell wall would inhibit the transmission of light, mesophyll cells have thin cell walls with only a small amount of ECM.

CHAPTER SUMMARY

10.1 Extracellular Matrix

- The extracellular matrix (ECM) is a network of material that is secreted from plant and animal cells and forms a complex meshwork outside of cells.

- In the ECM of animals, proteins and polysaccharides are the major constituents. These materials are involved in strength, structural support, organization, and cell signaling. (Figure 10.1)

- Adhesive proteins, such as fibronectin and laminin, help to adhere cells to the ECM. Structural proteins form fibers. Collagen fibers provide tensile strength, while elastic fibers allow regions of the body to stretch. (Table 10.1, Figures 10.2, 10.3)

- Differential gene regulation controls where in the body different types of collagen fibers are made. (Table 10.2)

- Glycosaminoglycans (GAGs) are polysaccharides of repeating disaccharide units that give a gel-like character to the ECM of animals. Proteoglycans consist of a core protein with attached GAGs. (Figure 10.4)
- Plant cells are surrounded by an ECM called the cell wall. The primary cell wall is made first. It is composed largely of cellulose. The secondary cell wall is made after the primary cell wall and is often quite thick and rigid. (Figures 10.5, 10.6)

10.2 Cell Junctions

- The three common types of cell junctions found in animals are anchoring, tight, and gap junctions. Plant junctions include middle lamella and plasmodesmata. (Table 10.3)
- Anchoring junctions involve cell adhesion molecules (CAMs), which bind cells to each other or to the ECM. The four types are adherens junctions, desmosomes, focal adhesions, and hemidesmosomes. (Figure 10.7)
- Two types of CAMs are cadherin and integrin. Cadherins link cells to each other, while integrins link cells to the ECM. In the cytosol, CAMs bind to actin or intermediate filaments. (Figure 10.8)
- Integrins can perform outside-in and inside-out signaling. This enables cells to communicate with the ECM. (Figure 10.9)
- Tight junctions, composed of occludin and claudin, prevent the leakage of materials between cells. (Figures 10.10, 10.11)
- Gap junctions form channels called connexons that permit the direct passage of materials between adjacent cells. (Figure 10.12)
- Experiments of Loewenstein and colleagues involving the transfer of fluorescent dyes showed that gap junctions permit the passage of substances with a molecular mass of less than 1,000 Daltons. (Figure 10.13)
- The cell walls of adjacent plant cells are cemented together via middle lamella. (Figure 10.14)
- Adjacent plant cells usually have direct connections called plasmodesmata, which are open channels in the cell walls. The ER of adjacent cells is also connected via plasmodesmata. (Figure 10.15)

10.3 Tissues

- A tissue is a group of cells that have a similar structure and function. An organ is composed of two or more tissues and carries out a particular function or functions.
- Six processes—cell division, cell growth, differentiation, migration, apoptosis, and cell connections—create tissues and organs.
- The four general kinds of tissues found in animals are epithelial, connective, muscle, and nervous tissues. (Figure 10.16)
- The three general kinds of tissues found in plants are dermal, ground, and vascular tissues. (Figure 10.17)
- Epithelial and dermal tissues form layers of cells that are highly interconnected. These layers can be one cell thick or several cells thick, and they serve as protective coverings for various parts of animal and plant bodies. (Figures 10.18, 10.19, 10.20)
- Connective and ground tissues are often rich in ECM and play a structural role in animals and plants. (Figures 10.21, 10.22)

TEST YOURSELF

1. The function of the extracellular matrix (ECM) in most multicellular organisms is
   a. to provide strength.
   b. to provide structural support.
   c. to organize cells and other body parts.
   d. cell signaling.
   e. all of the above.

2. The protein found in the ECM of animals that provides strength and resistance to tearing when stretched is
   a. elastin.
   b. cellulose.
   c. collagen.
   d. laminin.
   e. fibronectin.

3. The polysaccharide that forms the hard outer covering of many invertebrates is
   a. collagen.
   b. chitin.
   c. chondroitin sulfate.
   d. pectin.
   e. cellulose.

4. The single most abundant organic molecule of Earth is _____, and it is the main macromolecule of the _____.
   a. collagen, connective tissue of animals
   b. chitin, muscle tissue of animals
   c. cellulose, primary cell wall of plants
   d. integrins, cell junctions in plants
   e. pectin, secondary cell wall of plants

5. _____ are proteins that attach animal cells to the ECM.
   a. Cadherins
   b. Integrins
   c. Occludins
   d. Tight junctions
   e. Desmosomes

6. The gap junctions of animal cells differ from the plasmodesmata of plant cells in that
   a. gap junctions serve as communicating junctions and plasmodesmata serve as adhesion junctions.
   b. gap junctions prevent extracellular material from moving between adjacent cells, but the plasmodesmata do not.
   c. gap junctions allow for direct exchange of cellular material between cells, but plasmodesmata cannot allow the same type of exchange.
   d. gap junctions are formed by specialized proteins that form channels through the membranes of adjacent cells, but plasmodesmata are not formed by specialized proteins.
   e. all of the above.

7. Which of the following is involved in the process of tissue and organ formation in multicellular organisms?
   a. cell division
   b. cell differentiation
   c. cell connections
   d. cell growth
   e. all of the above

8. The tissue type common to animals that functions in the conduction of electrical signals is
   a. epithelial.
   b. dermal.
   c. muscle.
   d. nervous.
   e. ground.

9. Photosynthesis occurs mainly in the _____ tissue of plants.
   a. vascular
   b. dermal
   c. parenchyma
   d. collenchyma
   e. sclerenchyma

10. Which of the following is not a correct statement in the comparison of plant tissues to animal tissues?
   a. Nervous tissue of animals plays the same role as vascular tissue in plants.
   b. The dermal tissue of plants is similar to epithelial tissue of animals in that both provide a covering for the organism.
   c. The epithelial tissue of animals and the dermal tissue of plants have special characteristics that limit the movement of extracellular material between cell layers.
   d. The ground tissue of plants and the connective tissue of animals provide structural support for the organism.
   e. All of the above are correct comparisons between plant and animal tissues.

CONCEPTUAL QUESTIONS

1. List and explain the four characteristics of the extracellular matrix.
2. Distinguish between the primary cell wall and the secondary cell wall.
3. List and explain the four types of animal tissues.

EXPERIMENTAL QUESTIONS

1. What was the purpose of the study conducted by Loewenstein and colleagues?
2. Explain the experimental procedure used by Loewenstein to determine the size of gap-junction channels.
3. What did the results of Figure 10.13 indicate about the size of gap-junction channels?

COLLABORATIVE QUESTIONS

1. What role does the extracellular matrix play in animals?
2. What are the six basic cell processes required to create tissues and organs?

www.brookerbiology.com
This website includes answers to the Biological Inquiry questions found in the figure legends and all end-of-chapter questions.